THE TRUE STORY OF
BILLY THE KID

THE AUTHOR

PLATE I

The True Story of Billy the Kid

A Tale of the Lincoln County War

By

WILLIAM LEE HAMLIN

ILLUSTRATED WITH PHOTOGRAPHS

THE CAXTON PRINTERS, LTD.
CALDWELL, IDAHO
1959

Library of Congress Catalog Card No. 59-5484

Printed, lithographed, and bound in the United States of America by
The CAXTON PRINTERS, Ltd.
Caldwell, Idaho
83157

To

My Wife

PEGGY LEE HAMLIN

My Son

WILLIAM LEE HAMLIN, Jr.

My Granddaughter

EDNA LEE HAMLIN

This Book Is

Affectionately Dedicated

Foreword

THE westward expansion of the United States in the nineteenth century opened a literary gold mine of unprecedented richness. Then, and now, those who did not participate in the adventure were and are eager to read about it. One of the most productive veins, the romance of Billy the Kid, still is being worked, with profit, by historians and writers of fiction. For a number of valid reasons, there is a certain overlapping of history and fiction in this romance.

The story of the American frontier stimulates the imagination as no comparable population shift has done. Chronicles of the exotic country, the Indian wars, the granite characters of the pioneers, their incredible hardships and adventures — these were rich fare for citizens who stayed at home. Pushing west, and west again, was not for the timid, the rooted, the place-proud. Even so, the frontier adventure is not for us, for we cannot turn back the clock a hundred years, or even fifty, but we, like earlier stay-at-homes, can read of the West with interest and pride.

On-the-spot news coverage was not a feature of frontier journalism. Editorial opinion was more personal and significant than is usual today. In controversial matters, biased accounts were common. Facilities for checking the facts were few. Communications were inadequate. Imagine, then, the temptation to dramatize, to prejudice, to embellish. Evidences of these kinds of inaccuracies may be noted in contemporary letters and diaries, and in accounts of events by survivors in these latter days.

Carelessness in the safekeeping of legal documents, and the inevitable passage of years, are factors which complete the catalog of reasons for the obscurity of truth about some incidents on the frontier.

New Mexico, after the War Between the States, was, with Arizona, the *crudest* frontier. To the north of these territories, to the east and west, the forces of civil law were winning the long struggle, and order was emerging, however painfully. In the territory of New Mexico, a handful of hard men pitted the strength of their violent natures against distance, wind, drought, and each other. Geographically and physically, New Mexico furnished a made-to-order haven for outlaws—those wanted for crimes in other places—legal outlaws; and for certain untrammeled spirits—nature's outlaws.

It must be remembered that New Mexico was the forty-seventh state, admitted to the Union as recently as 1912. New Mexico is the only state which has two official languages—English and, in reluctant tribute to an older civilization, Spanish. The ancient capital, Santa Fe, has been a seat of government under the flags of the Pueblo Indians, the Spanish, the Mexicans, the Confederates, and, finally, the United States. Late acceptance to the status of statehood and the difficulties of blending Indian, Mexican, and American ethnic groups have been important factors in molding New Mexico and her people.

Students of the turmoil that was New Mexico have come to feel that today's criteria—legal, ethical, and moral—are not flexible enough to contain the New Mexico frontiersman. He was of a rare breed, rough, adaptable, and totally self-sufficient.

It is not remarkable that the territory of New Mexico produced William H. Bonney. This slight, fair boy, who died at twenty-one, emerges from the shadowy pages of history and legend, a study in paradox. Insouciant, charming, gallant, adhering to his own code of loyalty and justice, or ruthless, murderous, callous, the embodiment of evil—these conflicting opinions we may read of Billy the Kid, or hear from "old-timers," with a wealth of anecdote to confirm each view.

William Lee Hamlin, distinguished jurist and long-time student of New Mexicana, here presents a story of the frontier and the Lincoln County War between the years 1864 and 1881.

The author has chosen from material available in old legal records, contemporary news accounts, and stories of older citizens. Judge Hamlin obtained this information during extensive investigations in New Mexico. Out of the mass of conflicting data he has sketched a portrait of William H. Bonney which is, probably, very near the truth. The author terms the work a "posthumous brief for Billy the Kid," and shows this exceptional youth made hostage to fortune and inexorably drawn to tragedy in a drama played out in the classic Greek manner. Billy the Kid moves across the bloody scenes of his time as someone real and alive.

CAROLINE DAVIS, formerly *Curator*,
The Old Courthouse Museum,
Lincoln, New Mexico

Author's Note

THIS book is not presented as a history of the territory of New Mexico prior to its admission to the Union as a state, nor is it a historical romance, as such, of the then turbulent and lawless Lincoln County. Rather, it is an account of real people as they lived and of true events as they transpired during those tragic days.

I am well aware that there are many sources of information—frequently, misinformation—from which may be drawn a picture of those frontier days: fiction, hearsay, tradition, old records, but most factual are the recollections of those who witnessed the transition of our last great frontier into "A Land of Enchantment."

It was the author's great privilege to have known former Territorial Governor Miguel Antonio Otero, author of the book *My Life on the Frontier,* in which was sounded the death knell of a lawless territory and the birth of a great state. The many hours spent with this grand old man at his home in Santa Fe, listening to his experiences of those hectic early days, are numbered among my most cherished memories.

No less fortunate was my high privilege also to have known former Territorial Governor George Curry, then state historian, curator, and custodian of the Old Courthouse and Museum in Lincoln. Modest and unassuming, a characteristic of all great men, Governor Curry related to me the contributing cause, progress, and the termination of the "Lincoln County War," in which many brave men lost their lives, but, as in most such feuds, neither faction won. The days I spent in Lincoln visiting with the governor in his quarters in the Old Courthouse remain an unforgettable memory.

Others who generously provided me with graphic descriptions of those troublesome times were George Coe, the last survivor of the Lincoln County War; Amel Blazer, who as a youth witnessed the fight at Blazer's Mill, the battle in which "Buckshot" Roberts and Dick Brewer, members of the opposing factions, lost their lives; and Lucian (Luke) Dutra, a former *vaquero,* or cowboy in the employ of that great cattleman, John S. Chisum. (Dutra was not in the battle at Blazer's Mill.) Dutra witnessed the Kid's sensational escape only a few days before the date fixed for his execution by hanging. All of these have now passed on, but they and others have enriched the history of a great state.

All had known the Kid and Pat Garrett, his slayer. It was their collective opinion that the youth, though not always blameless, was neither a ruthless renegade nor a wanton killer, as he so often has been portrayed by writers of fiction. On the contrary, during the brief span of his twenty-one years, he was more frequently allied with the forces of law and order than otherwise.

There appears no instance, where men met death before his guns, when there were not involved justifiable or extenuating circumstances.

Portions of the story have been drawn from the recollections of descendants of the many old settlers and frontiersmen, both Anglos and Spanish Americans. Certain transitions, reconstructed scenes, and episodes are based upon my own conclusions following months of painstaking study and research.

In presenting this story, I seek the reader's kind indulgence.

William Lee Hamlin

Acknowledgment

In grateful acknowledgment and appreciation of the courtesy of:

Former territorial governors Miguel Antonio Otero and George Curry;

The Indiana Historical Society for the correspondence exchanged between Governor Lew Wallace and Billy the Kid;

Hon. William A. Keleher, attorney and counselor-at-law, Albuquerque, New Mexico, and author of *The Fabulous Frontier;*

Colonel Maurice Garland Fulton, Roswell, New Mexico, author and historian and former staff member at the New Mexico Military Institute;

Caroline Davis, Albuquerque, New Mexico, former curator and custodian of Old Lincoln Courthouse and Museum;

George Coe, Glencoe, New Mexico, the last survivor of the Lincoln County War;

Captain George Titsworth, New Mexico pioneer merchant;

Lucian (Luke) Dutra, Phoenix, Arizona, former range rider for the great cattleman, John S. Chisum;

Dr. E. L. Woods, Lincoln, New Mexico, pioneer physician and surgeon;

A. N. Blazer, who as a youth witnessed the battle between the posse and the outlaw, "Buckshot" Roberts, at Blazer's Mill;

Professor Irving McKee, Oakland, California, author of *Ben-Hur Wallace;*

Mrs. John W. Poe, Roswell, New Mexico, wife of Pat Garrett's deputy;

Sarah Salazar, Lincoln, New Mexico, sister-in-law of Hijinio Salazar;

Mrs. Ella Davidson, Roswell, New Mexico, reared in Lincoln during the factional feud;

The Macmillan Company, publishers, of New York City;

Rufus Rockwell Wilson, Inc., publishers, of Elmira, New York;

The *New Mexican*, Santa Fe, New Mexico;

The *Colorado Chieftain*, Pueblo, Colorado;

The National Archives and the Library of Congress;

The California State Library, Sacramento, California.

Table of Contents

	Page
Prologue	1
Part I	15
Part II	111
Epilogue	308
Postscript — The Last Years and Tragic Death of Patrick Floyd Garrett	311
Glossary	317
Roster of Those Who Lost Their Lives in the Lincoln County War and Its Aftermath	319
Statements Made to Governor Lew Wallace by the Citizens of Lincoln Relating the Chaotic Conditions Prevailing in Lincoln County	321
Appendix I and Commentary	332
Appendix II — Notes	348

List of Illustrations

The Author - - - - - - - - - - - - - Plate I, Frontispiece

Following page 172

Lincoln, New Mexico - - - - - - - - - - - - - - Plate II

Old Lincoln County Museum and Murphy-Dolan-Riley Headquarters as it Appeared in the Seventies - - Plate III

Leaders of the Murphy Faction - - - - - - - - - Plate IV

Alexander A. McSween; Susan McSween; Pat F. Garrett; and John H. Tunstall - - - - - - - - - Plate V

A Very Doubtful Reproduction of an Alleged Photograph of the Kid - - - - - - - - - - - Plate VI

Photograph Obtained from a Spanish-American Family - Plate VII

Old Photograph Names Seven as Texas Rangers and Includes Billy the Kid - - - - - - - - - - - Plate VIII

Burial Place at Fort Sumner; The Torreon at Lincoln - - Plate IX

New Mexico Counties in 1880 - - - - - - - - - - Plate X

Torreon Watchtower - - - - - - - - - - - - - - Plate XI

Floor Plan of the Old Murphy Building - - - - - - Plate XII

Marker at the Grave of Kathleen Bonney Antrim, Mother of Billy the Kid - - - - - - - - - - Plate XIII

Following page 364

Lew Wallace's Letter of Minute Instructions Arranging a Meeting between Himself and Billy - - Plate XIV

Billy's Note to Squire Wilson Asking Instructions - - Plate XV

Wallace's Reply to Billy (March 20, 1879) - - - - Plate XVI

The Kid's Long Letter in which He Agreed to the Governor's Plan - - - - - - - - - - - Plates XVII-XX

Billy's Letter to Governor Wallace Relating Incidents at the Greathouse Ranch - - - - - - Plates XXI-XXIV

Billy's Brief Request for an Interview and His Curt, Demanding Note of March 2, 1881 - - - - - - Plate XXV

Billy the Kid's Appeal of March 4, 1881 - - Plates XXVI-XXVII

Photostatic Copy of Death Warrant of the Kid in the Handwriting of Governor Wallace - - - - Plate XXVIII

Photostatic Copy of Pat Garrett's Return on the Warrant for the Execution of the Kid - - - - Plate XXIX

PROLOGUE

Prologue

THE American frontier, to be fully comprehended, should be visualized as a state of mind rather than as a locale, or a number of locales. The frontier was a primitive, driving force. Frontier society encompassed all the vices and virtues common to civilized man. These were intensified, their contrasts heightened, by the enforced social intimacy of frontier life. Frontiersmen were, necessarily, few in number in any one place. The complete commingling of a small, classless, unformed society forced each man to make a shrewd appraisal of his fellows. Nothing about himself or his associates surprised the frontiersman very much.

Frontier society, like any other, contained disparate elements, but the usual frontiersman had certain characteristics in common with his neighbor. He faced up to his difficult, primitive life with courage and resolution. If he lacked unusual tenacity, he failed—he went home where life was easier, or he died.

He had to deal with harsh nature on her own terms. His associates might be dishonest, unscrupulous, or even savage. He knew poverty, hard work, and daily living on a subsistence basis. The frontiersman had, or developed, a quality of *hardness*. It was his ticket to survival.

For his rewards he had a freedom of action unknown in more civilized sections, cheap and plentiful land, the golden promise of great riches, and the satisfactions of building. He built a house, a town, a district—perhaps the fabled empire of his dreams.

By a rigid, unwritten law, the name and person of a

good woman were held to be inviolate on the frontier. Most men of all stations, whatever their crimes, upheld that code and punished its violators, regardless of risk to personal safety. The chivalry of the frontiersman has not been overrated.

Every segment of the frontier population had frequent business and social contacts with every other segment. In New Mexico, these groups were, externally at least, clearly delineated and recognizable in the colorful scene.

The territory of New Mexico was best known as the terminus of the Santa Fe Trail. Colonization of New Mexico by the Spanish in 1598 laid the foundation for one of the most dramatic trade routes in the history of Western civilization.

For more than two centuries after the first colonists arrived, the only communication with the outside world was through Mexico. In 1805, Zebulon Pike began his historic trip west, and, after his report, pioneers from the States followed him.

James Purcell rode across the prairie from Missouri in 1805, and in 1821 Captain William Becknell, called "The Father of the Santa Fe Trail," blazed the route which was to remain in use until the railroad moved into the territory in 1880.

The Santa Fe Trail became even more important in 1822 when Mexico won her independence from Spain. Under Spanish rule, every effort had been made to prevent traders and trappers from the East from entering the territory. After New Mexico became a part of the Mexican Republic, a new era began. The long caravans which wound across the plains from Independence, Missouri, over Raton Pass, and into Santa Fe, found welcome. In the decade after General Kearny claimed the territory of New Mexico for the United States in 1846, one freighting firm alone had 3,500 wagons, 4,500 men, 40,000 oxen, and 1,000 mules on the trail, over which it hauled 16,000 tons of freight annually.

Stagecoaches followed the trail, with passengers west-bound to make their fortunes. Homeseekers used the route to bring their lumbering wagons and small herds of cattle. The Santa Fe Trail, route of commerce and travel, flourished in spite of constant threats by Indians and raiding outlaws. At the end of the trail was the Royal City of the Holy Faith of St. Francis of Assisi—Santa Fe—embodying all the flavor of the frontier. A complete cross section of the population of the territory of New Mexico was to be found gathered in Santa Fe.

Low in the shadow of the magnificent Sangre de Cristo mountain range to the east, the little city of adobe buildings was shaded by giant cottonwood trees. A small, sparkling river wound through the town and fed the little irrigation ditches. A brilliant blue sky arched overhead. Pungent piñon smoke and the sweet, spicy odor of roasting chilies scented the light, tangy air.

Although an occasional tall brick house stood proud, most of the populace dwelt in small, mud-colored homes built in the old Spanish style, presenting blank façades and barred gates to the narrow streets. The walls of the houses enclosed shaded patios, gay with flowers and grass. Stray chords from guitars, the tinkle of little fountains, and subdued laughter drifted over the walls. Life was sweet here, and slow-paced.

It was in the plaza, a large square in the center of the town, that the crush and frenzied excitements of trade and diversion brought a bit of the big world "outside" to Santa Fe. Here the smells of Santa Fe were less subtle. The inevitable piñon smoke, the reek of garlic, the scent of horseflesh, and the odor of humanity itself hung oppressively over the crowded square. Market stalls displayed produce—scarlet strings of dried chile, fine speckled cocks in wooden cages, a haunch of venison. Indian pottery, rugs, baskets, jewelry, knives, and hot tortillas were bartered in the open air.

When a wagon train, laden with goods and supplies, rumbled into town, its arrival signaled wild celebration. Fires were lighted in the plaza, around which, for a day and a night, there were bartering, singing, dancing, and drinking. Firearms were discharged into the air. The unwary found themselves menaced by the flying hoofs of cow ponies ridden through the crowd by careless *vaqueros*. Now and then a fight broke out. Then knives flashed briefly in sun or firelight as the combatants circled each other, surrounded by a respectful audience. No interference was attempted as this might have drawn additional partisans into the conflict. If both principals survived, the fight received no official attention. If not, one combatant was marched off to the *carcel* as the other received the last rites from a black-robed priest, kneeling in the dust.

Under the *portal* of the Palace of Governors, which fronted on the plaza, grave men could be observed coming and going on legal and political business, or standing in little groups, speaking in low voices of weighty matters.

In the old plaza at Santa Fe, amid scenes of activity and excitement, passed in review the people who populated the territory of New Mexico.

The trader, or merchant, dominated the scene. He was prosperous, authoritative. He had for sale the cloth, tobacco, manufactured goods, sugar, coffee, liquor, and salt his neighbors had to have. Whether just and reasonable or cruel and avaricious, he was a conspicuous figure.

The homesteader — the land-seeking farmer — was known by the bulky wagon which transported his family and household effects. He had a hopeful smile, and conducted himself with unusual decorum. But, if he appeared quieter than other Westerners, this appearance was deceptive. He was a man prepared to fight, to die if need be, for his family's future.

The ordinary rancher who operated a small spread was a well-mounted man in fine boots. He spent his days and nights in the open, tending his herd. His work was strenuous and endless. He battled the elements, the market, beasts of prey, raiding outlaws, and the contrary natures of the cow critters themselves. All the best of the man—his hopes, plans, and dreams—were invested in his herd. The rancher both feared and admired the cattle baron, who was only a rancher grown big—very big.

The cattle baron followed the frontier, moving his great herds into unfenced territory to have scope for his enormous operations. He established himself firmly, holding to lands and watering places to which he had no legal claim. He held them to the eleventh hour against all encroachments. The cattle baron was able to hold on by virtue of his wealth, by the very size of the herds he grazed, and by the strength of the cowboy army he employed to protect his interests. The cattle baron was, in effect, a general—directing the strategic movements of his herds and the protective-aggressive activities of his men.

The cattle baron, more than other frontier citizens, was subject to constant harassment by outlaws. Because of his great wealth, he was considered fair game by those outside the law who were drawn to this vast, rough, and sparsely populated country. The very circumstances of life in New Mexico, including the harsh and unscrupulous practices of the cattle barons themselves, forced some men to criminal activities.

Desperadoes, renegades, gunmen, and rustlers were usually referred to by the generic term "bad men." The bad man, as he appeared on the frontier, may have originated in any stratum of society. The bad man came in two models, with infinite variations, of course. One model was the despised and treacherous *counterfeit* bad man. He was a born murderer who, today, might be diagnosed as a homicidal maniac. He had no principles, no code beyond expediency, no regard for human life. He was a brute, a bully, and a coward.

For the *genuine* bad man, on the other hand, frontiersmen had a certain respect. The genuine bad man was likened to the great gray timber wolf—a killer, but a bold fighter with wild, natural dignity. The counterfeit bad man was often designated with the name of the coyote—a skulking, cowardly animal who seeks defenseless prey.

Gambling in the territory was not outside the law, nor was it a social offense. The honest gambler could be a leader in civic and business affairs in the community. Almost every man, from the lowly peon dealing three-card monte on his bright serape to the merchant playing with the rancher and the public official, gambled to a greater or lesser degree. Copper centavos and cattle empires changed hands at the gaming table with equal facility. It was only the dishonest gambler who was held in universal contempt.

The Indian's was the first family of New Mexico. He was aware of this distinction, and wore an invisible mantle of pride. Earlier, hostile group activity had indicated his resistance to the invasion of his domain. Shortly after the Civil War, the Indian population, finding resistance failing, made tacit peace with the white man. There were Indians who remained intractable and unpredictable, however, and the chain of Western forts which the United States had provided to keep the peace remained well-manned garrisons, ever alert to deal with individuals and small groups of renegades.

New Mexico, in the middle years of the nineteenth century, belonged essentially to the citizen of Mexican ancestry. As a Mexican national, he had been of mixed blood, even as the American is. A Spanish-Indian mixture was usual, but it appeared in varying degrees and was present along with other national and racial strains. When the territory of New Mexico was claimed for the United States, this Spanish-speaking American citizen retained his language, his cultural heritage, his integrated community and religious life, and his traditional point of view.

From the Indian, the Mexican had his pride and his attitude toward work—an attitude often mistakenly termed indolence. The Mexican, like his Indian forebears, was the most industrious of workers, until he had housed and clothed his family adequately and laid by food and supplies for the foreseeable future. When this was done, he took his ease, playing his guitar, or meditating. He did not adjust readily to the Anglo way, which was to work without ceasing, every day, every season. To him, a lifetime of sustained labor did not indicate an abiding faith in God. The brilliantly successful Mexican-American ranchers, businessmen, and scholars who were the leaders of their people in the territory seemed to achieve great things with ease and tranquility of spirit; if effort was involved, it was not apparent.

From his Latin blood, the Mexican-New Mexican derived a love of beauty, sentiment, and a deep interest in politics. Many distinguished men of Mexican descent have participated in the political life of New Mexico, and have served her people well.

In 1862, small irrigated farms and sheep ranching were the principal concerns of the native New Mexican. He dwelt on land which had been held by his father and grandfather, perhaps dating back to Spanish grants, and he was content that it should be so.

In the same year, events in the eastern part of the United States were conspiring to shape the destiny of New Mexico and of some of its citizens in strange ways.

Gold shipments from California and other far-Western states were continually moving eastward to reinforce the Union. In an effort to halt this movement and secure the gold for the Confederacy, General H. H. Sibley was ordered north from Texas. He met the Federal troops at Fort Craig in the territory of New Mexico, defeated them, and raided Fort Stanton to the north.

Fort Stanton fell to Sibley only after the garrison troops had destroyed the supply depot and partially demolished the fort by fire. Santa Fe, the oldest seat of government in United States territory, fell without resistance, and a government-in-exile was formed at Las Vegas in opposition to Confederate forces.

Fort Union was evacuated by Union troops, and, at Glorieta Pass, General Sibley was engaged by Union forces which had been reinforced by a column of volunteers. In this battle Sibley and the Confederate troops were routed. It was April, 1862. The gold route and the territory of New Mexico were again securely in Union hands.

At the time of Sibley's defeat at Glorieta, a column of thirty-five hundred California volunteers was making a forced march across the Western desert to attack General Sibley's rear. The column arrived too late to engage in the campaign but was, for some months, occupied against Apache hostiles. Eventually its members were mustered from the service, most of them at Fort Stanton.

Fort Stanton, named for Captain Charles Stanton, a gallant officer who lost his life in a skirmish with Apaches, is located among low, rolling hills, eight miles west of the present village of Lincoln. Lincoln was known for many years as La Placita del Rio Bonito.

Before, and for thirty-five years after the War Between the States, Fort Stanton was maintained as a frontier post, adjacent to the Mescalero Apache Reservation. It was at Fort Stanton that many volunteer troops were discharged from the service. Among those mustered out were Colonel Emil Fritz, Major William Brady, and Major Lawrence G. Murphy.

During the difficult years after the war, the scantily populated territory offered some business possibilities. Santa Fe, Las Vegas, and Las Cruces were the only sizable settlements. The few stores scattered about New Mexico did a lively business. Bars were fairly numerous and extremely busy. Several newspapers were published, and mining, cattle ranching, farming, and the practice of law accounted for the remainder of gainful occupations. The population of the territory in 1864 was approximately 90,000.

The number of practicing attorneys in 1864 seems to have been large in proportion to the size of the population. Development of new territory resulted in a quantity of legal business and afforded unusual opportunities to young attorneys.

Once the federal government had set the boundaries of the territory of New Mexico, the federal judicial system had begun to function fairly smoothly. However, territorial citizens were not always pleased with the men appointed from Washington to administer the affairs of the territory.

In many respects the status of law in the territory was shaky. Officials elected to administer the law were oftentimes unqualified. County clerks might be remiss in the keeping of records. Many county officials were unscrupulous in the issuance of search warrants, writs of habeas corpus, and civil instruments. The generally inferior quality of law enforcement personnel was a matter of public knowledge, and at least one newspaper blamed these conditions for all the troubles which subsequently developed in Lincoln County.[1]

Peace officers were frequently recruited from among the worst elements in the territory, and some of these officers were secretly affiliated with outlaws. Life was cheap, property rights were difficult of tenure, and taxes for the support of county governments were mostly uncollectible—or, if collected, were likely to be embezzled.

Before there could be effective law enforcement, there had to be fixed population—a family-based society—for by this influence only could law replace lawlessness, order supplant confusion. The prevalent lawlessness was more a matter of disorder than of immorality. Men went wrong with little temptation because the restraining influence of organized public opinion was largely absent. Into the resulting moral vacuum came bad men of all kinds—bad Mexicans, bad Negroes, bad white men—and the bad white men were the worst of these.

Thus it may be seen that, politically and socially, the citizen of New Mexico had not yet come of age. If he had been politically mature, he would have brought order out of the disorder, and he would not have countenanced the rise of "The Santa Fe Ring."

The members of the ring were professional politicians, appointees of a distant and indifferent federal government in Washington. As far as is known, the ring could not remove mountains; but its members were said to have removed land grants and mines and ranches from their owners. The methods of the members of the ring lay within the law, or within the scope of initiative

---

[1] *Thirty-Four* (Las Cruces, New Mexico Territory, April 30, 1879). See Appendix II, Note A, Prologue.

allowed them in carrying out their official duties. They were alert and quick to turn each situation to personal profit and advantage. The functioning of the ring involved a close liaison between officials in Santa Fe and local authorities. The well-oiled machine practically controlled every county in the territory for a number of years, and its mandates, issued from Santa Fe, were promptly executed.

Lincoln County, in 1869 and for a number of years after, embraced an area approximately as large as the state of Pennsylvania. Its western border extended almost to the Rio Grande, its eastern boundary reached beyond the Pecos River to Texas. If a map of the state of New Mexico is quartered, the southeast quarter almost exactly bounds Old Lincoln County.

In this area of 27,000 square miles, ranges of low, rolling hills and rich tablelands offered grazing for unlimited herds. The fertile valleys of the eastern and central sections were well-watered by small rivers with romantic Spanish names. Down the western slopes of the White Mountains tumbled Rio Tularosa. Along the eastern slope, Rio Ruidoso and Rio Bonito came together at a point in the foothills. At this confluence, the single stream became Rio Hondo, and made its tempestuous way to the Pecos.

The Mescalero Apache Reservation was here, in the high, timbered White Mountain Range. Fort Stanton was fully garrisoned with perhaps a thousand troops. Prospectors were busy in the rugged mountains. Little farms and villages, small ranches and large ones, and the transport and business resulting from these activities, gave the area an aspect of great prosperity, even though it was sparsely settled. Wild game was abundant, and furnished sport and food. But the wild life also offered economic hazards to ranchers, who lost animals to lions, bears, eagles, and coyotes, and whose valuable grass was heavily grazed by deer and antelope.

The little village of Placita del Rio Bonito, or Lincoln, was the hub of business and legal affairs for this vast section. The village had been settled, about 1850, by a few families of Mexican descent. For a long time the neighborhood had been shunned because of its proximity to the Apache, but these brave people established themselves in spite of forays by Indians and by Texas outlaws.

A prominent feature of the village landscape was the round stone Torreon, from which the populace maintained a watch for intruders. With the formation of territorial Lincoln County, in 1869, Placita changed its name to Lincoln and was officially designated the county seat.

The earliest families were for the most part peaceful and law-abiding, but, as more and more Anglos moved into Lincoln after the Civil War, they brought with them the seeds of the trouble that was to mean national publicity and shame for Lincoln County. Here were to be found representatives of all segments of frontier society, the best and the worst, mingling together in the course of daily living. The most dramatic scenes of the era were destined to take place in Lincoln.

This is a story of the origins and events of the Lincoln County War, and of William H. Bonney—Billy the Kid. Only conditions on the raw frontier could have evolved the Lincoln County War, and it was this conflict which shaped and forged Bonney, the man.

Billy the Kid, a slight youth who died at twenty-one years of age, excited special interest in his own time and later among historians and spinners-of-tales. So much has been said and written and sung of him that he has taken a place as an authentic figure in American folklore. Why did the person and the deeds of this boy have such an impact on the people who knew him and upon the history of New Mexico?

Billy was unprepossessing, physically. He is described by contemporaries as small—about five feet seven inches tall and weighing at most one hundred and thirty-five pounds. Yet he conveyed an impression of physical grace and perfect co-ordination.

The boy's slightly-curling brown hair was sun-streaked and worn long, after the fashion of the day. The slender face, above narrow, sloping shoulders, was distinguished by only two notable features—slightly protruding upper front teeth and remarkably expressive eyes, which appeared blue, gray, or smoky, mirroring the mood of the moment. His hands and feet were small, but his wrists were muscular and, proportionately, large.

Billy was neat and clean of person and polite and mannerly. He was well-spoken, talkative in moments of gaiety, but given to terse sentences and long silences when he was thoughtful or angry. He was high-spirited and capable of daring physical feats and sensational exhibitions of horsemanship and marksmanship.

The Kid, as he was almost universally called, was socially proficient at dancing and singing, and his gentle behavior and respectful deference to women were qualities acknowledged by his friends and enemies alike.

It has been said that Bonney had one or more sweethearts among the beautiful Mexican-American girls in the section, but no one has come forward to substantiate this. In any case, his relationship with the native Mexican-American citizens of Lincoln County was marked by an easy camaraderie and mutual respect. Many Anglos in the section were offensively arrogant, and they regarded the first citizens as ignorant creatures with outlandish accents, to be treated with contempt. Among these Anglos, their dark-skinned neighbors were referred to as "greasers." The sensitive Mexican-Americans were too proud to show their resentment of this and other discourtesies, but they were devoted to Billy, whose innate good manners implied respect for his fellow men.

Thus we have examined the appearance and attitudes of William Bonney, as gleaned from his contemporaries. The inner man, his motivations, his qualities of character, mind, and heart, must be judged by the reader as the tale unfolds.

PART I

Chapter I

LINCOLN was a village of huddled, mud-plastered buildings located in the narrow valley of the Bonito, the clear mountain stream which watered the community. The single street formed a long, lazy S, curving to the south at the east end of town, and reversing to curve north at the west. The steep hills on the north and south were covered with low-growing juniper and piñon. Little meadows and orchards thrived on the valley floor. The homes were neat and well kept. The birds sang in the early morning, and the bleating of lambs and voices raised in neighborly conversation carried far in the clear air. The valley was beautiful, sheltered, productive, blessed by nature.

It was to this valley village that Lawrence G. Murphy moved. He had been mustered from service after the Civil War, and, sensing a business opportunity, he stayed on at Fort Stanton to open a store.

Lawrence Murphy was of Irish parentage and he had had the advantage of a splendid education, having for a time studied for the priesthood. His appearance was distinguished and his manners were courtly.

Although Murphy was known as a heavy drinker, his indulgence appeared not to affect either his engaging personality or his keen mind. Beneath his benevolent manner, however, Murphy was ambitious and ruthless.

When his army service ended, Murphy, who held a commission as major, and Colonel Emil Fritz formed a trading company, adopting the name "L. G. Murphy & Company." Colonel Fritz, a German immigrant, assumed no active role in the business, and seemed content to accept his share of the profits as paid to him by Murphy. Apparently it was Fritz's capital which founded the business.

The firm operated on the military reservation at Fort Stanton as a post trader's or sutler's store. In 1873, as the result of an unpleasant incident, Murphy's military concession was withdrawn.

The trouble came about because of a quarrel between John H. Riley and James J. Dolan. Dolan and Riley were two young men who had become associated with the Murphy company. They were hot-blooded youths, both well under thirty, ready for any venture which promised danger or profit, and Murphy found many uses for them. They worked about the store, supervised the gambling in the "club" Murphy operated adjacent to the store, and helped with the gathering of Murphy's cattle and their delivery to the quartermaster in fulfillment of Murphy's profitable army contracts.

What Dolan and Riley quarreled about is not known, but, as a result of the disagreement, Riley withdrew from the firm (to rejoin it later). Threats were exchanged. One evening in July, James Dolan entered the quarters of Captain James F. Randlett at the fort. John Riley was there as the guest of Captain Randlett. The incident, what preceded it, and what was to follow, are best explained in Captain Randlett's own report of the affair:

D. Troop, 8th Cavalry
Fort Stanton, New Mexico
July 22, 1873

To the Honorable
Secretary of War
Washington, D.C.

Sir:

I enclose herewith a copy of writ served on me this day by order of the civil authorities (served by L. J. Gillum, sheriff) and request instructions. On arrival at this post in April, 1872, I found L. G. Murphy and Company post traders; their prices were exorbitantly large for all goods sold to the enlisted men of my command, almost to extortion. I remonstrated with this firm and was received with insult. I will, with the Honorable Secretary of War's permission, state the circumstances of the writ issued.

One Sunday morning, Dr. Bushnell of the Indian Agency invited Mr. Riley and myself to take a ride with him to select a new location for the Indian Reservation. Mr. Riley came to my house this day and told me at this time that he was at outs with the Murphy Company. After dining with Captain McKibben (Sunday), upon returning to my quarters, I discovered Dolan, an employee of Murphy and Company, in my rooms quarreling with Mr. Riley. I interfered and prevented further quarreling. I invited Mr. Riley as my guest to accept the hospitality of the house, which he accepted. On going to church the same evening, Mr. Riley said to me, "Dolan is going to shoot me for I saw him fixing his pistol." I told him to stay by me and no harm would come to him. After services by Dr. Barstow, on going to my quarters, Mr. Dolan approached Mr. Riley and discharged a pistol, a Smith and Wesson revolver. At that time Riley was saved by the throwing up of my arm. I entreated Dolan to be quiet which he would not do, being riotous, saying to me that Mr. Riley must retract something he had said or die. At this juncture I called the Sergeant of the Guard and had Mr. Dolan arrested. Mr. Murphy was also arrested, but was released by the commanding officer, Captain McKibben, the same evening. This firm I know to have been defrauding the Government since my arrival at the post. Their contracts with Indian agents have been fraudulent to my certain knowledge. So powerful is the Ring to which they belong that I am able to prove this firm has even attempted to force upon officers of this post contract goods inferior to samples from which they were bought.[1] I consider that L. G. Murphy and Company's store is nothing more nor less than a den of infamy and recommend the removal of the firm from the Reservation.

Respectfully submitted,
JAMES F. RANDLETT
Captain, D. Troop, 8th Cavalry
United States Army

[1] See Appendix II, Note A, Chap. I.

The "writ" to which Captain Randlett refers charged false arrest and false imprisonment. When Murphy and Dolan were handed copies of Randlett's letter, they realized they had underestimated the captain. Murphy arranged for immediate withdrawal of the charges against Captain Randlett, but it was too late. Prompt orders from Washington resulted in the removal of the company from the military reservation by Major Clendenning, then post commander.

That Lawrence G. Murphy should move his business eight miles down the valley to Lincoln was perfectly natural.

L. G. Murphy already had crossed the path of another prominent resident of Lincoln County, John S. Chisum—"The Cattle King of Bosque Grande." Chisum and Murphy were competitive cattle suppliers, and they were not friendly. Chisum's home, Spring Ranch, was located on the Pecos River, in the southeast quadrant of the vast area of Old Lincoln County.

John Chisum was a cowman. He had no peer in all the Southwest, with the possible exception of Charles Goodnight. Chisum was born in Tennessee in 1824 and moved, with his family, to Texas when he was thirteen years old. The years that followed have no place in this record until, in 1867, Chisum decided to move his herd, numbering ten thousand, from Texas into the territory of New Mexico.

He rounded up all cattle which bore his long-rail and jingle-bob brand[2]—and, perhaps, some which did not—and trailed them north and west to a point near the Pecos River now known as Malaga. Chisum scouted the river and selected Bosque Grande, forty miles south of Fort Sumner, for his first headquarters.

Chisum's operations were so vast and diversified as to

---

[2] See Appendix II, Note B, Chap. I.

stagger the imagination. His was a cattle empire extending one hundred and fifty miles along a never-failing river, with grazing for thousands of cattle on either side for as many miles as the animals cared to stray.

In this happy situation, the "Cattle King" wanted more cattle. He was too impatient to await the building of his herd by natural increase. Chisum gave some thought to the difficulties of small ranchers who were far from markets and who could not afford to trail their herds great distances. He quickly grasped the potentialities in this situation and went into Texas where he bought up many of these small herds. Chisum made part-payment in cash and signed a number of notes for balances due. He obtained nearly twenty thousand cattle in this manner, and returned with them to the Pecos grazing grounds, leaving behind unnumbered promissory notes of about the same value as Confederate currency after the Civil War.

Chisum was, first and last, a cattleman. It has been said of him that he lived with cattle, slept with cattle, and *ate* cattle—but not his own! That he was shrewd and unscrupulous and not eager to pay his bills cannot be denied, but these qualities were countered by humor, kindness, and unexpected generosity in Chisum's complex character.

John S. Chisum was the avowed enemy of L. G. Murphy and Murphy's associates, and tacitly aligned himself with the opposition in the trouble that was to come.

"The House," as the Murphy organization was locally known, commenced building the big store in Lincoln in 1873, immediately after moving from Fort Stanton. The building, substantially constructed of adobe and featuring many glass windows, was completed in 1874 and housed headquarters for Murphy's extensive operations. The store building was strangely imposing and conspicuous in little

Lincoln. It housed, on the first floor, Murphy's mercantile store, a bar, the post office, and Murphy's business office, a billiard room which served as the local "club," and a large storeroom. Upstairs were a Masonic meeting hall (which was sealed off from the rest of the second-floor rooms and entered by means of a ladder from the yard) and spacious living quarters occupied by Murphy, James J. Dolan, and, sometimes, by John Riley, who had mended his breach with Dolan and resumed association with the company.

The porch at the front of the building was covered, and its roof formed a second porch for the upper story. Here Murphy liked to sit on sunny mornings, smoking a fine cigar and observing with satisfaction the busy scene in the street below. Murphy was, in a very real sense, monarch of all he surveyed, secure in the possession of prosperity, power, and ease. But all this was destined to change, and the change would touch many lives with violence.

Murphy had a sound classical education. Perhaps, at leisure in the sun, he thought of the three fates of Greek mythology—Clotho, the spinner who spun the thread of life; Lachesis, the giver of lots who assigned to each man his destiny; and Atropos, whom none might deny, and who carried the shears which severed the thread of life at the moment of death. And yet it seems unlikely that Murphy recognized the hand of Lachesis, dispenser of destiny, when he met Alexander McSween.

Chapter II

ALEXANDER A. McSWEEN was born near Charlottetown, Prince Edward Island. Later he became a naturalized American citizen. Of Scottish parentage, McSween was deeply religious, intensely determined to maintain his rigid standards of social, business, and personal ethics. His life shows one interesting parallel to the life of L. G. Murphy. Murphy had been educated at a school where young men study for the priesthood, and Alexander McSween had studied for the Presbyterian ministry. Murphy adopted soldiering and business while McSween turned to law.

When asked why he had adopted the profession of law in preference to that of the ministry, Alexander McSween would reply, "Men very frequently are greatly in need of temporal as well as spiritual aid and advice. How better can I serve them than by being myself well versed in jurisprudence?"

And young Murphy? Nothing is known of the inducing reasons prompting him to abandon his ecclesiastical studies while a student at the academy. The War Between the States was in progress. Possibly it was the patriotic lure for a military career that prompted his decision.

He joined the "California Column" as a major and marched across the Arizona desert to reinforce the Federal troops then in the territory of New Mexico. When mustered out of the service, he remained to engage in commercial pursuits at Fort Stanton, and later at the village of Lincoln.

McSween practiced law for a time in Atcheson, Kansas, where he earned an excellent reputation. When he came to Lincoln, seeking a healthful climate in which to continue the practice of law, he brought with him his red-haired young wife Susan, whom he had met and married in Atcheson. As intense and determined as her husband, Susan McSween was more vigorous, practical, and realistic than he.

The McSweens arrived in Lincoln in 1875. They made friends readily, and McSween quickly built up his practice. One of his first clients was Lawrence G. Murphy. Murphy recognized the youthful attorney's ability, and the association was entirely amicable until Murphy asked McSween to defend several of his employees who had been found in possession of a small herd of cattle belonging to John Chisum. McSween believed the men to be guilty and declined to accept the case. Murphy applied pressure, and McSween reiterated his refusal. At this point the business relationship of Murphy and McSween was terminated, and the first fuel was fed to the flame that was to engulf all of Lincoln County.

John Chisum heard of the rift between McSween and Murphy, and Chisum came to Lincoln at once and retained McSween to aid in the prosecution of the men whom he had refused to defend. Murphy's employees were found guilty, but they escaped from jail and fled the country. During the trial, McSween established that John Riley, partner of Murphy, had acted in collusion with the thieves, seemingly with Murphy's knowledge. As a natural consequence of the trial, the enmity between Murphy on the one side and Chisum and McSween on the other was defined and deepened.

McSween dismissed the trial of the Murphy men from his mind as he interested himself in the affairs of a new client, John H. Tunstall.

Young Tunstall, born in England, was the son of a wealthy and distinguished family. He had traveled widely and was an accomplished linguist, although his Castilian Spanish was a constant source of amusement in Lincoln County where an archaic local patois was spoken.

Unlike many young Englishmen who came to the frontiers of the New World in search of adventure and freedom from conventional restraints, John Tunstall came in quest of profitable investments. After months of traveling and investigation, Tunstall arrived in New Mexico. He accepted the advice of Miguel A. Otero of Santa Fe to locate in Lincoln, where he meant to buy a ranch and open a mercantile business.

Tunstall purchased a quantity of supplies in Santa Fe, and, bearing a letter of introduction to Alexander McSween, he struck out for Lincoln, where he arrived in November, 1876.

McSween and Tunstall liked each other and found they had much in common. Soon they were close friends. While Tunstall was looking about for ranch property, Lawrence Murphy sent an emissary to McSween, offering McSween a sizable gratuity if the attorney would induce Tunstall to purchase a certain lower Bonito ranch from Murphy. Murphy could produce no valid title to the property, and McSween was offended by the proposition, which he bluntly refused. The tone of McSween's refusal did nothing to mend relations between the attorney and Lawrence G. Murphy.

Tunstall found a ranch to his liking on the Feliz River, about forty miles south of Lincoln. He stocked it with four hundred prime young cattle purchased from John Chisum. Tunstall acquired a *remuda* of fine horses, and, when he felt the ranch was completely stocked and equipped, he hired a foreman, Richard Brewer. Brewer was young, but he was reputed to be honest and a capable cattleman.

With Brewer in charge of the ranch and things running smoothly there, Tunstall turned his attention to the construction of a store building in Lincoln. He selected a location about a quarter of a mile east of Murphy's building, on the opposite side of the village's single street, and next to McSween's home. The building was a narrow, thick-walled adobe, a hundred feet or so in length, with an angle in front conforming to the bend of the street. Heavy shutters covered the windows, and two small openings in the west wall were designed for ventilation. The Lincoln County Bank, a new enterprise, was located in the west end of the building. The bank was financed by Tunstall, John S. Chisum, and a St. Louis investor, and Alexander McSween was active in its administration.

The store and the bank prospered from the first. Local ranchers and farmers who had suffered from the high prices and severe business practices of L. G. Murphy & Company, which had so long operated without competition, brought their business to the new firms. Murphy viewed the prosperity of Tunstall's store with growing concern. He mistakenly believed McSween to be Tunstall's partner in the store which was cutting away his profit, and chalked up another score against the attorney.

John Tunstall, judged by local standards, was extremely picturesque. In his high, polished riding boots, impeccably tailored breeches and jacket, and peaked cap, and flourishing a riding crop, he appeared as much out of character as would a conventionally clad cowboy in London's Trafalgar Square.

It is not easy to explain the meeting of minds which produced an instant sense of kinship and loyalty between John Tunstall and William H. Bonney. Measured by yardsticks of education, environment, and the social code by which each lived, two more different men than Tunstall and Billy the Kid could not be found. And yet, at their very first meeting was born a friendship and understanding destined to continue during the brief period Tunstall was to survive, and to change, irrevocably, the course of Billy's life.

Chapter III

WILLIAM H. BONNEY was seventeen years old the morning he met John Tunstall in Lincoln. Almost nothing is known of his birth, his family, or his early years. Tradition has it that he was born in Brooklyn, New York, on November 23, 1859, of parents who soon moved West in the hope of bettering their poor circumstances. At some point, the husband and father died, and the widow, with two small boys, moved on.

She spent some time in Santa Fe, and there she is known to have married one William Antrim. Her name appears in the marriage register as Katherine McCarthy. Nothing in Billy's story or in the legend explains this name. However, it is known that the Antrims soon left Santa Fe for Silver City in southwest New Mexico. Silver City was a busy mining community, and, until 1950, a plain wooden slab in the cemetery marked the grave of Mrs. Antrim.

Mrs. Antrim is remembered in Silver City for her kindness to underprivileged children and to persons down on their luck for one reason or another. She operated a boardinghouse and, while the family was not particularly prosperous, Katherine Antrim was able to be helpful to those less fortunate than she. When her son was twelve years old, he left Silver City. Perhaps Billy was involved in the stabbing of a local ruffian who had insulted his mother, as some tales have it. Possibly he couldn't be happy with his stepfather, as Billy, himself, said. The facts about these early years are so beclouded by tradition and legend that it is hard to learn what really happened.

It *is* known that Billy wandered about the West for a number of years. We have some illuminating anecdotes from this period, related by Billy and by others, which portray a lad remarkably competent to take care of himself in difficult circumstances—circumstances which could have broken many grown men—and did! It is reasonable to suppose that these experiences hardened and matured the youngster.

Good companions were not readily available to a boy in his situation, and some of Billy's associates were of doubtful character. One of these undesirables was Jesse Evans whom Billy first knew when both were boys in Silver City. Jesse Evans was a few years older than Billy, but, physically, much like him. For some months in 1877, Billy had hung about Lincoln with young Evans and a band of men who sometimes worked for Murphy and sometimes operated as a free-lance group. Probably they were occupied with rustling cattle.

Evans and the Kid rode in from the Ruidoso one afternoon and saw John Tunstall dismounting before his store. His unusual garb attracted their attention, and, as they reined up beside the Englishman, Evans broke into a boisterous laugh.

"What the hell can that be, Billy?" Evans asked, in Spanish. "And where did it come from?"

Billy made no reply, but sat his horse, gazing intently at Tunstall.

Tunstall answered Evans in German. To Evans' next quip, Tunstall replied in French.

Evans turned to the Kid in perplexity.

"Can this be the Englishman we've heard of?" he asked. "His lingo sure don't sound like Navajo or Apache."

Tunstall smiled, and, in Castilian Spanish, replied, "No,

lads, that was neither Navajo nor Apache; just a little German and French. I do not speak Spanish as well as you, so let us use the English tongue."

Evans was annoyed by Tunstall's pleasantry.

"Can you rope and tie that down, Kid?" he snarled. "This *hombre* is made up of Dutch, French, greaser, and Anglo. He thinks he's damned smart, and I don't like being rode by his spurs."

Billy laughed at his friend's discomfiture, and Evans dismounted and walked around Tunstall's horse.

"Just to even the score," Evans said, "I think I'll trade horses with this gentleman."

The Kid's blue eyes darkened when he saw Tunstall's look of concern.

"Hold it, Jesse," Billy said quietly. "There won't be a trade."

"Who says so?" blustered Evans. "Are you riding with this mixed breed?"

"I said it, Jess, and it rides that way," the Kid replied.

In the silence that followed, the boys stared at each other. Then, remounting, Evans said, "All right, Kid, you win the pot this time. Let's ride."

Tunstall watched the pair move up the dusty, narrow street toward the Murphy store. Tunstall was puzzled by the little scene, but he felt a certain warmth for the boy who had befriended him in what had turned into a tense situation.

A few days later, Billy the Kid came into Lincoln alone. He passed the Murphy building and rode to Tunstall's store where he bought tobacco, cigarette papers, and .38 shells. Billy was untying his horse when Tunstall came from the building. The tall Briton smiled and extended his hand in greeting.

"I want to thank you for the service you did me the other day," Tunstall said. "To side against your friend was not easy. I am very fond of that horse for personal reasons, and I could not have defended the animal for I am seldom armed. In any case," Tunstall added, laughing, "I would have been outclassed by the well-known dexterity of Mr. Evans."

"It was nothing much," the Kid replied easily. "Jess is a pretty good Injun, and we buried the hatchet. He gets on the prod sometimes, and I was afraid he'd go for his gun. He's mighty fast."

"So I have heard," Tunstall said. "But I've also heard there is a lad known as 'the Kid' who is a fraction of a second faster."

Billy smiled at the implied compliment.

"You can hear a lot of things about me in this neighborhood," he said. "But they're not all true, sir!"

"You have been employed by the Murphy Company," Tunstall commented. It was a statement rather than a question.

"At times," Billy replied, "but mostly I've been on my own."

Tunstall studied the boy carefully for a moment, then he said, "Billy, every man must plan the pattern of his own life. Methods of doing business differ, and the methods of the Murphy Company are not mine. I am afraid association with that group may bring you trouble—or worse. Would you consider going on my payroll?"

The Kid's boyish face lighted with pleasure.

"Mr. Tunstall," he said, "I rode in today meaning to meet up with you. I didn't intend to ask you for a job, but I hoped you'd offer me one. You have just hired yourself a rider, sir. I'll go out to camp for my war bag, and report back."

"It won't be necessary for you to come here," Tunstall told him. "I will give you a note to Dick Brewer. You can cut across country to the Feliz Ranch. That will make a shorter ride."

So, easily and quickly, in the fall of 1877, had begun an association difficult of explanation between John Tunstall and the Kid. The relationship was to last only a few months, but, after Tunstall's death, the memory of his kindness influenced Billy's course of action.

When the Kid had ridden away, a rancher who had witnessed the meeting came forward and spoke to Tunstall.

"Mr. Tunstall, it's not my way to horn in on any man's game, but you're new in this section. You may not know all about that boy. I hope you haven't made a mistake. That Jesse Evans—"

"Thank you for your advice," Tunstall said firmly, "but I like the boy. I feel that he is trustworthy and will be a useful and loyal employee."

The rancher shook his head doubtfully and turned away.

Billy rode directly to the Evans camp and stated that he intended to work for Tunstall. The announcement gave rise to protests and heated arguments. The others in Evans' band believed that this move on Billy's part constituted a treacherous desertion, somehow dangerous to all of them. Evans, always the wise leader, interposed when he saw that the Kid would not be persuaded to stay.

"Boys," he said, "we've all camped, fought, and starved with the Kid. He came here openly and told us what he intends. Let him go—maybe he'll come back!"

The men recognized Evans' authority, and they all agreed, with the single exception of Frank Baker, who declared the Kid to be "a damned traitor."

Billy accepted this remark as a direct challenge, and, for a tense moment, it seemed there would be gunplay in the camp. When no one interfered, and Baker did not move for his gun, Billy turned his back on the angry man and mounted his horse. With a single regretful glance for Evans, his boyhood friend, Billy rode slowly out of the camp.

Chapter IV

THE dark clouds of the coming trouble were rapidly lowering over Lincoln. Tunstall's store was cutting deep inroads in Murphy's business, and L. G. Murphy had been unable to devise any means of circumventing the expansion of his competitor.

Major William Brady, like Murphy, had been mustered out at Fort Stanton, and was a strong supporter of his former comrade-at-arms. Brady had been appointed sheriff of Lincoln County, and there was a feeling in Lincoln that Brady would execute any process emanating from the Murphy-Dolan-Riley headquarters and would serve no warrant or other process initiated by others without first consulting Murphy.

In September, 1877, some of John Tunstall's valuable horses had been stolen by members of the Jesse Evans band. The stolen animals were quickly driven over the Texas border and delivered to an unscrupulous horse trader. The outlaws made small effort to conceal the theft and seemed without fear of apprehension. When they returned from Texas, Evans and his friends camped openly in the Seven Rivers section, along the Pecos. Murphy, apparently anxious to make it plain that he was not connected with the raid, directed Brady to go to Seven Rivers and take Evans and the other horse thieves into custody.

Sheriff Brady, with the aid of a single deputy, was able to bring Jesse Evans, Frank Baker, Tom Hill, and George David to Lincoln. The four outlaws were lodged in the crude *carcel*[1] to await action of the grand jury. There were many in the village who said that Brady could not have arrested the four without their complete co-operation, and the sheriff's "bravery" in accomplishing this mission was a local joke.

A day or two after Evans and his associates had been jailed, Juan B. Patron, a citizen of Lincoln, learned that the prisoners had filed off their shackles and cut the logs in their cell. Patron made a report to Brady, and the sheriff accompanied Patron on an inspection of the miserable jail, where they found the situation as described.

Brady, however, took no measures to secure the prisoners, and, later the same day, the sheriff went to Tunstall's store where he accused McSween and Tunstall of plotting the escape of the prisoners. To Tunstall, who had been the victim of the thieves, this accusation was laughable.

That same night, the four prisoners escaped and made their way to the ranch which belonged to Dick Brewer, Tunstall's foreman. Brewer was away, and the outlaws took horses, saddles, and arms.

The escape and the raid upon Brewer's ranch became known the next morning, and a number of citizens called upon Brady with an offer to form a posse of twenty to pursue and recapture the escapees. The posse intended to place the prisoners under guard at Fort Stanton for safekeeping. Tunstall proposed to pay all the expenses of this undertaking. And thus it may be noted that there was some opposition to lawlessness in the area. Law and an orderly enforcement of it were desired by at least twenty men, nineteen of whom stood to gain nothing by the action they proposed. Their intention was to support and encourage local officials.

The sheriff declined the proposition, and added, "I arrested them once, and I'll be damned if I'm going to

[1] See Appendix II, Note A, Chap. IV.

do it again—and if any one of you attempts to take the law into your own hands without being deputized by me, you'll occupy the quarters those fellows just vacated!"

The sheriff's statement ended the matter, and, a little later, Evans, Davis, Hill, and Baker were coming and going at will in Lincoln. No steps were taken to apprehend them, and this incident caused a great deal of local resentment.

A few weeks after, Murphy, hard-pressed by creditors who sensed that his position was weakening, sent James Dolan to arrange a temporary loan at the bank owned by Tunstall. It was rumored in Lincoln that tax funds, collected by Brady as sheriff, and deposited in Murphy's vault for safekeeping, were not intact.[2] Alexander McSween, who was negotiating the loan for Dolan, had heard the rumors, and he asked Dolan, "If this is just a temporary matter, why doesn't the firm borrow from Sheriff Brady?"

Dolan replied that Riley had already obtained funds from the sheriff.

Here, it is necessary to go back a little in time to explain the source of the complication that brought about the death of Tunstall and defined the quarrel between the Murphy-Dolan-Riley faction and the friends of the Tunstall-McSween-Chisum coalition.

Emil Fritz, the original and silent partner of Murphy, died in Germany in June, 1874, while on a visit to his native country. Lawrence G. Murphy was probate judge of Lincoln County at the time, but he took no action to administer Fritz's estate until April, 1875, after nearly a year had elapsed. Then Murphy appointed William Brady administrator of the Fritz estate. Brady employed

---

[2] *Mesilla Independent* (Mesilla, New Mexico Territory, January, 1878). See Appendix II, Note B, Chap. IV.

Alexander McSween, who had just come to Lincoln, to make collections for the estate, and he instructed McSween that Dolan and Murphy should receive all funds collected, including the proceeds of a ten-thousand-dollar life insurance policy with the Merchant's Life Insurance Company, of New York. Brady told McSween that Murphy had placed this policy in the hands of Levi Speigelberg, of New York, without Brady's knowledge. Levi Speigelberg was a wholesaler of merchandise, to whose Santa Fe branch Murphy was heavily indebted.

In October, 1876, Brady resigned the administratorship, and Charles Fritz and Mrs. Emilie Scholand, brother and sister of the deceased Emil Fritz, and his legal heirs, were appointed joint administrators of the estate. Charles Fritz asked Alexander McSween to continue to represent the estate in the same manner as he had under Brady's administratorship.

McSween made a trip to New York on behalf of the heirs and demanded of Speigelberg the insurance policy and some other papers pertaining to the Fritz estate. Speigelberg declined to recognize McSween's demand upon the ground that he held an order from Brady, as administrator, to collect and pay the money to the firm of Speigelberg Brothers, of Santa Fe. This statement contradicted Brady's assertion to McSween that Murphy gave Speigelberg the policy without Brady's knowledge.

A number of conferences between Speigelberg representatives and McSween resulted in the policy and the other papers being turned over to McSween. McSween then entered into an agreement with Donnell, Lawson and Company to represent the estate in New York and collect the insurance from Merchant's Life, which had, in the meantime, gone into the hands of receivers.

A letter came to McSween in Lincoln, July 19, 1877, from Donnell, Lawson and Company, informing him that they had collected the full ten thousand dollars. After deducting their charges, the New York firm held $7,148.49, subject to McSween's order. The charges of Donnell and Lawson, the letter explained, were large because the policy was difficult of collection, and, during the negotiation period—November, 1876, until July, 1877—the matter almost came to suit. The explanation of the charges seemed in order to Alexander McSween, and he notified Mrs. Scholand and Fritz that he was prepared to pay over to them, as co-administrators of the estate, the sum of $7,148.49, less his own fees. By this time, McSween's difficulties with Murphy, Dolan, and Riley were multiplying, and so McSween also stated in his letter to the Fritz heirs that he did not desire to represent them further in settling the estate.[3]

McSween had prepared for his move by applying to the new probate judge, Florencio Gonzales, for audit and approval of the policy. The account was duly approved.

In December, 1877, Charles Fritz visited McSween in the latter's office. Fritz said that he was satisfied with McSween's handling of the insurance policy. McSween told Fritz that he planned a business trip to St. Louis, and he explained how his business would be handled in his absence. McSween assured Fritz that, as soon as Fritz, or someone, was authorized by the court to receive the net proceeds of the policy, McSween was prepared to pay over the full amount, less the charges of Donnell and Lawson and himself.

Christmas Eve, in Las Vegas, on the first leg of his journey to St. Louis, McSween learned that Thomas B. Catron, United States District Attorney, had sent out an inquiry for him. McSween notified Catron that he was in Las Vegas, and the same night the sheriff of San Miguel County went to McSween's hotel. The sheriff had re-

[3] See Appendix II, Note C, Chap. IV.

ceived instructions from W. L. Rynerson, District Attorney of the Third Judicial District, that McSween was to be arrested for embezzlement of ten thousand dollars belonging to the Fritz estate!

A puzzled Alexander McSween remained at his hotel on parole, and, when a warrant from Rynerson arrived, he was jailed.

It may be observed that Lawrence G. Murphy, although his prestige in Lincoln County was on the wane, had been able to enlist impressive legal and political support in his plan to discredit McSween professionally and, possibly, to ruin him financially.

Billy the Kid, busy at Tunstall's Feliz Ranch, knew nothing of these events as they were happening, and could not have anticipated how he would be affected, had he known.

Chapter V

McSWEEN, in the charge of a deputy sheriff, and with a party of friends, including John H. Tunstall, left Las Vegas January 4, 1878. The group went across country to Mesilla, where McSween was examined by Judge Warren Bristol, of the Third Judicial District. At the suggestion of Bristol, McSween consented to the continuance of his case until a grand jury, scheduled for April in Lincoln, should meet.

McSween and his friends, returning to Lincoln February 7, encountered Jesse Evans and James Dolan, together with Frank Baker and Jack Long, members of Evans' band. Tunstall and McSween were challenged and threatened by Evans and Dolan, but Deputy Sheriff Barrier of Las Vegas, in whose custody McSween remained, prevented an incident.

It was not until the McSween party reached Lincoln that they learned that Dolan had been acting as a courier and had raced into Lincoln a few hours earlier with a writ of attachment, issued by Bristol and dated February 7, the day of McSween's departure from Mesilla. Mrs. Scholand and Charles Fritz appeared as plaintiffs in the writ, and Sheriff Brady began at once to attach under it. He had been directed to attach McSween's property sufficient to secure the sum of $8,000. However, according to McSween's deposition,[1] sheriff Brady attached real and personal property belonging to McSween, John H. Tunstall, and McSween's brother-in-law, D. P. Shield, totalling more than $40,000 by McSween's valuation.

[1] See Appendix II, Note A, Chap. V.

Although Alexander McSween had been helpful to Tunstall in establishing his business, had served as the Briton's attorney in one or two matters, and had loaned him four thousand dollars, the two men were not partners in the Tunstall store or the Feliz Ranch ventures. Articles of partnership had been drawn up, but the agreement was not to become effective until May, 1878. Thus, Tunstall was not legally liable to attachment on McSween's account, but he offered no protest when part of his Lincoln property was attached. He expressed confidence in the outcome of the charges against McSween, and so allowed the illegal attachment.

About February 14, Tunstall learned that W. S. Mathews, an employee of Murphy, was at the Feliz Ranch with Evans, Baker, Hill, and Davis, as a sheriff's posse, to attach Tunstall's cattle and horses. Brewer, Tunstall's foreman, told Mathews the posse could round up the cattle, and take any belonging to McSween. Brewer added that he would not allow Mathews to remove Tunstall's property as there was no writ or order against Tunstall. Brewer's firmness had not been anticipated, since Tunstall had allowed his Lincoln property to be attached, and so Mathews returned to Sheriff Brady in Lincoln for instructions.

The same day, R. A. Widenmann, who worked for Tunstall, sought out the Englishman in Lincoln. Widenmann reported to Tunstall that Mathews meant to raise a large posse of Murphy men and remove the cattle by a show of force. Widenmann believed the posse would gather late in the day, February 16, at Turkey Springs, a few miles from the Feliz Ranch.

Tunstall heard other rumors also about the size of the proposed posse and the intent of its members, and he decided to go to the ranch and persuade his men to leave. He meant to allow the cattle and horses to be seized and then seek remedy in the courts. This sacrifice seemed worth while to Tunstall in the interests of law and justice, and to prevent bloodshed.

Later, Brewer, Middleton, Billy the Kid, and others informed McSween that Tunstall arrived at the Feliz Ranch in the evening, February 17, explained the situation, and instructed all his men to leave. When the men protested, Tunstall said that he would not sacrifice the life of a single man for all the cattle. He then sent a message to Mathews that no resistance would be offered.

With these arrangements completed, Tunstall and his men left for Lincoln, confident that trouble had been averted and that all would be well.

Alexander McSween, in his deposition before United States Commissioner Frank Warner Angel, Agent, Department of Justice and Department of the Interior, describes what followed:

On the night of the 18th, I was informed by Brewer, Bonney, Middleton, and Widenmann that Tunstall had been murdered on the road to Lincoln about thirty miles from his ranch by Evans, Baker, Dolan, Morton, Corcoran, Gallegos, Wallace Ollinger, Roberts, Hill, George Davis, R. W. Beckwith, Tom Green, George Hindman, John Hurley, and others to the number of eighteen men. They said that at the time of the murder they were some distance from Tunstall. He, however, tried to make his escape, but failed to do so. I was also informed by Tom Green, who was present when the murder was committed, that Morton, who was acting as deputy under Mathews, called out to Tunstall, "Stop! I want to see you. I don't want to hurt you." Tunstall then dismounted and walked towards Morton, and delivered to him the Colt's pistol he was carrying. A few minutes later Evans took aim at Tunstall and shot him, the ball taking effect in his breast. As Tunstall fell on his face, Morton fired another shot at Tunstall out of Tunstall's own revolver, the ball entering the back of his head and coming out in the forehead. Morton then walked to Tunstall's horse and fired another shot from Tunstall's revolver at the horse. The horse dropped dead, and the murderers carried Tunstall's body and laid it close by the side of the horse, putting Tunstall's hat under the dead horse's head.

This was the single climactic event which brought on the bloody and infamous Lincoln County War, and it was at this point, precisely, that William H. Bonney emerged from the shadows of his youthful years to stand, fully revealed, in the light of the inevitable consequences of the death of John H. Tunstall.

Chapter VI

McSWEEN ordered Tunstall's body brought into Lincoln for burial, and requested a post mortem[1] and inquest. The day following Tunstall's death, February 19, acting upon affidavits filed by McSween, J. B. Wilson, Lincoln justice of the peace, issued warrants of arrest for certain members of the posse and placed these in the hands of Atanacio Martinez, constable, for service. Martinez wisely felt he needed help and requested Waite and Billy the Kid to join him in making the arrests. When the trio called at the Murphy store to contact the wanted men, Brady summarily jailed all three.

All of these developments were known in Lincoln, and, on February 22 a meeting of citizens was held and a committee named to learn of Sheriff Brady why he had not allowed service of the murder warrants, why Bonney and Waite were still being held, and what bond Brady would accept from McSween on the property under attachment in the Fritz matter. The committee received no satisfactory reply to these questions.

Brady placed deputies in Tunstall's store, and McSween, dissatisfied with their conduct, charged Brady with appropriation of goods. Peace Justice Wilson ordered Brady to appear before the scheduled grand jury to answer the charges.

Since Billy the Kid, Constable Martinez, and Fred Waite had failed to serve the warrants, Justice Wilson, on March 1, appointed a number of special deputies, headed by Dick Brewer, to arrest those charged in Alexander Mc-

[1] See Appendix II, Note A, Chap. VI.

Sween's information with the murder of Tunstall. When Brewer learned that two of the wanted men, Morton and Baker, were at Dolan's ranch on the Pecos, a hundred miles from Lincoln, he quickly organized his posse. Among its members were Billy the Kid, Charles Bowdre, Frank McNab, Fred Waite, Jim French, John Middleton, Hendry Brown, J. G. (Doc) Scurlock, and one other, McCloskey. Brewer was doubtful about McCloskey as he had reason to suppose McCloskey was a partisan of Murphy. However, the man seemed anxious to accompany the posse, and Brewer allowed him to do so.

The posse scouted for several days, and, on March 6, found a party of five on the lower Penasco River. The five men put spurs to their horses and fled. Members of Brewer's posse pursued. The fleeing men ran a few miles and then split into two parties, and one group of three made for the hills.

Morton and Baker continued their flight, heading in the direction of Dolan's ranch. Billy recognized them and spurred ahead to lead the chase. After a time, lucky shots brought down the horses of both fugitives. Morton and Baker succeeded in reaching an abandoned adobe house, where they made a stand.

After two days of sporadic shooting, Morton called to Brewer that he and Baker would surrender if Brewer would guarantee their safe conduct to Lincoln. Otherwise, Morton said, he and Baker would stay on in the house to the end.

Bonney favored the latter course, and declared his feelings to Brewer.

"Just tell them to come out fighting like men and take their chances," he urged. "That will be a hell of a lot better chance than they gave John Tunstall."

"I agree with you, Billy," Brewer said, "but I am acting as a sworn officer of the law, deputized to arrest these men. I have no choice."

From a position behind a tree, Brewer called, "It's all right, Morton. Throw your guns out the door and come out one at a time, reaching for the clouds."

When the men came out, Morton, who had been on friendly terms with Billy when both were riding with Jesse Evans, offered his hand to the boy in friendly greeting.

"You black-hearted son-of-a-bitch," Billy said, "I don't know you, and I don't want to."

Billy stood for a moment, his eyes searing the face of the man who had shot Tunstall; then he turned and walked to his horse.

The posse and the two prisoners traveled to John Chisum's South Spring Ranch to remain overnight. Morton requested writing materials and spent the evening writing a letter, which, although not always consistent with the known facts, alibies Morton very well and indicates his confidence of finding protection in Lincoln.[2]

March 9, the posse left the ranch on the long journey to Lincoln. At Roswell, the group delayed long enough for Morton to post his letter. It was addressed to a cousin in Richmond, Virginia. Morton asked M. A. (Ash) Upson, Roswell's eccentric postmaster, to register the letter. This was a fairly unusual request, and Upson, surprised, asked Morton if he expected anything to happen to him and to Baker en route to Lincoln.

"No, I don't, Ash," replied Morton. "Brewer has promised to deliver us safely in Lincoln, but I know some members of the posse would be glad to murder us, and, if that should happen, I want my people back home to be informed."

"Before anything can happen to you," offered Mc-

[2] See Appendix II, Note B, Chap. VI.

Closkey, who had overheard Morton, "they will have to kill me first. You have my word on that."

McNab, who was standing near, dropped his hand to his gun and confronted McCloskey.

"Damn you for a yellow, double-crossing coyote. How in hell you got in this posse, I don't know—unless Dolan planted you, somehow. Watch your step, *hombre,* because I'm watching you!"

During this highly charged interchange, Billy the Kid watched quietly.

The party resumed its travel toward Lincoln. There have been conflicting accounts of what occurred on the journey. Here is the report of Billy the Kid to McSween, in Lincoln, confirmed by Dick Brewer, on his official return of the warrants:

> We knew some members of the posse were determined to kill Morton and Baker on the way back to Lincoln. I hadn't wanted to take them prisoners, but, since they were, I didn't want to kill unarmed men, either. I had hoped they would take their chances and come out of that old house fighting like men. I knew Baker to be a coward, but Morton was a real fighting man, even if he did shoot Tunstall. Brewer had given his word, and, while I didn't like it and cussed him plenty, I intended to help him carry it out. When we left Roswell, we believed the three riders who had escaped us before would head for Dolan's ranch and return with a bunch of warriors to free Morton and Baker and give us some hell, so we were plenty careful.
>
> McCloskey and Middleton rode close beside the prisoners. Brewer had told Middleton to watch McCloskey, for he didn't trust him. Charlie Bowdre and I scouted some distance ahead, while the rest of the posse acted as a rear guard. About thirty miles from Roswell, Frank McNab and Hendry Brown rode up to McCloskey and Middleton. Frank put his gun close to McCloskey's head, saying, "So you're the damned bastard who said you'd have to be killed before anything can happen to these *hombres.*"
>
> McNab fired as he spoke, and McCloskey fell from the saddle, dead. Middleton had no chance to interfere, and, if he had, he'd have been killed, too. I heard the one shot and turned to see what had

happened, and saw Morton and Baker in a full gallop, away from the group. There was confusion. A number of the possemen were milling around the spot where McCloskey had fallen, while others, led by Dick Brewer, were riding after the prisoners, firing as they rode.

My first thought was that Morton and Baker had somehow got guns—maybe from McCloskey—and made their break. I expected them to separate, which would have been good sense, so I told Bowdre to follow Baker and I would look after Morton, but they stuck together.

I was riding Old Grey, and he is some ground-gainer. I cut across at an angle and yelled to them to pull up. Morton only waved his hand, and they both spurred their horses, hard. I was still out of range, but I forced Old Grey to shorten the distance while I got my rifle from the boot. When I got within less than a hundred yards of them, I pulled up short and dismounted to aim. I fired twice, first at Baker, then at Morton. I got them both—pretty lucky shots. Perhaps it was just as well, for I'm certain, had they reached Lincoln, Brady would have arranged their escape. That is just the way it all happened, Mr. McSween.

After the shooting, the Kid walked to where the victims lay. He ignored Baker's body, but stooped and turned Morton's face to the sky and momentarily looked down at his former friend. He asked no questions just then, as to how the escape attempt originated, and appeared sober and thoughtful, showing neither elation nor regret. Perhaps he was thinking of the death of Tunstall.

McSween was saddened by the report of violence, but he seemed satisfied with the explanation of Bonney and Brewer, and, apparently, public sentiment was, too, for when the grand jury met in April it took no official notice of the affair, and no indictments were returned.

Chapter VII

WHILE these grim events were unfolding, Alexander McSween's own troubles were running counterpoint. He had made an appearance bond, even though his bondsmen had been threatened, but Rynerson had refused it. A second bond was executed, and it, too, was rejected. McSween continued in the custody of Deputy Sheriff A. P. Barrier, who had accompanied him from Las Vegas in January. Barrier declined to deliver McSween to Brady as Barrier's knowledge of the local situation convinced him that to do so would jeopardize McSween's life.

The death of Tunstall had served to crystallize the opinions of residents of the area toward the Murphy-Dolan-Riley-Brady group, and the weight of that opinion was unfavorable.

A few days after Tunstall's funeral, a small delegation of military men from Fort Stanton came to the McSween home in order to learn, unofficially, how matters stood. This delegation, headed by Colonel Purrington, post commandant, and accompanied by Sheriff Brady, found a number of McSween's friends at his home. These men, farmers and stockmen for the most part, explained that they proposed to protect McSween's life. The colonel heard and seemed to accept McSween's account of events, and his interpretation of them, and left with his party.

Dolan had been dispatched to Mesilla, armed with affidavits to support the issuance of an alias writ for the arrest of McSween, and a writ for Deputy Barrier's arrest for contempt of court, based upon the deputy's refusal to surrender his prisoner to the custody of the sheriff of Lincoln County. When Dolan's errand became known, friends of McSween and Barrier entreated them to leave town. The two men slipped out of Lincoln at night and found refuge at various ranch houses.

March 10, McSween arrived at Chisum's South Spring Ranch and remained there until March 29. On that day, McSween, in the company of John Chisum, Barrier, and others, returned to Lincoln to attend court, which was scheduled for April 1. They arrived in Lincoln about noon of April 1 and learned, for the first time, of the grim events of the morning.

William Brady, sheriff of Lincoln County, and George Hindman, his deputy, "Dad" Peppin, and Court Clerk J. B. Mathews left the Murphy store on the morning of April 1. The men were on an errand for Judge Warren Bristol. The spring term of court had been scheduled to convene in Lincoln on April 1. Over in Mesilla, Judge Bristol was fully informed of the turbulent conditions in Lincoln, and he had come to feel that discretion was the better part for him. He decided to postpone the session of the court until some later, and safer, date. His decision is understandable, but perhaps it was ill-advised. A firm and courageous jurist in Lincoln at that critical time might have been instrumental in bringing about peace.

In a letter to Brady, Judge Bristol directed the sheriff to satisfy the legal formalities by opening and then adjourning court, and announcing that it would be reconvened at an undetermined date. Brady, Hindman, Peppin, and Mathews carried rifles and wore sidearms as they walked east along the village street toward the small adobe structure which served the town as schoolhouse, court, and assembly place.

Brady and his men had passed San Juan Church a few

paces when they were fired upon from behind a low adobe wall by a group which included Billy the Kid, Jim French, Charles Bowdre, and several other partisans of McSween and Tunstall, all of whom had just arrived in Lincoln. Brady was killed at once, and Mathews and Peppin took cover behind a near-by building to return the fire. Hindman, wounded, lay in the dusty road under the bright April sun, pleading for water.

Ike Stockton, a newcomer to Lincoln, witnessed the shooting. Stockton was a bad man in his own right and was subsequently hanged for murder in Colorado, but he was moved by the pleas of the dying Hindman to run a hundred yards to the Bonito and return with a hatful of water. No shot was fired by either faction as Stockton raised the wounded man's head. Hindman drank deeply, and died.

After a short time, the firing ceased. Billy the Kid believed Mathews and Peppin had abandoned their hiding place to report to Murphy, and so Billy leaped the adobe wall and bent over Brady's body, in the open, to pick up the rifle Brady had been carrying. A shot came from the rear of the adjacent building, and the bullet struck the stock of Brady's rifle in Billy's hand and glanced, tearing a painful wound in the boy's side. The Kid stood, coolly immobile, until he observed a slight movement at the corner of the building from whence the shot had come. Then, firing rapidly at the corner, he walked backward, covering his own retreat, and rejoined the men behind the wall.

Billy, knowing that the gunfight would invite quick retaliation from the Murphy group, directed Charles Bowdre, Tom O'Folliard, Harvey Morris, and Fred Waite to ride at once to the Feliz Ranch to bring Dick Brewer and the rest of the men to Lincoln to protect McSween. Then

Billy and his four remaining companions circled to enter McSween's house from the rear.

A number of persons who were gathered at the McSween home had full knowledge of the gun battle. Mrs. Ealy, wife of the Presbyterian minister, who was a guest of the McSweens, was the first to speak to Billy.

"Billy, you have done a terrible thing. I pray God will forgive you. Sheriff Brady's men were not looking for you. They were on their way to the courtroom! Many of our friends will see this as deliberate slaughter, and it will do our cause great harm."

Mrs. Ealy's remarks surprised and perplexed the boy. He stood silent and thoughtful, absently pressing his hand to his side. It was only then that kindly Mrs. Ealy noticed that Billy was hurt and summoned her husband, who was a physician as well as a minister, to care for his wound.

In the early afternoon, McSween and the others arrived from Spring Ranch. McSween was told of the gun battle, and his shoulders slumped. He looked suddenly tired and discouraged—almost ill.

"Governor," Billy said to McSween, "I'm sorry it happened this way. We believed Brady was coming for us. We thought they meant to flank us and reach the side wall by the Torreon. Then we wouldn't have had a chance."

McSween seemed unable to speak.

"I'm not trying to shirk the blame, Governor," Billy said. "I knew this might bring a lot of trouble, so I sent for Dick Brewer to come at once with the rest of the boys. The four who stayed are on guard in the patio, and they can hold off the Murphy men until Dick can get here."

McSween's face was ashen, and his hand trembled as he put aside the Bible he had been holding. He did not lack spiritual courage, but he had suffered severe shock.

McSween's face was grave. "Billy, I deplore what has happened. Violence is the thing John Tunstall and I tried so hard to avoid. I cannot condone the taking of human life! Besides, I will be blamed for these deaths, and our just cause will suffer. May God help me now, for I don't know what is best to do!"

Several bystanders were quick to advise that Billy be sent away, but McSween did not appear to hear them. Susan McSween observed her husband's indecision, and she sensed the uncertainty and growing tension in the room. She assumed command of the situation by asking Billy to recount everything that had happened since the McSweens had seen him last. Susan listened quietly while Billy told of the pursuit of Morton and Baker, their capture, and their deaths.

He said that the posse, under Brewer's command, had remained at the Feliz Ranch until they began to fear for the safety of Mr. and Mrs. McSween. Bonney and eight friends had ridden to Lincoln, at Brewer's direction, to protect the McSweens if necessary. As they dismounted near the wall, they saw the heavily-armed Brady approaching. Billy and the others crouched low behind the wall. A rifle was fired, and the battle began. Billy stated that he did not fire first, and that he had not fired at either Brady or Hindman.

"Why did you foolishly risk your life to get Sheriff Brady's rifle?" Susan McSween asked.

"It was not his, ma'am," the Kid said. "It was mine."

"Then how did it come into the possession of Sheriff Brady?" Mrs. McSween demanded.

There was silence in the big room.

"John Tunstall was the only friend I ever had, besides my mother," Billy began, softly. "He gave me my first real job, and, when I started work, he gave me a new saddle and Old Grey—and there is no better horse, anywhere. One evening, in his office, I admired a fine rifle on the wall. He took it down and gave it to me. I thought more of it than anything I ever owned, except Old Grey."

The boy paused, and his eyes, searching the faces of the listeners, seemed very blue.

"Mrs. McSween," Billy said, "I owe my life to Mr. Tunstall's gift after what happened today. You remember Waite and I went to Murphy's store with Constable Martinez to try to serve warrants on some members of that posse that killed Mr. Tunstall? Well, Sheriff Brady jailed us. When I was released a few days later, the sheriff returned my gun and holster, but refused to give me my rifle. I got it back today."

Susan McSween had been listening intently as Billy talked. Now that she had heard his story, she did not look to her stricken husband for action.

"I want you to remain here, Billy," she said decisively. "Doctor Ealy will attend to your wound. This violence has been unfortunate, and it will bring us new trouble. Very well, then, we will meet it as we have done before. Please remain on watch with your men until Brewer arrives."

Chapter VIII

LATER in the evening, McSween submitted to arrest by Dad Peppin, who explained he was acting sheriff. The charge was the old one—embezzlement—and the warrant was the alias warrant obtained by Dolan while McSween was absent from Lincoln. This was not the violent move McSween and Billy had anticipated, and McSween seemed relieved to go with Peppin.

McSween's friends were uneasy, however, and applied to Colonel Purrington for his protection. They insisted that the prisoner be held at Fort Stanton for safekeeping. Purrington had been friendly to McSween when he investigated the circumstances of Tunstall's death, but now the colonel seemed reluctant to have McSween at the fort. Finally, however, he agreed.

Before he removed McSween from his home, Peppin searched the house for arms. According to McSween and his friends, Peppin had no warrant for the search, and it had not even the color of legality.

Billy the Kid is not mentioned in accounts of the late evening of April 1. Quite apparently, he and his four companions had left the premises at the time of Peppin's search, for Peppin arrested, without warrants, George Washington (a Negro), Shield (McSween's brother-in-law), Widenmann, and Robinson. The four were charged with implication in the deaths of Brady and Hindman. The ostensible search for arms was probably a search for Bonney and the others, and when he failed to find them, Peppin lodged charges against four men he well knew had no part in the gunfight.

McSween and his four friends went to Fort Stanton in the company of Purrington, to await the convening of court. During the week the prisoners remained at Fort Stanton, Colonel Purrington was relieved of his command, and Colonel N. A. M. Dudley assumed command of the post.

April 8, ruling on the embezzlement charge against McSween, Judge Warren Bristol, who had come to Lincoln a week late, held that the matter should be submitted to the grand jury, and he approved bail bond for McSween's release.

The grand jury examined the charges, questioned a number of witnesses, and presented the court the following findings:

> Your Honor charged us to investigate the case of Alex A. McSween, Esq., charged with the embezzlement of ten thousand dollars, belonging to the estate of Emil Fritz, deceased. This we did, but were unable to find any evidence that would justify that accusation. We fully exonerate him of the charge, and regret that a spirit of persecution has been shown in the matter.[1]

This, then, was the conclusion of an action that had brought untold unhappiness and loss of time, money, business, and property to Alexander McSween, dating from December 24, 1877, to April 10, 1878. During that period, McSween had been several times arrested, imprisoned, transported about the state as a prisoner, forced to make exorbitant bonds, hounded into hiding, threatened, and abused. The same action had been the direct cause of the death of John H. Tunstall, Morton, Baker, McCloskey, Brady, and Hindman.

The vindication of McSween by the grand jury did not resolve the difficulties at Lincoln. Murphy, Dolan, and Riley still had their financial troubles, McSween was bitter, five men were dead, and feelings were inflamed.

---

[1] See Appendix II, Note A, Chap. VIII.

Chapter IX

LINCOLN COUNTY was without a sheriff for a few days after the death of Brady on April 1. Peppin, who had been one of Brady's deputies, simply usurped the duties and privileges of the office. Peppin's position was weak, however, and Alexander McSween took recourse in the law for which he had such great respect. He prepared and filed with the Board of County Commissioners a petition for the appointment of John N. Copeland to fill the vacancy. The commissioners acted promptly, and, on April 10, Copeland was formally sworn in as sheriff.

The Tunstall-McSween faction experienced a sense of satisfaction at having a sheriff whom they believed to be honest and capable, but Copeland's tenure proved brief. Upon complaints to Territorial Governor Samuel B. Axtell by Murphy, Dolan, and Riley, Copeland was removed. The governor's removal order alleged that Copeland had failed to make a proper bond as the ex officio tax collector of the county. The governor designated George W. (Dad) Peppin as sheriff. This act of Governor Axtell's was one of the principal reasons for his subsequent removal by President Hayes.

During Copeland's period of service, there was a lull in the factional fighting, although McSween and Billy the Kid continued determined to bring the killers of Tunstall to justice. One of those they most wanted was Al Roberts. Roberts had been present when Tunstall was slain. He was no more or no less guilty than other posse members, but, since the death of Tunstall, Roberts had been waging a private war against friends of Tunstall and McSween wherever they might be found.

Roberts had acquired the name "Buckshot" from having been wounded in a gunfight by a charge of those lethal pellets. The wound left him permanently lame, and he could not raise his rifle above his waist with his right arm, but fired from the hip in the manner of a man shooting a pistol.

Buckshot had lived a colorful life, and was rumored to have killed four Texas Rangers before fleeing to New Mexico. In Lincoln County he found work and security with Murphy, by whom he was employed in an unspecified capacity.

When he came to Lincoln County, Roberts made a number of friendly calls upon Frank Coe, a well-known young rancher whose homestead was well up on the Ruidoso River. Coe felt that Roberts was not to be trusted, but he did nothing to arouse Robert's animosity, and Roberts visited the Coe homestead freely.

Roberts was believed to have been assigned by Murphy to liquidate Billy the Kid, Bowdre, Brewer, O'Folliard, and one or two others who Murphy thought were especially dangerous to him. These killings would have served the dual purpose of avenging the deaths of Morton and Brady and of weakening, significantly, the McSween fighting force.

Buckshot made an attempt to shoot Billy the Kid and Bowdre from ambush. Because the range was great, his shots were not effective, but Bowdre received a flesh wound, and this made him fighting mad. He and Billy recognized their assailant, and Bowdre was for taking immediate action to kill Roberts. Billy the Kid was able to prevail upon Bowdre to ignore the attempt, for the time. Billy knew that Murphy had procured an appointment as deputy constable for Roberts.

It was at Blazer's Mill, located on the edge of the Mescalero Apache Reservation, that Buckshot Roberts met the posse headed by another deputy constable, Dick Brewer, on April 8. Brewer had organized the posse ostensibly to capture one George Davis, who headed a daring group of rustlers operating in the extreme southwest corner of Lincoln County, with headquarters on the Tularosa slope at Rincanalla. However, it seems likely that Brewer expected his posse to meet Buckshot Roberts.

Members of the posse included Billy the Kid, who had come to be Brewer's right-hand man, Frank Coe and his cousin, George Coe, Bill Scroggins, Charlie Bowdre, Hendry Brown, Jim French, John Middleton, Tom O'Folliard, Stephen Stevens, Doc Scurlock, Fred Waite, and Brewer, the leader. The posse made a search of the area without finding a trace of Davis, and stopped at Blazer's Mill on the return journey to Lincoln.

Dr. Emil Blazer, a retired dentist, owned the only lumber mill in the section and supplied building materials throughout the county. Blazer had a large establishment, and many of the men in the posse, as well as Buckshot Roberts, had been guests of the doctor from time to time.

The posse arrived at noon. The horses were turned into the corral, and the men, as was the hospitable custom, were invited to remain for the midday meal. Brewer asked Blazer for news of Buckshot Roberts, explaining that he held a warrant for Roberts' arrest. Blazer answered evasively. He did not want to become involved in the factional dispute which, by now, was coming to be called "war." Blazer had no quarrel with any of the principals. His mill was a long distance from Lincoln, and he was both peaceful and businesslike by inclination.

Brewer directed George Coe and John Middleton to stand guard while the other posse members had a noonday dinner. They had just gone inside when Roberts appeared, riding his big bay mule. Coe, Middleton, and Roberts were all surprised, but Roberts calmly dismounted near a small log outbuilding. He was armed with two six-shooters, a Sharps rifle, and a wide cartridge belt containing a plentiful supply of ammunition. The sentinels had covered Roberts when he came into view, and now they called a warning to Brewer, inside. Within seconds, Roberts was held under the sights of thirteen rifles.

Brewer invited Roberts to surrender. Roberts debated the issue, and, as he did so, the canny old gunman edged into the outbuilding. From there he called out a challenge to the posse.

The posse deployed at Brewer's order, and Frank Coe stepped forward to see if he could persuade Roberts to surrender. Coe failed to move Roberts' resolve to shoot it out, and he withdrew. At that moment, Bowdre, George Coe, John Middleton, and Billy the Kid stepped around the corner of the building. Bowdre, with Roberts squarely in his sights, ordered Roberts to drop his gun. Then Roberts and Bowdre fired simultaneously. Bowdre's bullet passed through Roberts' middle, inflicting a fatal wound, but the old man did not go down. Roberts' shot struck the buckle of Bowdre's belt and deflected, dropping Bowdre with a painful wound in the groin.

Another shot struck George Coe, mangling his right hand and severing his trigger finger. Coe dropped his rifle, and Roberts' third shot passed through a fold of his shirt. John Middleton fell with a bullet through his chest, and he appeared to be dead. Billy the Kid, not fully recovered from the wound he had received in the gunfight with Sheriff Brady and the deputies, felt the leather band torn from his hat by a near miss.

While Roberts' rapid fire was doing all this damage, posse members were firing at him, and he received other wounds besides the first shot fired by Bowdre. Roberts was dying, but, still firing, he pulled an old mattress to the floor and lay upon it with his rifle aimed at the door so that he could only be taken from the front. Here the situation seemed stalemated.

Blazer came out from cover and argued with Buckshot that he should give up so that his wounds could be treated. Roberts refused. He declared to Dr. Blazer that he was dying and meant, if possible, to take Billy the Kid, Bowdre, and Brewer with him.

Dr. Blazer advised Brewer to withdraw his men and wait for Roberts to die. Brewer feared a trick by Roberts and said he would stay to finish the matter. Placing his men so that they covered all points but the front door of the cabin, Brewer circled widely to lie behind a pile of logs about fifty yards before the door. Roberts was not visible, and no sound came from the little building.

Brewer eased his revolver across a log and fired several times into the room, then quickly dropped prone behind his barricade. There were no answering shots, but, wary as Brewer had been, he had underestimated Roberts. Buckshot knew Brewer's position. He put his sights upon the place and waited. Moments passed before Brewer cautiously raised his head, hoping to glimpse Roberts. Instantly, a rifle shot sounded, and Dick Brewer fell back, the top of his head literally blown away by a single ball from Roberts' Sharps.

The leadership of the posse, by unspoken consent, was assumed immediately by Billy the Kid. Billy accepted the assurance of Blazer that Roberts was dead, or dying, and he left with his men for Frank Coe's ranch where the injured could be treated. Middleton was in critical condition, and both Coe and Bowdre would need surgery. Billy thought it unwise to take the wounded men to Fort Stanton as the new commandant seemed sympathetic to the enemy. To return the wounded to Lincoln would make the whole group vulnerable to hostile action by Murphy's town forces, and so Billy began to make a plan to convey the wounded men to Roswell.

Their problem was solved when the posse had gone about ten miles from Blazer's Mill. Five mounted men approached the spot where the posse had halted to watch, with some misgivings. The posse members were in no position to flee, and they had no inclination to do battle, and so they were overjoyed to learn that one of the riders was Dr. Gordon, post surgeon at Fort Stanton. The other four cavalrymen were escorting him to the Mescalero Indian Reservation to attend the Indian agent, who had been injured.

Dr. Gordon was able to treat the injured men, and he left instructions for their further care. He also agreed to go to Blazer's Mill to look after Roberts. At the mill, Dr. Gordon found that Dr. Blazer's carpenters had constructed rude coffins from discarded lumber, and, in the evening, Brewer and Roberts were buried side by side near the site of the battle.

The encounter at Blazer's Mill was one of the most desperate fights ever waged by one man against overwhelming odds. Months later, Billy the Kid told a friend about the affair.

"Yes, sir," Billy said, "that old wolf licked our crowd to a standstill. He killed Dick Brewer, almost killed Middleton, wounded Bowdre, and shot off George Coe's trigger finger. And, Jim, he almost parted my hair with a bullet, but he took off my hatband instead!"

Thus Billy the Kid expressed his admiration for the courage and tenacity of Buckshot Roberts, one dying man who bested a posse of thirteen. This was a tribute from one brave man to another.

Chapter X

WORD of the fight at Blazer's Mill soon reached Lincoln. By now the situation in Lincoln County was an acknowledged war, and the series of outbreaks were regarded in the light of engagements, or battles. There remained little doubt that the fighting would continue until the points of difference were resolved, or all the warriors were dead. A number of citizens removed themselves and their families from Lincoln County — temporarily, they hoped.

The cohorts of L. G. Murphy were glad to learn that Dick Brewer, the able young general of McSween's forces, was dead, and that disabling injuries had eliminated Middleton, George Coe, and Bowdre. On the other hand, the Murphy forces lost an able man when Buckshot Roberts, the old warrior, fell at Blazer's Mill. Murphy surmised that young William Bonney would step into the place of Dick Brewer as leader of the McSween forces, and in this he was correct. The Murphy men were acquainted with the intelligence and courage of Billy, but they knew him to be very young, and they did not believe he represented a threat to their success.

More alarming was the fact that citizens of the character of George and Frank Coe were espousing the McSween cause. The Coe cousins, both young ranchers, were highly respected, and Murphy was reminded once again that his hold on the community was slipping. Murphy's relations with his associates in Santa Fe were becoming less cordial, and his creditors were ever more insistent.

Further, John Copeland was not acceptable to Murphy as sheriff.

It became apparent that Murphy would have to devise some new and brilliant strategy, and so, in mid-April, he summoned his lieutenants to "the house" for a conference. James Dolan, Billy Mathews, George W. (Dad) Peppin, Marion Turner, John Kinney, and Bob Beckwith were present.

Murphy reviewed events since the death of Tunstall. He then suggested that the removal of Copeland from the office of sheriff and the death of Billy the Kid were desirable objectives for immediate action, and he asked for suggestions from the group as to how these things might be accomplished.

Marion Turner offered the first suggestion—that warrants be secured for all of McSween's men, charging each of them with one or another of the killings which had followed Tunstall's death. If Copeland did not display alacrity in serving these, Turner concluded, there would be grounds for his removal. Murphy agreed that the idea was sound, but inquired who was to furnish the sworn affidavits alleging the crime of murder.

When no solution to this problem was offered, Billy Mathews asked that the military be requested to intervene. Murphy replied that he had conferred with Colonel N. A. M. Dudley, who had succeeded Colonel Purrington as post commander at Fort Stanton. Colonel Dudley had said that he had received orders from General Hatch at Santa Fe stating the military was without authority to act in the Lincoln County disorders unless aid was solicited by civil authorities, in case of emergency.

Dolan and Beckwith, the youngest of the lieutenants and both fighting men, proposed a plan they had been discussing in low tones while the others were talking. They had counted the McSween supporters in Lincoln, and added to those the number who would rally round Sheriff Copeland. They counted twenty-five. Dolan and Beckwith suggested that Murphy might send word to all his men from Pecos and Seven Rivers to drift into Lincoln by twos and threes. The plan called for these gunfighters to appear in a manner which would not arouse notice so that the McSween men, headed by Billy the Kid, would not be alerted to come in from the Coe Ranch.

With twenty or thirty extra men in town, Murphy would be able to lead from strength and effect the removal of Copeland and the death of Billy the Kid. The plan was agreed upon, and William Johnson, who commanded the far-flung outposts of the Murphy empire, was notified that the elimination of Billy the Kid, McSween, Sheriff Copeland, and Isaac Ellis, a local partisan of McSween, would receive recognition in the form of substantial rewards.

Sheriff Copeland was not a stupid man. He observed the influx of gunmen almost as soon as it began, and he viewed the situation with grave concern. Copeland held warrants for a number of the men for the murder of Tunstall—warrants which previous officers had not served. He sought McSween's advice.

"I believe this is a move devised by Murphy to create trouble," McSween said. "If you attempt to take the wanted men, open conflict will result, and I believe that is what Murphy wants. There will be more of the violence and bloodshed which I abhor. We must not fall into that trap!"

Copeland expressed doubt about what seemed to him a timid course.

"It is not a question of your courage or willingness to perform your duty," McSween assured him. "But it would be unwise to try to serve those warrants at present."

Copeland chose to follow McSween's advice, for a time at least, and this puzzled Murphy, who knew the sheriff was fearless. Murphy waited, uneasily, for the sheriff to move.

Some relatively minor, and seemingly pointless, outbreaks occurred about three weeks after Copeland's appointment as sheriff.

A few days after Copeland's interview with McSween, two Mexican Americans, friends of Juan Patron, who was a McSween partisan, were found lying beside the road at the edge of Lincoln. The men had been murdered, and no clue pointed to a motive, or to the identity of the killer, or killers.

On May 1, Frank Coe was riding toward his ranch with Al Saunders and Frank McNab. The party was fired upon from ambush, and McNab was killed. Saunders was critically wounded, and Coe saved himself only by throwing himself from his horse. Coe was captured and held a prisoner until the following day. It was only because Coe was known to have been friendly to Buckshot Roberts that he was released and permitted to go on his way.

Frank Coe sent word to Sheriff Copeland that William Johnson and Bob Beckwith were members of the attacking party and were responsible for the death of McNab and the wounding of Saunders.

In Lincoln, the same day the Coe party was attacked on the Ruidoso, sporadic firing was heard at intervals from the hills on both sides of the village and from the brush along the Bonito River. This seems to have been a ruse to entice the sheriff and his deputies into open conflict. The small population was terrified. Householders fled in panic to place their women and children with outlying ranchers for safety. The sheriff placed guards at the McSween home and in the Torreon at the east end of town for the protection of those who remained in the village, and little Lincoln assumed the aspect of an armed camp.

McSween, on May 3, secured warrants from J. G. Trujilla, justice of the peace of Precinct Two, charging Johnson and Beckwith and about twenty others with the death of McNab. These were handed to Copeland for service. Copeland discovered that Murphy's armed men in the village now numbered about forty, and he decided to appeal to the military for help in preventing bloodshed when he arrested Johnson, Beckwith, and the others.

After Copeland had signed a memorandum asserting that a state of emergency existed in the village of Lincoln and that the lives and property of her citizens were imperiled, Dudley agreed to bring a detachment of troops to Lincoln. Copeland returned to Lincoln, and Dudley sent a letter to Murphy by special messenger. Dudley wrote Murphy of the sheriff's request for troops and added that he intended to comply. The colonel advised Murphy to get word to his followers to offer no resistance when the troops arrived, and to submit to arrest. Dudley promised that the Murphy lieutenants would receive further instructions from him.

Lawrence Murphy received Colonel Dudley's communication with satisfaction. The sheriff had brought about what Murphy had desired, but had not been able to effect—the intervention of the military—and Murphy read a great deal between the lines of Dudley's letter.

A detachment of cavalry rode into Lincoln the next morning, and, with Sheriff Copeland assisting, took twenty-one prisoners, all of whom submitted to arrest in good humor. The prisoners were immediately removed to Fort Stanton, under guard.

Two days later, on May 6, McSween and several others went to the office of Peace Justice Trujillo to testify against those arrested, including Johnson and Beckwith, in the matter of McNab's murder. To their great surprise, Lieutenants Goodwin and Smith, with a platoon of soldiers, were present, and all the witnesses were placed under arrest, without being allowed to testify. The military party made the arrests under warrants issued by Dave Eaton, justice of Precinct Three, based on affidavits signed by Dad Peppin, J. B. Mathews, and a military officer, charging the witnesses with conspiracy, and with assault with intent to kill.

Sheriff Copeland vigorously protested and denied the charges on behalf of the prisoners, whereupon the sheriff was abused by one of the lieutenants and ordered to offer no interference. The officer reminded Copeland that he had asked the military to take charge and added, contemptuously, "You're getting your wish!"

McSween, Patron, Ellis, and Salazar were held three days in the guardhouse at Fort Stanton, and then released. In the meantime, when witnesses were not allowed to appear at Precinct Two against the twenty-two men accused of the murder of McNab, Justice Trujillo ordered their release—and so the strategem was successful.

Viewed by modern standards, such uses of the law and the army are difficult to understand. In the Lincoln County War, both sides sought to use the authorities available to them to resolve matters satisfactorily. These authorities were employed, almost literally, as weapons of war, and, under some circumstances, they proved as effective as heavy cannon. On the frontier, vice, corruption, and ignorance of the law were common among minor officials. Murphy had been a military man himself, and had the sympathy of many of the officers at the post. He also carried heavy debts for some of them for liquor, gaming, and merchandise, and the fact that he stood well in the favor of most of the officers and men is not surprising.

Most of the prisoners released from custody by Trujillo were directed by Murphy to leave town. Murphy desired, for the next few weeks, to avoid violence. His fertile mind was busy with new strategy to bring Lincoln and the county again under his influence. But he had a thorny problem in Copeland, and Murphy decided the sheriff must be removed by due process of law, since other means had failed.

Murphy was able to persuade Rynerson, the district attorney, that the sureties on Copeland's bond were insufficient. Judge Bristol then declared the bond void. Governor Axtell was fully informed of all the circumstances by Murphy, and the governor appointed George W. Peppin to fill the office of sheriff until there should be a general election. There was no appeal from Axtell's order, and the Murphy forces were pleased to be in control, again, of local law enforcement.[1]

In the new sheriff, Murphy had a valuable man. Murphy placed little reliance on Peppin's ability or resourcefulness, but he was a useful medium for issuing orders to the Murphy supporters who served as posse members. This plan served the dual purpose of placing responsibility upon Peppin for the actions of these men and giving their activities legal status.

Peppin, or, more accurately, L. G. Murphy, appointed Marion Turner chief deputy. Turner, formerly a staunch friend of John S. Chisum, had become the cattle king's most implacable enemy, and was induced to espouse the Murphy cause because Chisum was known to be back-

[1] See Appendix II, Note A, Chap. X.

ing McSween. Turner was a man of more than ordinary attainments and great courage, and he lent strength and prestige to the Murphy faction.

Murphy's next move was to secure from District Attorney W. L. Rynerson a ruling that the action of Justice Wilson in appointing the posse headed by Dick Brewer to capture the slayers of John H. Tunstall was illegal. Predicated upon this ruling, the killings of Morton, Baker, and Buckshot Roberts were held to be acts of murder and vengeance, unauthorized by process of law. Whereupon, warrants were issued for all persons present at the deaths of Morton and Baker, Roberts, and Brady and Hindman. This action had the effect of outlawing almost every one of the McSween partisans.

There were now outstanding against Billy the Kid five separate warrants charging him with murder. Billy admitted that Morton and Baker were killed by him in the escape attempt, but these were the deaths investigated by the April grand jury, which declined to bring indictments. There existed no proof that William Bonney had fired at either Brady or Hindman in the gunfight in the village street, and Billy specifically denied that he had done so, while candidly stating that he had attempted to shoot Billy Mathews in the same fight because of Mathews' part in the death of Tunstall. In the matter of Buckshot Roberts, the old warrior himself and everyone present knew that Bowdre had fired the fatal shot. However, there was no denying that Billy had been present on each of these occasions.[2]

[2] See Appendix II, Note B, Chap. X.

Chapter XI

WHEN Copeland was replaced by Peppin, Alexander McSween's concern increased, both for his own safety and for Tunstall's property, for which he felt morally responsible until Tunstall's father should arrive from England. McSween sent word to Billy the Kid to come to Lincoln as soon as it seemed reasonably safe.[1] Billy, Bowdre, Brown, Scurlock, Middleton, and Tom O'Folliard rode in as soon as they received the message. All heavily armed, they approached Lincoln from the west. As they were passing "the house," they observed Sheriff Peppin standing in front of the building. The Kid reined Old Grey to a halt, and his companions ranged themselves behind him. He greeted the sheriff.

"Hello, Dad. We heard you had some papers to hand us, so we just rode in to save you some trouble. We'd admire to hear what you have to say."

The sheriff studied the group of smiling youths only a moment before declining to accept the implied challenge.

"Another time will do, Billy," Peppin said. "Just now you can all go to hell!" and the sheriff walked into the building.

Billy laughed and rode at the front of the men to the McSween home, where they learned that McSween wanted help in protecting the Tunstall property, particularly the valuable horses which McSween had sent to the Brewer ranch. McSween explained that he had placed five paid guards with the horses, but it was rumored that Jesse Evans planned to raid the ranch in force. McSween

---

[1] See Appendix II, Note A, Chap. XI.

wanted the Kid and the others to go to the ranch to reinforce the guards. He hoped that the presence of this large body of men guarding the horses would induce Evans to change his plans.

Billy agreed, and, with McSween's admonition against violence ringing after them, the little party rode away.

Everything was quiet at the Brewer ranch, but a day or two after the reinforcements had arrived, a friendly neighbor brought word that Jesse Evans was camped near by with several men. Without waiting for breakfast, the Kid and his companions saddled quickly and moved out to intercept Evans. Billy divided his party, hoping to flank the enemy. With Brown, he ascended the ridge to the east of the Ruidoso River. Bowdre and the others followed the ridge along the west bank.

They scouted a mile or so, and then Billy heard shots from Bowdre's direction. The Kid circled to a position at the rear of the spot and saw that Bowdre had been captured, and the shooting had been only a skirmish, without casualties. With a wild Apache cry, Billy spurred Old Grey headlong into the center of the Evans group which had Bowdre covered. The others took advantage of the momentary confusion, and, when the dust had settled, Billy and his men were covering the Evans party.

Jesse Evans and Billy talked, briefly, about the events of the last few months. We can only wonder what thoughts were in Billy's mind as he looked at Evans, his boyhood friend, and the reported slayer of John Tunstall.

"Oh, and one thing more, Jess," Billy said at the end of their conversation. "I've heard there's a party from Seven Rivers hanging around here, pining to pick up the Tunstall horses at the Brewer ranch. If you happen to meet them, tell them they're welcome to the animals, but I'll be there to receive them—and I'll be *glad* to!"

The Kid turned Old Grey and rode leisurely in the

direction of the Ruidoso, followed by Bowdre and the others.

The tension in Lincoln was increasing daily, and, after several councils-in-camp, the friends of McSween agreed that the men led by Billy would return to Lincoln and remain quartered there until the war should, somehow, be finished. Even McSween reluctantly consented to this plan. Although there was no warrant against him, McSween felt the danger to himself, and he had been moving about and remaining away from his home. He was, by now, weary of the role of refugee. The decision to bring his friends into Lincoln in force to remain at his home meant hazarding his life and property, and Alexander McSween knew this.

Chapter XII

SUNDAY afternoon, July 14, 1878, McSween and about forty men rode into the deceptively quiet little village of Lincoln and established themselves at the McSween home and in several other strong adobe buildings at the east end of town. Billy the Kid and the best of the fighting men stayed with McSween as a special bodyguard.

Deputy Marion Turner had been scouting the countryside for Billy and his men. He returned to the village to find them there and well barricaded, and a hasty meeting was called at "the house."

Turner believed guards should be posted at strategic spots to make sure all escape was cut off for the McSween forces, and Sheriff Peppin immediately detailed a number of men to fill these positions.

Turner then wrote an unsigned note: "Tell the women to leave at once. We are coming to take you. If this warning is not heeded, we will not be responsible for their safety." Turner arranged to have this note delivered to the McSween home by a Mexican woman, and then turned his attention to planning a siege.

But first, Turner, Dolan, and John Kinney went to McSween's house. From a safe position, Turner called for those inside to come out, unarmed, and surrender themselves. Billy the Kid replied, and his voice was both amused and contemptuous as he called a refusal from inside the house.

In the McSween home there were now eleven men and three women. The men were McSween, Billy the Kid, Francisco Zamora, Vicente Romero, Jim French,

Doc Scurlock, Hijinio Salazar, Harvey Morris, Chavez y Chavez, Ignacio Gonzales, and Tom O'Folliard. Mrs. McSween, her sister Mrs. Shield, and Mrs. Ealy were also in the house. In the Tunstall store, next door on the east, were three great fighting men: George Coe, Charlie Bowdre, and Hendry Brown. Don Martin Chavez stationed the remaining forces in the Old Torreon, east of the Tunstall store, and in the Montano and Patron buildings, across the street. The forces Peppin and Turner had mustered were about equal in number to the McSween forces, totalling nearly forty for each side. Frontal attack by either group would probably be inconclusive, and would certainly result in many casualties. For the time being, the situation appeared to be at a standstill.

The McSween faction accepted the leadership of Billy the Kid, and he elected to assume a defensive role.

At "the house," Turner addressed his men. "Sheriff Peppin, myself, and the other deputies are confronted with a difficult and serious situation. As peace officers, we are charged with arresting for murder a number of men now defying us here in Lincoln. They have refused to surrender and have enlisted a large number of others to prevent us from executing our duty, and those others have placed themselves in the unlawful position of protecting and harboring the outlaws. We must deal with all of them accordingly."

Turner continued to outline the situation and concluded by asking James Dolan to write a note to General Dudley at Fort Stanton. The note read, in part:

> I have the honor to respectfully state that mostly all the men for whom I have United States warrants are in town, and are being protected by A. A. McSween and a large party of his followers. They are in the houses of A. A. McSween, Ellis Sons, J. B. Patron, and José Montano. They are resisting, and it is impossible for me to serve the warrants. If it is in your power to loan me one of your howitzers,

I am of the opinion the parties for whom I have said warrants would surrender without a shot being fired. Should it be in your power to do this, in favor of the law, you would confer a great favor on the majority of the people of this county, who are being persecuted by a lawless mob.

The note was signed by the hand of Sheriff George Peppin.

One of Turner's lieutenants, apparently desiring to make sure of Dudley's sympathetic assistance, dispatched a few men to hide near the trail and fire over the head of the cavalryman who was expected to bring Dudley's reply. The plan proved a good one. A lone courier arrived in Lincoln in late afternoon, and he reported the ambuscade. The post commander had sent a note declining to intervene, but he tempered his refusal by expressing willingness to lend such aid as was possible under existing War Department regulations.

Peppin sent a reply to General Dudley[1] by the returning courier:

LINCOLN, N.M.
July 16, 1878

Gen. N. A. M. Dudley
Commdg. Fort Stanton, N.M.

GENERAL:

I have the honor to acknowledge the receipt of your very kind favor of date; am very sorry I can't get assistance I asked for, but I will do the best I can. The McSween party fired on your soldier when coming into town. My men, on seeing him, tried their best to cover him, but of no use. The soldier will explain the circumstances to you.

I take this opportunity of thanking you for your kindness in name of all my posse.

Respectfully,
Yr. Obt. Srt.
GEORGE W. PEPPIN, *Sheriff*

[1] See Appendix II, Note A, Chap. XII.

During the terrible days between July 15 and July 19, 1878, the Lincoln County War reached its climax. Forces numbering nearly eighty men were aligned against each other. The McSween partisans, under the leadership of Billy the Kid, waited, strongly established in several stout buildings at the east end of town. The Murphy faction held "the house" at the western limits of the village, and stationed riflemen in concealment on the slopes of the hills overlooking Lincoln.

Most of the women, children, and elderly people had fled to find relative safety at outlying ranches.

Billy the Kid posted riflemen on the roof of the McSween home, where, from behind a low parapet which served as a breastwork, they commanded the empty road from both the east and the west.

Except for sporadic firing, Tuesday, July 17, was quiet. The little village seemed empty and deserted. Although no casualties had resulted, bullets had splintered the windows of McSween's home, breaking all the glass and damaging Mrs. McSween's fine furniture. At midday, the burning July sun raised shimmering heat waves from the dust. With the coming of the cool darkness, all firing ceased, but no glow of candle or lamplight appeared in the village. No sound disturbed the absolute quiet except the subdued murmur of the Rio Bonito, hurrying to meet the waters of the Ruidoso a dozen miles away.

In the early dawn of the eighteenth, Susan McSween, Mrs. Shield, and Mrs. Ealy were preparing breakfast for the men when the firing from the hills was renewed. The front windows of the McSween house were the targets. Billy directed the men on the roof to return the fire, but, as the attackers were well hidden among the rocks and trees, efforts to dislodge them appeared hopeless. The men on the roof could only try to discourage any nearer approach of the snipers. The purpose of the attack, directed by Turner, was to drive the defenders from the roof, if possible.

Two of Turner's finest marksmen, Charley Crawford and Lucio Montoya, were directed to find new positions higher on the hill, from where the defenders would be exposed to their fire. From a high ledge, these two sent volley after volley against those stationed on the roof, and Billy was forced to order his men to abandon their post.

There followed a brief lull while Turner's two riflemen changed their positions. Then Crawford and Montoya directed their fire against the Patron and Montano houses. This maneuver was wholly unexpected, and three of the surprised defenders were seriously wounded.

Fernando Herrera, who had hunted buffalo on the plains, was known as one of the best long-range riflemen in the territory, and he was among the members of the McSween faction stationed in the Torreon.

Herrera was annoyed by the activities of the riflemen on the hill. He inspected his large-bore buffalo gun and carefully cleaned and oiled it. He selected several cartridges, coated them with grease from a tallow candle, and dropped one into the breech.

Herrera made a stealthy exit from the round stone fortress and found a place beneath a low window in an adobe hut beside the Torreon. He surveyed the ledge which sheltered Turner's sharpshooters through field glasses. His movements were unhurried. He rolled and lighted a cornhusk cigarette, then another, and yet another. He tossed these out the window and watched the little spirals of smoke to calculate the direction and velocity of the light breeze.

When he was satisfied with these observations, Herrera rested his heavy weapon on the window sill. He estimated the distance to the ledge of rocks where the riflemen lay, adjusted his sights, and aimed at a spot where he had detected a slight movement. Patiently he waited for some moments until something stirred at the same spot. Fernando reacted instantly with a steady pressure on the trigger of his rifle, and, seconds later, Crawford half rose and pitched forward, rolling to the foot of the long hill. The heavy ball had pierced his body, fracturing his spine.

Herrera's extraordinary feat has become a near legend in New Mexico. His target was barely perceptible up the incline of a steep hill, and the distance exceeded nine hundred yards. Herrera's was a shot unequalled among the exploits of frontier riflemen.

At midmorning, several officers with an escort of troops rode down to Lincoln from Fort Stanton. The officers had been detailed by Dudley to serve as a board of inquiry to investigate the attack upon Private Robinson of the Ninth Cavalry Troop "by the McSween faction," as reported by Sheriff Peppin. The defenders were ignorant of the plot and so were not alarmed by the appearance of the cavalrymen.[2]

No member of the Military Board of Inquiry was sent to the McSween house to obtain verification of Sheriff Peppin's serious charges. Upon evidence provided by "the house" and upon the self-evident fact of the shooting of Crawford, the McSween faction was, in effect, tried and found guilty of having fired upon a United States soldier with intent to kill, and of the murder of a local citizen —Crawford. The soldiers returned to Dudley with their report.

The Kid watched the departure of the soldiers from Lincoln. He spoke cheerfully to McSween.

"Well, Governor, looks like we're still on our own. I believe Dudley would back Peppin's game if he could.

[2] See Appendix II, Note B, Chap. XII.

I don't get this play, but I guess the cavalry isn't going to interfere."

McSween was worried. "I don't know, Billy," he said soberly. "I hoped they would stop the fighting somehow." He dropped his head a moment, then he looked up at the faces of those about him.

"Our cause is just, my friends, and the Supreme Power will defend the right," McSween said.

"That may be, Governor." The Kid smiled as he spoke. "But if Dudley and Peppin are hatching up something —well, all we can do is wait!"

Thursday, July 18, was a relatively quiet day. There was little firing on either side. McSween's men did not know that, after the departure of the military, Peppin had issued a cease-fire order to his men. Dolan had gone to Fort Stanton to confer with Dudley.

When Dolan had left the fort, Dudley assembled a number of his officers and secured the signatures of most of them to a prepared statement that, in their opinions, after careful consideration, soldiers should be stationed in Lincoln for the safety and protection of the women and children, and for the safeguarding of property. This move was designed to protect and justify Dudley, in the event that notice of the matter should be taken by the War Department.

Dudley placed the signed statement in the headquarters safe, then addressed his officers. "I believe, gentlemen, the Secretary of War will find no valid criticism for the action we are about to take. Return to quarters and await further orders."

As Friday, July 19, dawned, the McSween defenders took heart. The soldiers had not reappeared, and the men believed War Department orders had prevented Dudley from supporting Peppin. However, they had underestimated Dudley.[3]

About midafternoon, a detachment of cavalry and a squad of artillery, with a Gatling gun and a twelve-pounder, entered Lincoln under the personal command of General Dudley. At "the house" the soldiers were greeted by loud cheers from the Peppin deputies inside. The military party moved down the dusty road until it arrived at the front of the McSween home, where the order to halt was given. Dudley dispatched an orderly into the house with a note directing McSween to appear.

Alexander McSween was confident that the troops had arrived to bring about a truce, and he went quickly into the yard, followed by everyone who had been in the house. This curiosity and confidence on the part of the McSween men caused them to leave their rear unguarded—a grave error.

The general sat his horse as he spoke to McSween. "I am here, sir, to protect the lives and property of the residents of this village—especially the women and children, who are endangered by the random firing of your men. That must cease at once," Dudley said.

"We will comply with your order, sir," McSween replied, "if Sheriff Peppin will receive and obey a like command."

"I have no authority to give orders to the sheriff, or in any wise to interfere with his performance of his official duty," Dudley said. "I believe he holds warrants for the arrest of a number of the men you are harboring."

McSween said nothing.

"If you will surrender these men," Dudley continued, "further conflict will be avoided. I am leaving a cannon and men here in the road. If any shots pass over the

---

[3] See Appendix II, Note C, Chap. XII.

heads of my men, they will fire upon your house with the cannon. I suggest you consider carefully."

Dudley did not give McSween an opportunity to reply that this vague proposition was unacceptable. Instead, Dudley and his staff continued down the road past the Patron and Montano houses to the Torreon.

Outside the Torreon, Dudley summoned Don Martin Chavez, leader of the McSween forces stationed at the east end of town. Dudley delivered to Chavez orders similar to those issued to McSween, again emphasizing the safety of the women and children, almost all of whom were known to have left the village.

"Further," Dudley said, "you and your men are non-residents. You came here from the Hondo to prevent the arrest of men for whom the sheriff holds warrants. Your action constitutes an attempt to obstruct the law —a very serious offense!"

"I am deploying my men from this point west to the Murphy store," Dudley continued. "If another shot is fired, a field piece will go into action against the building from which it comes."

When Don Martin failed to reply, Dudley showed his irritation. "You do understand English, do you not?" he snapped.

"I do, *Señor,*" Chavez replied.

"In that case," Dudley said, "if you desire to avoid trouble, take your men and leave Lincoln at once," and the colonel rode away, the soldiers at his heels.

Don Martin stood a long moment, his bare head lowered, considering the problem. He was a brave man, and an honorable one. How could he leave McSween and his other friends in time of peril? Yet the gringos now controlled this area, which had been the home of his people for centuries. As the acknowledged leader of a number of loyal men, could he, Don Martin, invite disaster for them by defying the orders of the commander of the Federal troops? Because of his inherent chivalry, Chavez felt dishonored by his decision, but there seemed to him no alternative. He rejoined his men and ordered them out of Lincoln.

While Dudley was talking to Chavez, the men who returned to the McSween house made a frightening discovery. During the parley in the yard, they had all surrounded McSween and Dudley, leaving the house unguarded. Andy Boyle, Jack Long, and one or two other Turner deputies had seized this opportunity to pile brush and branches against the northwest wing of the house and set fires. Jack Long even slipped into the long living room at the front of the house and drenched the furnishings with oil before he fled with the others.

A breeze was blowing, and the fire could not be controlled. However, because of the stout adobe construction of the big house, Billy believed the progress of the fire would be slow. The only water for fighting the fire was in the Rio Bonito, some distance behind the house, and the path to the river was fully covered by Turner's snipers.

The sheriff's forces were jubilant. They had observed the departure of Don Martin and his men, and they knew that all the remaining McSween forces were gathered in the house from which dense smoke was now issuing.

Inside, Billy wasted little time in vain regret that the house had been left unguarded. When it became apparent that fighting the fire was hopeless, he pulled a chair into a quiet corner and applied himself to thinking over the possibilities of the situation. He knew that all the defenders of the McSween house faced death in the flames, or flight in the face of the certainty of a hail of bullets from the rifles of the enemy. Only darkness, if they could hold out until then, would offer a slender hope of escape for some.

There was intermittent firing by both sides during the afternoon, but, in spite of Dudley's threat, the cannon remained silent.

McSween addressed a note to Dudley before dark. The attorney offered to surrender himself to the military on condition that he be assured safe conduct to Fort Stanton and his companions be allowed to leave the village. Susan McSween protested that this gesture would prove vain, but when she was unable to persuade him to her point of view, she took the note from her husband's hand and stepped out the front door.

All firing ceased as she beckoned a soldier on sentry duty some distance away. She handed the note to the soldier with the request that he deliver it to Dudley and return with a reply.

The answer was returned quickly. Dudley refused the proposal on the ground that the matter was one for the civil authorities.

McSween read the reply and handed it to Billy the Kid without comment. Then McSween picked up the open Bible and was immediately lost in his reading.

"See here, Governor," Billy said, "things are getting pretty hot around here. Better lay down that Book and take this gun. We'll be needing all hands when the fire forces us to run for it."

McSween waved aside the proffered weapon. "Billy," he said firmly, "I will die here before I'll be responsible for shedding one drop of human blood."

The boy's eyes darkened momentarily, as they always did when he was angered; then, quickly, they lightened to their natural, dancing blue.

"Well, I guess we undertook to fight your fight, Governor, but some of the boys are going to feel you're letting them down."

McSween, head bent over the Book, did not reply.

"If we're going to be a man short," Billy said, crossing the room to return to his post, "I'll just have to do the fighting for two—me *and* you, Governor."

To the men inside the house, the hot July night seemed terribly slow in coming. The fire moved slowly, inexorably through the house. The west wing was a smoking ruin, and the fire ate into the living room. Here, Jack Long had done his work well. The oil-soaked furnishings burned hotly, and the defenders retreated to the five rooms of the east wing.

Outside, riflemen watched, sealing off every avenue of retreat. The coming darkness worked against them and gave the besieged men hope of escape.

Susan McSween, usually immaculate and smart, was wilted by the heat from the fire and the July weather. Her face, white with strain, and her fashionable gown were smudged with soot. But her red hair seemed to blaze like her indomitable spirit as she spoke to the men.

"Eventually we will be forced into the open to be shot down," she said. "I am going to appeal to Dudley, personally, to intervene before it is too late."

Billy's blue eyes searched Susan's resolute face. "Mrs. McSween," he said, "you know Dudley will do nothing. He could have stopped the fighting long ago, if he would. He's as much a member of the opposition as Dolan, Turner, and the others."

The boy smiled gently at Susan McSween. "I think," he said, "that you and Mrs. Shield and Mrs. Ealy should leave now. The rest of us will hold out until full dark and then make a break. There's one chance in a million that some of us will get through."

"Nevertheless, I shall see Dudley. I can do no less than fail," Susan said.

She touched her hair with a slender hand, then walked through the remaining rooms and out into the dusk.

Mrs. McSween approached a young corporal of cavalry and asked him to conduct her to Colonel Dudley. The soldier replied courteously, and he and the red-haired woman walked out of sight of the anxious watchers in the house.

At Dudley's headquarters, the troops had bivouacked, and the commandant was established in a tent where the colonel, Captain Blair, and two or three others sat around a table littered with bottles and papers. Several lanterns were suspended from the ridgepole of the large, square tent, and these cast a yellow light over the interior.

The young corporal saluted and reported the presence of the visitor to Colonel Dudley.

Susan stepped into the lamplight, her head high. "I am Mrs. McSween," she said. "I am here to implore you to order this conflict to cease. My home will soon be destroyed, but for that I care little. I ask only that you act to spare the lives of those trapped inside—victims of the men responsible for this tragic situation."

"I am without authority to interfere, madam, much as I may regret it," the colonel answered, indifferently.

"Are you and these soldiers here going to stand idly by while those within my home are burned to death? Or shot if they attempt to escape?" Susan asked.

"I am here," Dudley said angrily, "to protect the women and children and law-abiding residents of this village. I cannot interfere with the civil authorities in the exercise of their official duties."

"There are no women and children here, Colonel Dudley," Susan said, the anger in her voice matching the colonel's. "They have fled the village in terror, not of our men, but in fear of imported Rio Grande outlaws and the others sworn in as Sheriff Peppin's deputies! Are arson and murder the official duties of the sheriff with which you cannot interfere?"

Dudley struck the table with a clenched fist. "I want to hear no more of this," he shouted. "No one can dictate to me respecting my duty or my authority. Get out!"

Susan McSween left the tent. Outside, the young cavalryman had waited to escort her home. He walked quietly beside her. When she thanked him, silhouetted in the light from her burning home, he came to attention and saluted, silently offering tribute to her courage.

The wind died as darkness came. Four rooms of the McSween house were untouched by the fire which was moving but slowly now. Alexander McSween appeared dazed, but Billy was cheerful, giving orders and encouragement in a lighthearted manner. When Susan McSween returned, she was told that Mrs. Shield and Mrs. Ealy had been induced to leave. No one needed to ask if her mission had succeeded.

Vicente Romero was dead in the dark yard beside the house. In an effort to save himself he had suddenly dashed from the place, shouting, "I surrender," as he threw his gun away. A volley from the riflemen struck him, and he fell almost as soon as he was outside.

Billy, who had been attempting to dissuade Romero from the flight, said, "There's your answer, *compadres*. They don't want our surrender; they want our lives!"

The death of Romero suggested a new thought to Susan McSween. Now she could prove to Dudley that surrender was impossible, and only military intervention could save the lives of those in the house.

Billy and her husband both argued that Mrs. McSween should not return to Dudley. They believed this course to be futile, and they wished to spare her whatever was possible. Billy urged that Susan follow Mrs. Ealy and Mrs. Shield to a place of relative safety.

It was very dark now, and the glow of the flames lighted Billy's boyish smile as he spoke to the woman whose face was in shadow. "The time is nearing when we must make a break, ma'am. Some of us may get through, but there will be a lot of shooting, and you must not be here. Please go, ma'am, while there's time."

Susan McSween placed her hand on the boy's arm. "Billy," she said, "I have heard you say, if there were a chance in a million, you would take that chance. That is what *I* mean to do now."

Susan went out into the night. Two shots were fired at her before the marksmen, apparently identifying her in the light from the flames, ceased firing. The young corporal joined her in the road. They walked a few paces, then the soldier stopped. He faced Susan.

"Mrs. McSween," he said, "I wish you wouldn't go to Dudley. Some other men are at the headquarters now, and they are growing boisterous and profane. May I conduct you to some place of safety, instead?"

"Thank you for your kindness," she said, tears glistening in her eyes, "but the lives of my husband and his companions are at stake. I must go to Dudley. He is my only hope."

The junior officers had left Dudley's headquarters, and the colonel had been joined by Boyle, Peppin, Long, and Kinney. The tent flaps had been folded back, exposing the interior to the hot night. Susan brushed aside the sentry who attempted to halt her and stood before Dudley.

"Are you here again, madam?" Dudley inquired, unnecessarily, "Please leave, and don't come back."

"Colonel Dudley," Susan said quietly, "I am here to ask you as a brave officer of the United States Army to intervene to save the lives of my husband and the men trapped in my burning home. Surrender is impossible. One man, Vicente Romero, was shot down as he attempted to surrender, and lies dead in the yard. I appeal to you, as a soldier and a gentleman—"

The outlaw, Kinney, interrupted with a loud laugh. "I've heard you called a lot of names, Dudley," he said, "but this lady called you a 'gentleman.' That tops 'em all! Why not do as the lady asks? Go up and put out the fire. Send the boys home. Tell 'em the war's over!"

Dudley glared at Kinney, then he turned to Susan. He spoke decisively, but not unkindly, her appeal to his chivalry seeming to soften the soldier. "I regret to inform you, there is nothing I can do."

"Then why are you here, and why did you order Don Martin Chavez to leave?"

"He was instructed not to interfere with the civil authorities, and he withdrew voluntarily," Dudley said. "I resent being questioned in this fashion, but I am willing to repeat that I am here for the protection of innocent citizens, women, and children."

"Since you refuse to intervene, Colonel Dudley," Susan said, "what means is there of preserving the lives of those in the burning house?"

"I can only suggest that they come out, surrender, and submit to arrest," Dudley said, impatiently.

"Will you protect them from violence as they leave the house, unarmed?" Mrs. McSween asked.

"Assuredly not, madam," Dudley replied. "That is the responsibility of Sheriff Peppin. This discussion is closed."

Susan McSween no longer had a doubt that she had appealed in vain, and her hopelessness dispelled all fear and confusion. She lifted her chin and spoke clearly and firmly, with the desperate confidence of one who no longer has anything to lose.

"You are suggesting, sir, that these men surrender to Peppin and his men? Has it not been reported to you that Vicente Romero, a brave man, attempted to do just that and was instantly killed as he walked out of the building, shouting his wish to surrender, showing his empty hands? Do you ask that the others should take the same action and meet the same fate?"

Dudley was very angry now, and ordered the woman to leave, as he had done before.

Stubbornly, dauntlessly, Susan stood her ground. "You will have cause to regret this day as the most unfortunate of your career," she said slowly. "The deaths of the men about to die are your responsibility. If I live, I swear before heaven to see that you are punished."

There was silence in the tent. Dudley stared at Mrs. McSween. He was almost dazed with surprise.

"If law and order ever come to this unhappy community," Susan continued in measured tones, "I will charge you with murder, with arson, and with harboring and protecting criminals. I will carry my case to the War Department, and to the President, if necessary. You are worse than the renegade, Kinney, who sits beside you. He makes no pretense at honor, and, in that, he is your superior."

Dudley had been sorely tried, and the last taunt roused him fully. He half rose from his chair and, flushed and stammering, loudly ordered Susan to leave the premises, adding, "I'll permit no common—"

"Do not complete that remark, sir," Susan interrupted. "I go, with this promise; I shall devote my life and what may remain of my fortune to obtaining justice for you." And Susan McSween vanished beyond the circle of yellow light.

"What a woman, General, what a woman!" the outlaw, Kinney, said. "She read your cards as easy as if they came from a marked deck—and take it from me, soldier, she meant what she said!"

The colonel's reply was unintelligible.

"By God, what a woman!" Kinney repeated, as if thinking aloud. "If I could find myself one like her, I'd turn dirt farmer and settle down. Red hair, too!"

Kinney poured a long drink, gulped it down, and walked out of the tent.

Susan and her escort directed their steps toward the glow of the fire.

"I heard what was said, ma'am," the soldier said. "To-night, I wish I were a civilian. Somehow, I'd—"

The boy did not finish his sentence. Susan said nothing.

"My name is George Loomis," the corporal went on, at length. "My enlistment is up in about two months. When I am on my own and can serve you in any way, get word to me."

Susan took his hand. "Thank you, Corporal, for your courtesy and kindness. I shall be in need of friends, and I will not forget you. Now, return to your post, with the blessings of an unhappy, but grateful woman."

Two rooms of the house remained standing, but the wall of one of these was licked by flame even as Susan entered.

Billy went to her at once. He was calm, even cheerful.

"Well, ma'am, I surmise old Dudley wouldn't listen to you," he said. "Now, I've got some orders to give, and the first is for you. There's very little time, and you must leave us at once."

"Very well, Billy," Susan McSween said. "I have failed to help you. If I remain now, I shall only be in the way, so I will go. I will pray that you may all escape."

She crossed the smoky room to the corner where her husband sat on a wooden chair. Susan pressed a kiss upon his forehead and turned to leave.

"Don't worry, ma'am," Billy said. If the governor will get himself together and follow orders, maybe we can save him. *Hasta la vista,* ma'am, and wish us luck!"

Susan left her home. She looked back once.

Chapter XIII

BILLY surveyed his companions. In the room were Francisco Zamora, Ignacio Gonzales, Hijinio Salazar, and Chavez y Chavez, Harvey Morris, Jim French, Doc Scurlock, Tom O'Folliard, and McSween. Billy made it nine fighting men, counting himself and excluding McSween.

"*Compadres*," Billy said, "make sure every chamber is loaded. Eject the empty shells from under your firing pins. Every shot will count."

All the men knew what faced them, but Billy was calm and self-assured. If he felt any concern, the others could not detect it. They drew strength from his presence and from his direct and smiling glance.

"Governor," Billy said to McSween, "we're about to move into the last room, and we'll leave from there. Please take this gun. Our chances are small, but every shot we fire will reduce the odds against us. Come on, now, Governor."

McSween put the Bible aside and stood up.

"No, Billy. It is written, 'Thou shalt not kill.' I place my faith in God. His will be done."

Billy looked at the broken man and considered how he might fit McSween into the escape plan. He decided to appeal to McSween's sense of justice, to try to make McSween feel responsible for the lives of the men fighting his cause. Billy guessed that these arguments would weigh little when balanced against McSween's rigid religious and ethical concepts, but he had to try. The chances of all the men depended upon a fixed plan—there must be no confusion, and McSween must not be permitted to jeopardize the others.

"Well, now, I respect your sentiments, Governor," Billy drawled, "but why are we all here? A powerful lot of blood has been shed on your behalf. You owe a lot to these boys, and you have made yourself responsible for their lives. Encourage them by your example. Show yourself their leader and their friend."

This was a long and eloquent speech for Billy, and it came at a time when action counted most, but it left McSween entirely unmoved.

A shower of burning embers fell from the ceiling around the heads of the two men.

"All right, Governor," the Kid said, resignation in his tone, "but from now on you must follow orders. Move into that room before the roof falls on our heads."

In the last room, Billy rolled and lighted a cigarette, then he gave the final orders, speaking sometimes in Spanish, sometimes in English, and pausing frequently to make sure that everyone understood.

"*Compadres,* the time is now. I promised Mrs. McSween we'd try to pull the governor out of this squeeze, if possible. His chances aren't worth a white chip. And," he smiled, "ours are about as good."

The men crowded around Billy laughed a little.

"Our hole card is a poor one to draw to," he continued soberly, "but there must be no stampede."

"Hijinio," Billy said to Salazar, "when we leave, you make a run for the gate in the north wall, and lead Zamora, Gonzales, and Chavez to it. Keep low and don't bunch up. If you make it, cross the river and head for the hills. I think your chances are better this way. Those coyotes will be more interested in cutting us Anglos down—especially me and the governor—and some of them might hold their fire when you boys come out."

Salazar and the others agreed to the plan, and Billy turned to the Anglos.

"All right, boys, we'll deal the game this way. When Salazar and his boys have cleared the door, you, Harvey, make a break for the gate at the northeast corner of the wall."

Then to French and Scurlock, he said, "You next, Jim, then you, Doc. Same gate. Do you both get it clear?"

"We'll play it your way, Billy," French answered for both men.

Outside, in the smoky darkness, Bob Beckwith moved quietly into the shadow of the gutted west wing. The fire was all on the east now, and there were areas of darkness where the other part of the house had stood. Beckwith covered the only possible exit, and waited, for he knew there would be a break very soon. Inside the room, Billy continued to make plans, unaware of the proximity of an enemy.

"When Doc clears the door," Billy said to McSween, "you follow and run like hell. Head for the northeast gate. Keep low. Don't stop or look back. Those are orders!" The Kid's blue gaze held McSween's eyes for a long moment before he turned to O'Folliard.

"Tom, you and me will cover the rear. That will put the governor between us and the other boys. I can't figure a better plan to bring him through. Some of us won't make it, but if the governor cashes in and I haven't done my best for him, I couldn't face Mrs. McSween."

"Don't worry too much, Kid," jibed O'Folliard, who was as young as Billy and seemed as cool. "Could be you might not be nowhere around after tonight to express them regrets!"

"You can go to hell, Tom," Billy grinned. "And you may be right!"

The flames had died down momentarily, and only a dim glow and heavy smoke came from the burning room. Billy was well pleased.

"There won't be a better time," he said. "You'll not be able to see, but fire at every gun flash. Are you boys set, Hijinio? Then go—keep low, spread out, and run! Good luck, *amigos!*"

Behind the first group, Harvey Morris led out Jim French and Doc Scurlock.

Beckwith, standing concealed, held his fire. He wanted the Kid and McSween.

Volleys of shots sounded from the directions of both gates in the wall. Turner had planned carefully, and his men caught the escapees in a deadly crossfire. Francisco Zamora and Ignacio Gonzales were killed instantly. Chavez y Chavez was gravely wounded but escaped into darkness.

Hijinio Salazar, leader of the first group, fell with bullets in his back, chest, and side, but he was fully conscious. He knew that the slightest movement on his part would invite death, and so he lay, absolutely still, where he fell.

At the northeast exit, Harvey Morris died, leaning against the wall beside the wooden gate. French and Scurlock paused there in a hail of fire to render aid, but they saw that Morris was beyond help and blocking the gate. After a momentary delay, the two men scrambled across the wall and reached cover along the river.

McSween hesitated to follow Morris, French, and Scurlock through the door. Vital seconds passed as the distance between him and the trio lengthened.

"For God's sake, Governor, move if you want to live!" Billy urged. Turning to O'Folliard, Billy ordered, "Cover him, crowd him, drag him, if you must!"

McSween was at the door when Beckwith stepped from

hiding and fired from about ten paces. O'Folliard was so close behind McSween that he received the shot intended for the attorney in his right shoulder. The impact caused O'Folliard to drop his gun. As he stooped to retrieve it, McSween appeared to hesitate, and Beckwith fired three rapid shots at McSween. Alexander McSween fell where he stood.

O'Folliard, wounded and weaponless, gave up fumbling for his pistol, leaped the fallen McSween, and made for the river, to fall, unconscious, in the underbrush.

Beckwith's zeal and his anxiety for the reward offered for McSween's death undid him. He ran out into the open, shouting to his concealed companions, "I got McSween, and I claim the reward!"

In his excitement, Beckwith did not see the shadowy form of the Kid as he ran back to kneel beside McSween. Billy saw at once that the weary McSween had passed beyond the blood and violence he hated.

Beckwith's friends had ceased firing, and Billy's voice came to him clearly in the stillness. "You're right, Bob, he's dead, and you've earned your reward."

"It's the Kid," Beckwith shouted, firing at Billy.

"Poor shooting, Bob," Billy taunted, as shots from the other riflemen began to come his way. "You should have learned not to hurry in a pinch. Now, for the reward—"

Beckwith was lifting his gun when Billy fired twice, so rapidly the reports sounded like one. Beckwith went down with a bullet in his forehead and another in his heart.

Ben Litchfield, one of Turner's imported deputies, had heard Beckwith's shout identifying Billy and, hoping to add luster to his reputation by killing the Kid, rose from his cover and fired. He missed, and a bullet from Billy's gun struck him in the face, shattering his cheek bone and destroying his left eye.[1] Litchfield fell back behind the wall.

The firing by the besiegers became heavier as soon as it was apparent that Beckwith was out of the fight and the lone defender in the shadows was Billy the Kid. Billy made for the northeast gate with bullets from a score of guns raising dust about his feet, cutting through his clothing, and carrying away his hat. He reached the gate, unscathed, and paused, as had French and Scurlock, to see if Morris required aid.

By now Morris had fallen clear of the gate, and, bending low, Billy passed through, followed by gunfire from the deputies and from the carbines of the soldiers who had joined the fight. He reached the river and made his way along its course, keeping to the underbrush. Ten miles to the east, at Hondo, he secured a horse and went to friends in San Patricio. There, within a few days, he was joined by French, Scurlock, and O'Folliard and Bowdre.

All firing had ceased with the escape of the Kid, and the besiegers now took stock of the situation. Liquor was brought, and the frame outbuildings on McSween's property were set ablaze to light the scene. Andy Boyle and a deputy named Pierce moved about in the fiery glow, identifying the dead. Boyle had had a good deal of whisky, and he stumbled over the body of Hijinio Salazar who lay quietly, feigning death.[2]

"That's Salazar," Boyle told Pierce, "a Lincoln greaser fighting on the wrong side. I'm glad we got him." Boyle looked closer at the prone form. "Say, Pierce," he said, "maybe he ain't dead. Better make sure," and Boyle drew his pistol.

"Come on, Andy, put up your gun," Pierce said.

---

[1] See Appendix II, Note A, Chap. XIII.
[2] See Appendix II, Note B, Chap. XIII.

"Don't waste a shot on him. He's dead, all right. Let's have another drink."

Hijinio Salazar's life was spared by Pierce's indifferent remark. Boyle turned away, and Hijinio, heroically controlling his pain and fear, tried to hold his breath.

Someone shouted, "Here's McSween. Beckwith got him all right!"

One of the strange deputies knelt by the body and picked up something. "By God," he exclaimed, "he carried a Bible instead of a gun!" and the man shoved at the body with a booted toe. The next moment he was staggered by a well-directed blow from Kinney.

"If you or anyone else repeats that play, it will be his last." Kinney's voice was deadly. "Give me the Book." He drew a soiled scrap of paper and a stub of pencil from one of his pockets. In the light cast by the burning outbuildings, he wrote: "Mrs. McSween, it wasn't me who killed your husband. I have only saved his Bible for you. Respt. J. Kinney."

Kinney placed the note between the pages of the Bible. He raised McSween's head and pillowed it upon the Book, then he covered the upturned face with his own shabby jacket. "I'll kill the first man who attempts to disturb that body laying there," he said. "Does anybody want to call my hand?"

The men in the group fell back. Most of them knew nothing of Susan McSween's appeals to Dudley, and they could not know how Kinney had been affected by her courage and resolution.

Dolan and Sheriff Peppin approached in time to hear Kinney's last remark.

"Getting soft, Kinney?" Dolan asked.

"Yes, Dolan, soft as a lead bullet. That's my nature," Kinney snarled.

"What's in the note?" Dolan asked.

"A private matter," Kinney replied.

"Let it ride," Dolan said. "But from the score in this fight it looks to me like some of your boys had dust in their eyes."

"How would you add it up?" Kinney inquired coldly.

"Well," Dolan answered, "Beckwith got McSween, but the Kid got Beckwith. Litchfield is over there, all shot up. Your men got four of the Mexicans and let one get away, but they were the deuces in the deck. Where are the aces—Billy, French, Scurlock, O'Folliard? Looks to me like they won the pot. Add it up different, if you can!"

"Your tally sounds about right, Dolan, but you're forgetting one thing," Kinney said. "We were mighty short-handed."

"Meaning what?" Dolan asked. "You had not less than thirty men here, counting the soldiers!"

"But, Dolan," Kinney smiled, "we were short two great fighting men—you and Peppin were absent!"

All the men were listening now, and they moved to choose their leaders. The men brought in from Dolan's ranch moved to stand beside and behind him, and the imported fighters drifted close to Kinney.

"Where were you during the fight?" Kinney continued. "You and Peppin were busy with Dudley, and there was no chance of a bullet parting *your* hair."

Dolan's gun hand clenched and unclenched, and Kinney laid his hand on the butt of his pistol.

Dolan was a brave man, and an angry one. "Those are fighting words, Kinney," he began hotly, but Marion Turner, Peppin's outstanding deputy, stepped between the two men. Turner's courage and authority were recognized by both factions, and his action prevented possible bloodshed among the victors.

"Men," Turner said, "there will be no personal quarrels here." Turning to some of his own men, Turner directed,

"Take Litchfield to the store and send to the post for Dr. Appel. Take Beckwith's body to the storeroom and notify his family. And remember," Turner added, "this war is over!"

During the night, the remains of the McSween home and the Tunstall store, next door to the east, were plundered. Sam Corbet, caretaker placed at the Tunstall store by McSween, was forced to flee in order to preserve his life, and he could obtain no protection from the sheriff.

At the approach of daylight, Dolan ordered his riders to return to the Seven Rivers Ranch on the Pecos, and Kinney and his followers withdrew in the direction of the Rio Grande.

The clear notes of the bugle announced dawn at the military encampment. Presently the detachment of cavalry, followed by the field pieces and baggage van, passed in close formation up the road in the direction of the post. Colonel Dudley rode at the head of the troop, which traveled smartly at "trot."

When the last echo of hoofbeats had died away, silence enveloped the little village. Low over the roof tops the light, acrid smoke from the destructive fires of the night before had settled, but no cheerful breakfast smoke rose from other humble chimneys to mingle with it. The chatter of children was absent. There was an oppressive air of doom.

Dr. T. F. Ealy, the missionary-physician, emerged from his home into the morning sunlight. With his family, he had remained in Lincoln through the battle, and, during the final bitter hours, he had given shelter to Mrs. Shield and to Susan McSween. He went slowly toward the cooling ruin. He would need help for the work ahead, but upon whom could he call? His thoughts turned to George

Washington, the Negro who lived in a small cabin a little way outside the village.

Washington agreed to help Ealy, and they went to the McSween premises together. A few of Lincoln's Spanish-speaking citizens who had gone to the hills several days before drifted back into town and joined Washington and Dr. Ealy.

Under the direction of the doctor, the bodies of McSween and Morris were removed to the Ealy home for Protestant services. There was no cemetery in Lincoln, and so Dr. Ealy ordered the slain Mexicans, shrouded in blankets, to be interred where they had fallen. The small community did not have a regular priest, and Dr. Ealy read the burial service for those of a faith differing from his own.

He knelt long in silent prayer, and, as he rose and raised his hand in final benediction, those in the little crowd around him solemnly and reverently made the sign of the cross, all joining in petition for the repose of the souls of the slain youths.

The riverbank was searched for casualties, and, when none was found, it was assumed that Billy the Kid, French, Scurlock, O'Folliard, and Chavez y Chavez had escaped, as well as Hijinio Salazar, who had played dead among the bodies in the yard.

Other refugees drifted into town, and among them was Pedro Gonzales, the carpenter, who set to work building pine coffins for the burials of McSween and Morris. Behind the Tunstall store there was a narrow, level strip of earth where, five months before, John H. Tunstall had been buried. At his side, two new graves received the bodies of Alexander McSween and Harvey Morris.[3] And there would be yet another unmarked grave in the narrow strip of earth between the store and the river.

---

[3] See Appendix II, Note C, Chap. XIII.

Hijinio Salazar, the wounded man who had lain motionless among the bodies of his comrades through the long night, afterward related his own story:

"It was one very bad night for me. I think we make a serious mistake for not doing just as Billy told us. He said, 'Spread out and run like hell,' but we all reached the gate near the same time. Maybeso, we were like a covey of quail. It is easier to shoot at many men close together than just at one, if he runs fast and dodges. We were all very much scared, and forgot to do what Billy said. Chavez ran very fast and a little ahead, and, although wounded, he made his escape.

"Francisco Zamora and Ignacio Gonzales died, and I fell with three bullets in my body.

"No, *Señor,*" Salazar replied in answer to a question, "Billy did not send us out first to draw their fire. I have heard this spoken by his enemies often, but it is an untruth.

"He directed us to the northeast gate and the one farthest from the adobe wall where he believed Turner's men were hidden. He could not know they had circled to cover both gates. Besides, he had told us it was the Anglos they most wanted to kill, especially himself and *Señor* McSween, and this would give us the better chance. It is true there was very little choice, but Billy never thought first of his own safety.

"Remember, *Señor,* he was the last one from the burning house and the last to leave the yard, where he had made a lone fight against all of Dolan's and Kinney's men."

The aging Mexican paused, and a faraway look came into his eyes.

"You will pardon an old man if his thoughts wander back to his young friend, the Kid, who was so often and unjustly accused of crimes in which he had no part.

"When I fell, I knew should I move I would quick be one dead man, so I laid very still. At first I did not feel great pain, only very sick. I wanted to sleep that which is called 'faint,' I guess.

"I think to myself, 'Hijinio, if you sleep now you maybe breathe loud and make noise and maybe move your arms and legs,' so I make myself stay awake. Soon I have great pain and am almost wild for one big drink of water, and laying on the ground in the dark, I cannot see well, but I hear Beckwith say he has killed Señor McSween. I think I was about only thirty feet away. Then I hear Billy talk to Beckwith and then two shots, and I know Beckwith is dead, because Billy never misses.

"Many shots follow from the wall, and I was afraid Billy had been killed, but not so. Very soon there was no more shooting, and many men come from the wall into the yard. Much whisky is brought, and they sing and dance like Apaches.

"Andy Boyle is very drunk, and he kicked Francisco and Ignacio and laugh. Then he saw me and jumped hard on my chest. He said maybe I am not dead, and he will shoot me some more to make sure.

"Old Man Pierce told him to put up his gun, for I was already plenty dead. They laughed and drink some more, then went away—much seems like a bad dream. It was beginning to grow light, and I managed to crawl to the stream about a hundred and fifty feet away where I drank much water.

"I was very weak from the loss of blood, and I think I what you call 'pass out,' for when I wake I saw the sun above the hills.

"On my hands and knees I followed down the Bonito until I came to the rear of my brother's house. When I reached the door, I found no one there. They had hidden, as did many others.

"I got up on a bed, and for a long time I remember nothing more. I was later told by my brother José, when he and his wife returned, they found me unconscious. He had risked his life by going to the Murphy-Dolan store to appeal for aid to Dr. Appel, whom he had observed entering the building.

"When I came awake again, Dr. Appel had finished caring for my wounds. He said to me, 'Hijinio, you are one lucky boy, and you will get well. I found two bullets, but one I did not. When you are stronger, you come to the post, and we will hunt some more.'

"I did not go, *Señor,* and sometimes that bullet still reminds me of that night, now so long ago.

"You wish to know how I escaped death for the second time that day? Very well, if you are not weary of hearing an old man talk so much about the days before you were born.

"Dr. Appel was ready to leave, and three of the gunmen came by the back door, saying they had come to kill me. I think they had overheard José's request for help.

"Dr. Appel was one very brave man. He took a big army pistol from his leather bag and turned to the men. He spoke slowly, but there was something in his voice, 'I am an officer in the United States Army, and I will kill the man who draws his gun. You are three against one, and I may lose my life, but if I do, I promise all of you will hang. Get out, and quickly.'

"The men backed to the door, always facing Dr. Appel and his gun, and disappeared.

"You wish to know more of Billy the Kid? I tell you the truth. Many people everywhere will say, 'Old Hijinio Salazar has lied,' but he does not!

"Billy was the bravest man I ever knew, and I have known many brave men. I do not believe that he knew the meaning of fear. When faced with danger he was always calm, but he acted quick, like a flash of light.

"He appeared never to think of what he should do—

his mind and hand acted at once. I never saw Billy take a drink of liquor, although he was much in saloons where there was much drinking. In those days, *Señor,* such were the only places men could meet and talk and gamble. He was always loyal to his friends and risked his life in their cause as he had for McSween. He was good to my people, and, during those early days, most of the *gringos* were not.

"Billy always seemed to smile and be happy. Among all of the good God's creatures there are none more quick to sense those whom they may trust than children and dogs—Billy loved them both, and they loved him.

"I knew Pat Garrett well, *Señor,* and he gained a great reputation because of having killed Billy, who was then unarmed. Some years later, he himself died, as did Billy, by an assassin's bullet."

Hijinio Salazar, who in his youth had eluded death by courage and sheer force of will, lived his entire life in the once-turbulent but subsequently quiet little village of Lincoln.

There, in 1936, he died, well past three score and ten, and in a neglected cemetery on the outskirts of the village is his grave. At its head stands a plain, white marble monument. His epitaph is one of modest simplicity:

HIJINIO SALAZAR
Born Died
February 14, 1863 January 7, 1936
Pal of Billy the Kid[4]

Now, we will return, briefly, to events that were taking place in Lincoln during the month of February, 1878. The general situation cannot be better described than by here incorporating a portion of the diary of Mrs. Ealy.

[4] See Appendix II, Note D, Chap. XIII.

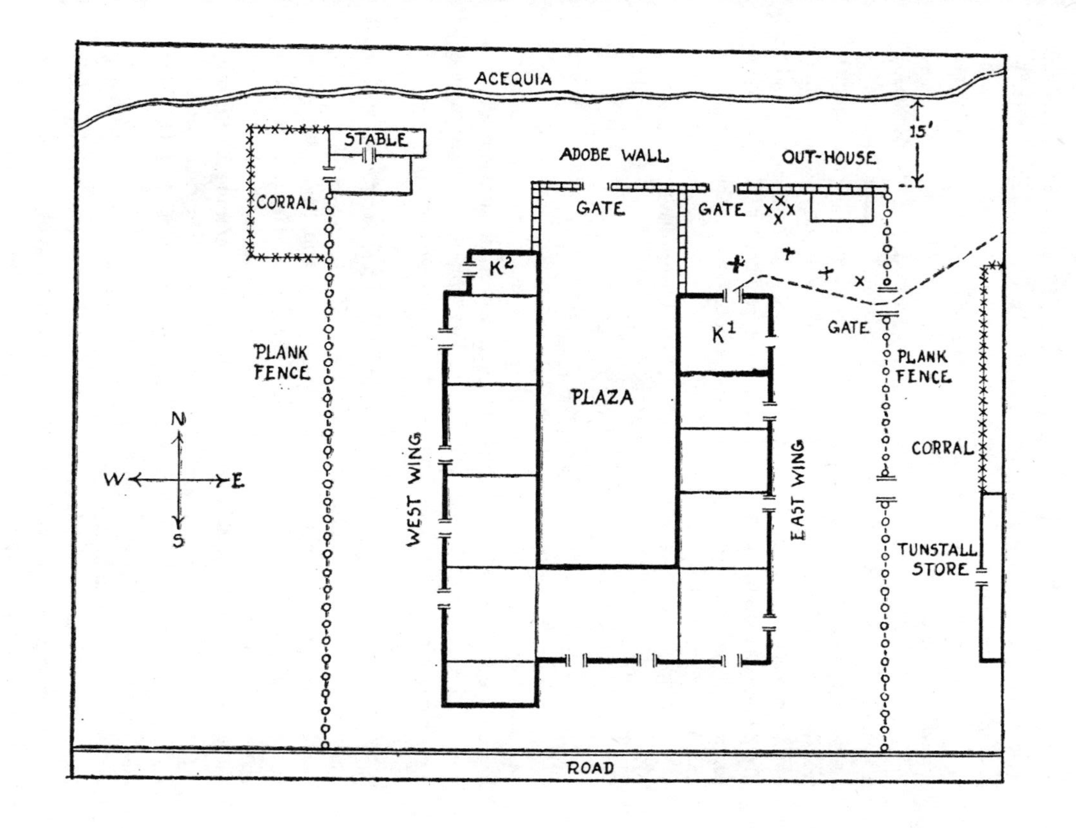
ACEQUIA
15'
STABLE
CORRAL
ADOBE WALL
OUT-HOUSE
GATE
GATE
GATE
K¹
K²
PLAZA
PLANK FENCE
PLANK FENCE
WEST WING
EAST WING
CORRAL
TUNSTALL STORE
N
W
E
S
ROAD

It was after dark on the evening of Feby. 16 when we arrived at Fort Stanton. The trip from Trinidad, where we had left the train, had been long and tedious; five days of weary wagon travel. Our new home-to-be in Lincoln was still ten miles away. How eager we were to reach our journey's end.

Then came the news Mr. Tunstall had been killed, and Mr. McSween was under arrest charged with a serious criminal offense. Two factions were in the midst of a warfare and the whole of Lincoln County was being rocked to its foundations. Lincoln Village was the center of the disturbance, and it was to Lincoln we had been sent by the Presbyterian Missionary Board, following a request of Mr. McSween for a minister, a doctor and a teacher. Should we continue in spite of the terrifying rumors?

Major Burt at Fort Stanton said it would be sheer madness to venture into the seething town, but what else was there to do? Dr. Ealy, Miss Gates, my two small children and I had just gone through a trip wearisome in the extreme, and the very thought of returning without days—yes, weeks of rest—was unthinkable. Besides, Dr. Ealy was also a missionary and had no connection with the feud. Surely, he could go to Lincoln undisturbed. Such a decision he reached, and both Miss Gates and I were glad to support him in it, even though with shivers of apprehension when we thought of encountering any of those western ruffians.

We had not long to wait for such an encounter, for the following morning, as we drove into town, three of the Murphy, Dolan, Riley men, all armed with rifles, stopped the wagon, and began to search our belongings. Their excuse was that they were searching for firearms and ammunition. It was a stormy entrance into our field of work. Dr. Ealy protested that his sole purpose in coming to Lincoln was to preach, teach and practice medicine. His explanation met with no favor in the minds of the desperados, and they looked at Dr. Ealy and even at us, with undisguised hostility.

Just then I would have been willing to start back on the long, lonesome trail to Trinidad, the rail point, and return home. Dr. Ealy explained further that we had come at the request of Mr. McSween, who had asked the Presbyterian Society for a minister. At this pronouncement, there appeared upon the faces of the men, a look of actual hate. The entire truth came to me in a flash. It was Mr. McSween against whom this deadly hatred was directed, and we were now in the feud regardless.

We were permitted to continue our way, following the directions grudgingly given us by the Murphyites.

Mr. McSween came from his house and greeted us kindly but sadly. He told us about Tunstall's death; how he had been shot down in cold blood near his ranch by the friends of the three men who had searched us, simply because he objected to their stealing his cattle, and was about to take the matter into the courts. The easiest way, they thought, was to silence Mr. Tunstall once and for all. The next night his body was brought to McSween's home. Among those who attended it were William Bonney, then known as The Kid, Dick Brewer and Fred Waite; men who were in Tunstall's employ. The body was in a miserable condition. Mr. Tunstall had been twice shot, and his forehead and face had been beaten into an almost unrecognizable pulp.

The youths were anxious to take the execution of justice into their own hands, but were restrained by Mr. McSween as a clash would be inevitable.

Mrs. McSween was away at the time, and I was asked to play two or three hymns. I shall never forget Billy's expression during the service. On his face were drawn lines of grief, but his eyes almost frightened me; they appeared to glow with a deadly hatred. He later told me Mr. Tunstall had been the only friend he ever had except his mother.

The service was a fearsome one for no one knew when hostilities between the two factions might be resumed; there being many men on both sides then in Lincoln, ready to use their guns at a minute's notice. Col. Dudley came down from Fort Stanton with a number of soldiers to observe what was going on, but said little regarding the feud he could easily have prevented. Instead, he spent his time drinking with Murphy at his store.

Fighting went on intermittently. One week one faction appeared to be in control, and the next week, the other. Death became very common. Dr. Ealy conducted funeral services for the killed of both sides without distinction. During the five months we remained in Lincoln, Dr. Ealy conducted thirty-eight such services, and only one person had died of natural causes. Frequently some of those young warriors would come to my home and ask me to play the organ and sing. Billy appeared to be especially fond of music and had some knowledge of Christian hymns. He told me at one time he had attended church and Sunday school with his mother. He really had a very good voice, and I was frequently secretly amused as I listened to the discordant sounds meant to be harmony. The youths came with their guns and belts filled with cartridges, and I imagine I was as often off key as they as they stood about me. I felt a nervousness, though it was not fear, for they always behaved very well. I was impressed with the quiet mein of Billy. He appeared to be a born leader. Should one of his friends grow a little boisterous, Billy would just look at him, his eyes steady, but with what appeared always to be a smile. The noise would instantly subside, with, "All right, Kid,"; then to me, "I'm sorry, Mrs. Ealy. Guess I was just feeling a little bit too good." When they were leaving, there was always an expression of courteous appreciation.

Then came the week of the four or five days fighting, in which Mr. McSween and a number of other men were killed. I shall not attempt to relate its terror. On Monday morning, just as Dr. Ealy was opening the shutters preparatory for school, one of the little Shield's boys came running in. "There must be no school today, Dr. Ealy, as both parties are in town, and the danger is very great." And so it proved. Our abode was within one hundred feet of the McSween home, which was eventually set on fire and men killed as they were forced to abandon it after a long and hopeless struggle. Some escaped; one of whom was Billy, the Kid. The rest is history.

PART TWO

Chapter XIV

THE tragic conclusion of the conflict on the night of July 19 did not bring peace to Lincoln.

The population was restless and uneasy. Other lives were yet to be sacrificed in the aftermath of the bitter feud. Many of the partisans fled the territory. Others resorted to outlawry, particularly rustling, in order to survive. Business was so unsettled that there was little legitimate employment.

During the five months from February 18, when John Tunstall died, to July 19, 1878, nineteen men had lost their lives, and an undetermined number had been wounded. The dollar loss has never been computed, but it must have been great.

Officials of a heretofore indifferent administration in Washington were forced to recognize the gravity of conditions existing in the territory of New Mexico.[1]

President Hayes removed Samuel B. Axtell from the office of territorial governor. General Lew Wallace, soldier, statesman, and author, was appointed governor of the unruly territory late in August. Wallace was vested with extraordinary powers to aid him in the effort to restore order.

Wallace took office October 1, 1878, and one of his first official acts was the issuance of an "Amnesty Proclamation," under date of November 13, 1878.[2] Pursuant to its provisions, free pardons were promised to all of either faction who would lay aside their arms and re-

[1] See Appendix II, Note A, Chap. XIV.
[2] See Appendix II, Note B, Chap. XIV.

turn to peaceful occupations. However, the proclamation contained a "joker." Amnesty could not be pleaded by any person to bar conviction under indictments already found and returned, charging crimes and misdemeanors. This provision narrowed the proclamation's effectiveness materially, as a large number of indictments were then outstanding.

After the battle which ended July 19, Billy the Kid found occasional employment with small ranchers, and spent much of his time at the gambling tables in Fort Sumner. There remained in the area only the Kid and a handful of the other followers of the "lost cause." In certain quarters it was thought that this remnant ought to be eliminated.

Bitter enmity, its exact origin unknown, had arisen between Billy the Kid and John S. Chisum. The trouble has been variously attributed to a dispute about unpaid wages due Billy, and to Chisum's failure to provide the financial support he allegedly promised the McSween cause during the Lincoln County War.

In any event, Chisum reported that the Kid was raiding his herds. The "Cattle King" overlooked no opportunity to name the Kid leader of a "band of cattle thieves," and, in spite of his well-known frugality, Chisum even offered a reward for the Kid's arrest and conviction. However, Chisum neglected to specify the *amount* of such reward.

Billy the Kid lived a free life and a wandering one. Already legends had started to gather about his small person, and he was beginning to serve as a convenient scapegoat for every unsolved crime in a great section of the territory. This was a game his enemies were glad to play. Inefficient peace officers blamed Billy for criminal acts perpetrated by unknown persons. Guilty persons who knew the boy's reputation were able to spin webs shifting suspicion away from themselves and pointing to the phantomlike Kid.

Warrants for Billy's arrest were placed in the hands of every peace officer in the southern half of New Mexico. In most instances the officers made small effort to apprehend the Kid, for not a few sympathized with him, while others, knowing of his skill with arms and believing the tales about him, were afraid.

Susan McSween, meantime, endangered her safety by pursuing her determination to secure justice for the death of her husband and the destruction of her home. True to her promise, she brought to the attention of the authorities the conduct of Colonel N. A. M. Dudley on the occasion of the three-day battle. Her life was threatened, from time to time, and Governor Wallace, who was making his headquarters at Fort Stanton and Lincoln until he could clear up the loose ends of the feuds, detailed three men to guard Mrs. McSween.

Colonel Dudley moved defensively and procured several affidavits purporting to show Susan McSween a woman of bad character. The affidavits were couched in offensive, even obscene, language and were given wide circulation.

Governor Wallace requested that Dudley be relieved of his command at Fort Stanton and cited before a Military Board of Inquiry. His investigations suggested this course of action.

General Hatch, commander of the Military Department, with headquarters in Santa Fe, consented to issue an order suspending the colonel, pending his appearance before the Board of Inquiry. The governor assumed personal supervision of the case.[3]

Wallace was quick to perceive that the testimony of Susan McSween would require extensive corroboration, since several means were being used to discredit her.

---

[3] See Appendix II, Note C, Chap. XIV.

The governor interviewed a number of witnesses in secret. Most of them talked freely to His Excellency, but declined to agree to appear before the Military Board of Inquiry. They expressed fear of reprisals from the military, from powerful members of the Murphy faction, and from unknown sources. Only a few of the bolder and more courageous agreed to testify at the inquiry. When Wallace told Susan McSween of the difficulty of securing witnesses, she had a suggestion.

"There is one who knows more than any other about all the events from the time of Mr. Tunstall's murder to the present, sir. I may be able to persuade him to appear against Colonel Dudley."

"Who is this witness?" the governor asked. "And would he not fear to appear, even as the others?"

"He is William Bonney, sometimes called Billy the Kid, and I believe he is completely fearless."

"Ah, yes! I have heard of the part he played the night your husband met his death. He must be—well—an unusual lad. But, Mrs. McSween, I understand he is out of the vicinity because of an indictment charging him with the murder of former Sheriff Brady. Can you contact him?"

"I believe I can get a message to Billy," Susan said thoughtfully, "although it may require several days."

"Very well, madam, let us hope you meet with success. Try to arrange for me to meet with him, if possible."

Susan chose George Washington, her late husband's trusted Negro friend, to bear a note to Billy. It read:

BILLY: Governor Wallace wishes to talk with you. Will you come to the Ellis house as soon as possible? We are greatly in need of your help.

SUSAN MCSWEEN.

Governor Wallace provided the messenger with a good horse, and Washington followed a tip that Billy was at the Yorley ranch near San Patricio, helping with a cattle branding.

The next day, Washington returned to Mrs. McSween.

"Billy said, ma'am, he will come to see the governor soon. He sent his respects to you, and said if I forgot to tell you, he would lift my hair for sure!" Washington laughed, showing brilliant teeth, as he passed a hand over his head which was as smooth and black as polished ebony.

The next evening, Billy rode into Lincoln, dismounted, and entered the hotel. Governor Wallace was using the hotel office as a study, and he was busy there with some official documents. When he heard a light step, the governor spoke without looking up, "Yes? What is it?"

"I am looking for the governor, sir. He sent for me," Billy answered quietly.

His Excellency put aside his pen and fixed his attention upon the slight figure standing, hat in hand, just inside the door.

"There must be some mistake, son," he said kindly. "I don't know you, and I can't recall having summoned you."

Billy stepped nearer the desk and handed a paper to the governor.

"If you will read the note, sir, I believe it will explain."

A glance at the note brought an exclamation of surprise from General Wallace. He looked closely at the youth standing before him. Billy was nineteen years old, small and slender. His brown hair was long and curled a little, and he looked back at the governor with clear, blue eyes. The boy smiled, drew himself very straight, and saluted smartly.

"William Bonney, reporting present, sir. Does he pass the general's inspection?"

"At ease," the governor said crisply, responding to the

boy's byplay. The distinguished soldier rose and extended his hand.

"I am glad to see you, Billy, but I was taken by surprise. Somehow, you don't look like I expected."

"That I can understand, sir," Billy said easily. "You may have been told I have horns and a tail, but I never wear them when I go visiting!"

Governor Wallace smiled, and Billy continued seriously, "Mrs. McSween sent word you wished to see me. I will do anything for her if you will tell me how I can help."

"Then tell me," Wallace said, "just what occurred here during the week ending July 19, when McSween and the others were killed, and the McSween home burned. I would particularly like to hear your account of the actions of Colonel Dudley during the last twenty-four hours of that time."

Thoughtfully, carefully, and without displaying any emotion, the Kid related the incidents, from the hour of his arrival in Lincoln until he fled after killing Bob Beckwith. He described Dudley's rejection of all appeals to stop the fighting and save the lives of those trapped in the burning building.

The recital was spoken as if it were another who had enacted the Kid's courageous role on that flaming July night.

"Your account fully corroborates that of Mrs. McSween," Wallace said when Billy had finished. "At my request, General Hatch has suspended Dudley, and has ordered his appearance before a Military Board of Inquiry to answer the charge of dereliction of duty on that unfortunate occasion. The date for the hearing has not been set, but we believe it will be soon."

The governor paused and studied Billy a moment, then continued, "There are those who could provide valuable evidence, but they decline to testify, apparently fearing reprisals. This fear may or may not be justified, but, in any case, it is their duty to aid in bringing peace to Lincoln."

"Perhaps you should shorten your loop a little, sir," Billy said quickly. "Those men are not cowards. Many of them are small ranchers and homesteaders and have wives and little children. It is for their families they fear."

Wallace was not surprised that Billy knew to whom he referred. He had believed for some time that the Kid had friends and sources of information in Lincoln.

"I meant no reflection upon their courage, Billy," Wallace explained. "I respect their reasons, and possibly I might feel as they do in the same circumstances. However, let me ask you but one question—are you willing to appear before the Board of Inquiry and testify to what you have told me?"

The Kid's blue eyes assumed their angry, smoky color as he thought for a moment of the events of the war.

"If you want my testimony, you have my promise, sir—if I live! I believe I can bring with me Tom O'Folliard, Jim French, and Doc Scurlock, if you wish. There are indictments against all of us, but we want to see things cleared up, and we want peace and safety for our friends in Lincoln."

Billy paused for breath. He was making a very long speech, but he had more to say. "I am concerned for the safety of Mrs. McSween, sir. She is very determined, and she puts herself in a dangerous position."

"Have no anxiety," Governor Wallace said. "I have three men watching over her, and she is under their constant surviellance, although much of the time she is unaware of their presence."

"Thank you, Governor. That lifts a big load off my stirrups, since I can't stay around to ride herd over her."

Billy went to the door, then turned to the governor.

"I have talked more than is my habit, sir," he said. "And it is not my place to advise you. If I shove in my chips at the wrong time, just declare the game closed—but I'm afraid this young lawyer, Chapman, who came from Las Vegas to help Mrs. McSween, is talking too much. He writes to the papers at Mesilla and Las Cruces. He is getting lots of people pretty hostile, and that does Mrs. McSween no good. Besides," Billy concluded, "if he don't quit riding them, he'll get himself killed!"

The governor nodded his agreement. "I have seen some of these articles, and you are quite right. The situation here is still explosive. I mean to speak to Mrs. McSween and suggest that she instruct Chapman to be more circumspect in the future. And now, Billy, wait a moment. As we talked, I have been trying to plan for your safety if you testify."

"Thank you, Governor," Billy said wryly. "No one has been much interested in my welfare, except Mr. Tunstall. So far, I have managed to look out for myself. I know of nothing you can do, with those indictments against me."

"Of course you are ineligible to plead amnesty because of the indictments," Wallace admitted. "And it is out of my jurisdiction to order their dismissal, but there is a way I can help you."

The Kid's face lighted with interest as he waited for the governor to continue.

"Surrender to the authorities, stand trial, and, if you are convicted, I will pardon you. To do this is clearly within the scope of my authority as chief executive of this territory."

The boy's look of hopeful anticipation faded as the governor finished speaking.

It wouldn't work, sir," Billy said. "If I were tried,

I would stand convicted even before the evidence was in, but that isn't the real joker in the deck." He paused, rolled and lighted a cigarette. Then he said, "It's this way, sir. I ride into town, hand my gun to the sheriff, and then what?"

"What do you mean?" Wallace asked.

"They know that filthy hole they call a jail won't hold me. I've been in—and out—of it!"

Billy sighed deeply, then he said, "They'd take me to the guardhouse at Fort Stanton, and from there I'd never get to trial. I'd be shot 'trying to escape,' or 'by persons unknown'—or some other way. Your pardon wouldn't be much good to me then, would it?"

After a moment the boy touched his hat to the governor, and Wallace followed him outside. Billy mounted Old Grey. "Get word to me when you want me," he said, "and I will come. *Hasta la vista!*"

And Billy rode over the hill, in the direction of San Patricio.

Wallace went inside and slumped in his chair, lost in thought. The situation was complex, with hidden aspects, the governor sensed, although he lacked all the information needed to put the puzzle together. If Wallace could by some means grant amnesty to the Kid, further action against the boy by the authorities would necessarily end; and one of the troublesome problems of restoring order in Lincoln County would be solved.

The pending indictments against Billy were the crux of the matter. The only solution that presented itself to Wallace was an appeal to Judge Warren Bristol for their dismissal. Others had employed this means to the advantage of Billy's enemies, so why should it not be used for the benefit of the boy?

The governor turned to his desk and prepared a note to Attorney Ira Leonard of the little town of White

Oaks, near Lincoln. Leonard was interested in the proceedings against Dudley.

The governor requested that Leonard proceed to Mesilla and petition Judge Bristol to dismiss the indictment against Billy the Kid, even as he had dismissed those pending against the Murphy partisans.

Wallace sent a similar note to District Attorney W. L. Rynerson, in which he said that he believed such action would be in the interest of law and order.

Chapter XV

WITH the final collapse of the old Murphy financial structure, Thomas B. Catron, of Santa Fe, who held a blanket mortgage on the properties, had taken over. His brother-in-law, Edgar A. Waltz, was placed in charge of Catron's interests in Lincoln, with instructions that "cash and cattle" should, in the future, be the rigid policy of the firm.

The former outlaw element was giving the village a wide berth. In Lincoln there was now comparative quiet, attributable largely to the presence of Governor Wallace. The village returned to its former uneventful routine, and no one missed the excitement. Residents once more went abroad with security. Children played and laughed along the dusty road. Outwardly, it seemed that peace had come to Lincoln.

The mountain air was clear and crisp the morning of February 18, 1879, just one year from the day of John H. Tunstall's death. Billy the Kid, Fred Waite, Tom O'Folliard, and John Middleton rode boldly into Lincoln, in spite of the indictments against them. They knew the strangle hold of the old enemy had been broken, and George Kimbrell, an efficient officer, had been elected sheriff.

It had been tacitly understood between Governor Wallace and the new sheriff that no immediate action should be taken against those ineligible to plead amnesty unless some new and overt act of lawlessness should be committed. It was not that His Excellency condoned the earlier offenses; he was, rather, awaiting developments, and desired to prevent any incident which might delay his effort to restore peace and order.

So it was that, when the four youths rode into the village, they were met by Tom Longworth, Sheriff Kimbrell's deputy. Longworth stepped into the road and held up his hand.

"Rein up, boys! Don't you think you are crowding your luck a little?"

"*Buenas dias,* Tom. *Como está usted?*" Billy called.

"Plumb forgot how to talk Anglo, have you? Maybe you never did know how! If it'll make you sleep any better, my health is fine," Longworth answered.

"And, further," the deputy continued, "I think it would be good sense if you Shorthorns would keep out of town for a spell. Things are pretty quiet, right now, and we don't want to start another stampede."

"We rode in peaceful, Tom, and you have my word we'll sidestep trouble. Besides, I hear Dolan wants a powwow with me. The boys came along to keep me company. I couldn't disappoint Jimmie," the Kid grinned, "since he says he wants to bury the tomahawk."

"Well, maybe so," the deputy answered, "but don't bet all your chips on that!"

The riders dismounted and stood about the deputy.

He continued in a low voice, "You boys can go into town, I guess, but—well—you know General Hatch has relieved Dudley of command at the post, and he's sore as a range steer that's had its horns sawed off. Most special, he resents the governor, Mrs. McSween, and that boy lawyer of hers. It may be that hell will break loose again, some place."

"How do you mean, Tom, and who?" Billy asked.

"Sheriff Kimbrell thinks some bad medicine is brewing, but he can't get his loop on who it's for. We try to keep things quiet here, but if someone don't get a handful of buckthorns under his saddle blanket, I'll be a squaw man!"

His listeners remounted, and the Kid rode close to Longworth.

"Keep an eye on Mrs. McSween, will you, Tom?" he asked quietly.

"We try to do that, Billy, but I don't believe she's in any real danger, right now. One more thing—you mavericks do your grazing quiet and peaceful while you're in town!"

"All right, Tom," the Kid replied. "You have our promise—but if we forget to remember, better send to the post for help. There are only four of us, so just one regiment should be enough to round us up!"

"I don't believe I will have to send for the troops, boys," Longworth replied, laughing. "Your word shines with me," and he watched the four out of sight.

The quartet kept faith with Deputy Longworth and spent most of the day visiting friends among the Spanish-American families. Late in the afternoon, they went to the store formerly owned by Murphy and Dolan. The men were greeted by Edgar A. Waltz, Catron's brother-in-law, whom Catron had placed in charge of his interests in Lincoln. Waltz had had no part in the Lincoln troubles, and he wanted no unpleasantness at this late date. When he recognized his guests, he immediately retired behind one of the high counters. This maneuver elicited good-humored laughter from his callers.

"Why the stampede?" the Kid asked. "We came in peaceful, just looking for Dolan. We heard he's craving a peace talk. Where is he?"

"Mr. Dolan is not here, and I know nothing about his business," Waltz said firmly.

"All right, sir, just tell him, if he's looking for me,

I'm down at the Ellis place," Billy said, and he and his companions left the building.

When they had gone, Waltz wrote a note to Dolan, who was at Fort Stanton, and dispatched it by a messenger on a fast horse.

It was late in the evening when Dolan, Waltz, Mathews, Jesse Evans, and two imported gunmen, Campbell and Van Sickle, came to the Ellis house. Although they did not like the look of the party, the Kid, O'Folliard, Middleton, and Waite stepped out into the road to meet them.

Van Sickle immediately confronted the Kid, challenge in his manner. His hand rested on the butt of his gun.

"So you are the Kid—fastest gun hand in New Mexico," Van Sickle sneered. "I've a mind to kill you where you stand for murdering Bob Beckwith. He was a friend of mine."

O'Folliard, Middleton, and Waite started forward, but Billy motioned them back.

"Don't start beating your war drum, *hombre,*" Billy said quietly. "I don't know who you are, but murder is a pretty big word."

His eyes were on Van Sickle's hand. If Van Sickle drew, or if Billy did, it would signal a battle. Billy wanted to keep faith with Deputy Longworth, and, further, he had the feeling that something other than loyalty to a fallen friend prompted this flagrant provocation by a stranger. Billy had a great curiosity to learn what motivated Van Sickle.

"You've been hearing wrong about one thing," Billy continued evenly. "Your friend Jesse Evans over there can outdraw any man east *or* west of the Pecos. After him, I may be next best, and you can find out easily—if you have the guts."

Billy added the last phrase in a very soft voice. He waited, and, when Van Sickle didn't move or speak, he continued, "I killed Bob—you got that right—just after he shot down Mr. McSween. He fired at me, and missed. I didn't. That's the spread. Now I'm waiting to see your hole card!"

Jesse Evans stood to one side, listening, a half smile on his face. He knew Van Sickle was inviting an early death, and he waited, quite detached, to see the little scene played out.

Evans was aware that Billy had hated him since the day Jesse rode out with the posse which killed John Tunstall. He also knew of Billy's fierce loyalty to his old companions, and he never believed he would meet the same judgment Billy had meted out to some other members of that ill-fated group. However, Jesse was not sure of Billy, and he was alert and cool when he met his former friend, never completely trusting the strange kinship between himself and the Kid.

Evans did not intend to interfere between Billy and Van Sickle unless another member of either group should make a treacherous move. If that happened, Jesse meant to side with Billy. Jesse barely knew Van Sickle, and disliked him.

Dolan and Van Sickle's friend, Campbell, had drawn aside and were talking. They seemed to be in disagreement.

Dolan turned away from Campbell to speak to Van Sickle, "Forget the war talk, Van. The Kid came in for a peace talk, and this is a hell of a way to start it. We'll go down to Patron's and celebrate the truce."

Dolan's remark broke the tension, and, as the men walked up the road, Jesse Evans fell into step beside Van Sickle, his supposed comrade-at-arms.

"Well, *hombre*, you played in luck," Evans said contemptuously. "You called the right card when you said you heard the Kid was the fastest gun hand in New

Mexico. And he knows damned well you never knew Bob Beckwith. It looked for a while, though, like you and Bob might meet up somewhere tonight!"

With that thrust at Van Sickle's vanity, Evans quickened his steps and showed Van Sickle his back.

The party now numbered ten men, four with the Kid and six in Dolan's following. When they entered Patron's saloon, O'Folliard went at once to one end of the bar, and Middleton and Waite took places at the other end. The Kid stood in the center, at Campbell's right. The stratagem was not unobserved by the others. They saw at once that, in case of trouble, Billy could step back, leaving Dolan's men in a line of cross fire—actually, in the center of a triangle. Dolan was thoughtful. Because of the Kid's reckless courage, he had supposed the boy would ride into Lincoln alone. The presence of his three companions, all on guard, posed unexpected complications.

Juan Patron, the keeper of the bar, had been a loyal supporter of the Tunstall-McSween faction during the war, and he felt some concern when he identified his visitors. That Billy, O'Folliard, Waite, and Middleton should be with Dolan and his friends was surprising, and, Patron thought, boded no good. Showing nothing of what he thought, Patron's greeting, spoken in Spanish, was courteous. He arranged glasses along the bar.

"Permit me first to be your host," he suggested.

The glasses werc filled, and Mathews proposed a toast in a loud voice, "Well, *compadres,* here's down the river, hoping it's long and deep."

Everyone drank except Billy, who stood still, an empty glass near his hand. Patron had not filled a glass for Billy, for he knew, as well as the others, that the boy always refused liquor. A little frown furrowed Billy's brow as he heard the toast proposed by the man he had tried so earnestly, if unsuccessfully, to kill the morning of April 1, 1878.

Another drink was poured, and another. Campbell was in an ugly temper. Turning savagely to Patron, he snarled, "So you're the damned greaser who said you'd admire to see Dudley hung?"

"No, *Señor,* I did not say so."

"Are you calling me a liar, you dirty—"

"I have said that the *Señor* is mistaken."

"Well, damn you," Campbell replied, "they can hang Dudley for all I care, but I'll make sure *you* won't be around to see his neck stretched!"

Campbell's hand dropped to his side, but, as his gun cleared, he felt his wrist in the firm grasp of Billy's left hand. The Kid rested his right hand at the top of his own holster. The grasp of Billy's hand tightened, Campbell's gun was discharged, and the bullet lodged itself in the front of the bar.

"You're some careless with a gun, Campbell," Billy drawled. "That wild shot might have hurt someone—maybe even you."

Campbell and Billy faced each other. Campbell's smoking pistol was still in his hand; Billy's remained in its holster. The little room was full of the smell of gunpowder, and gunsmoke mingled with the smoke from the sputtering lamps.

"All right, Kid, accidents can happen," Campbell grumbled. "But next time you can be sure nothing is going to get tangled up with my gun hand." Campbell replaced his gun and turned back to the bar.

Patron had been only a little frightened, believing that he could rely upon his friends. He extended his hand across the bar and said, casually, "*Muy gracias,* Billy. I felt no alarm as I saw you were watching." Patron leaned nearer to Billy and added in a low voice, "Look out for

Campbell. He is a very bad man." Patron noticed that the men were leaving. "Thank you. Good night," he said pleasantly.

George Chapman, the young attorney retained by Mrs. McSween, was quartered in the Tunstall store. The ten men coming up the street from Patron's place saw the one-armed lawyer leaving the building. Billy was instantly apprehensive. He was not enjoying the evening, but he was reluctant to end it without learning what Dolan intended by way of a peace move.

Chapman's zeal in the service of Mrs. McSween had invited the enmity of Colonel Dudley and his supporters. Rumors were about that the elimination of Chapman, Patron, the Kid, Mrs. McSween, and Governor Wallace had been "decreed." The rumors proved impossible to pin down, but those in authority, including Deputy Longworth and Governor Wallace, gave credence to them, and it was the circulation of these rumors that accounted for the tension in the apparently quiet village.

Although he sensed the reckless mood of the men in Dolan's party, Billy believed the young lawyer was not in danger while he and his friends stood by. Therefore he said nothing when Campbell accosted Chapman.

"Who in hell are you?" the gunman demanded roughly. "And where do you think you're going?"

"My name is Chapman, and where I am going is my business," was the curt reply.

"I'm making it mine," Campbell said. "I asked a question, and I ain't heard your answer."

Chapman's reaction demonstrated both his courage and his lack of discretion. He merely pushed silently past Campbell to continue up the street. He was confronted by a revolver in Campbell's hand.

"Not so fast, damn you," Campbell said. "I hear you're real handy with your pen and have been writing a pack of lies to *Thirty-Four* at Las Cruces. Something tells me you may not write any more for a while."

The Kid started forward at this thinly veiled threat, but Jesse Evans laid a restraining hand on his arm.

"Hold it, Kid," Evans whispered. "If that lawyer will use his head, you won't need to draw to this stacked deck. They've thrown two hands in the discard tonight, and this may be the third."

Campbell had not finished. "You sing so pretty, we'd admire to have you give us a serenade," he said.

"I will not be intimidated by a crowd of drunken ruffians," Chapman said. "Please stand aside and allow me to pass."

"Damn you," Campbell swore. "You've been asking for it. I'll let you pass with a one-way ticket straight to hell!"

While he was speaking, Campbell fired the revolver. Chapman, one-armed and weaponless, slumped in the road, shot through the heart.[1]

The Kid and his companions stared at the inert form in the road; then, silently, as if by arrangement, they drew apart to leave. Waltz and Van Sickle had slipped away, leaving Dolan, Mathews, and Campbell near the fallen Chapman. Evans walked over to the Kid.

"Billy," he said, "this was a damned-fool piece of business. It don't make sense."

The Kid looked at Evans and made no reply.

"I met Dolan up the road," Evans explained. "He told me there would be a peace talk, and I agreed to ride along."

Still the Kid made no reply. He merely moved his eyes from Evans to the gunman, Campbell, and back to Evans. He had given his promise to Longworth, but his

---

[1] *Thirty-Four* (Las Cruces, New Mexico Territory, Feb., 1879). See Appendix II, Note A, Chap. XV.

impulse was to terminate the career of Campbell forthwith. The Kid's feelings about Evans were mixed, as they had been since the day of Tunstall's death. Billy's loyalty to old friends, the integrity of his promise to Longworth, and his desire to avenge the death of Chapman, who was a friend of the cause for which he had fought—these were at war within him. The night seemed suddenly cold, and Billy shivered.

The Kid was rarely undecided, and so Evans was not aware of the source of his preoccupation. "This was no fight," Evans said. "And don't you let Campbell find a chance to dry-gulch you. I ain't sure whose gun hand he is, but—"

"Thanks, Jess," Billy interrupted. His voice sounded muffled. "Maybe Campbell will make his try when I'm not tied down. Right now I'm wearing Longworth's hobbles and can't shake them."

"Longworth's hobbles?" Evans was surprised. Then, understanding, he nodded. "It's this way, Kid—when I saw how things were going, I decided I'd side with you and your boys, but I didn't intend to show my hand unless there was a showdown."

"Well," Billy said, "maybe you would have joined us, Jess. I would have saved Chapman if I could, but it happened so fast. If I had horned in, others would have been killed, and I gave my word to Longworth."

"And I guessed wrong when I held you back," Evans said. "Now watch yourself and try to forget Chapman. He ran his bluff and was called—and his hole card was only a deuce!"

Billy, Waite, Middleton, and O'Folliard went toward the horses they had left in the corral beside the blackened walls of the McSween home. Campbell followed along, boasting. The Kid's heroic restraint of the long evening was wearing very thin. He stopped, faced Campbell, and spoke deliberately, "Campbell, I'm not drawing cards in what has already happened. That will be up to the sheriff, but I'd like to say that killing that unarmed man was the act of a dirty, yellow coward."

Campbell dropped a hand to his gun, but he did not draw.

"You say you haven't finished your job here," Billy said, stepping closer to Campbell. "Well, here's a thought for you—threats have been made against the life of Mrs. McSween. If she meets with harm, I will look for you, and I will find you, and I will kill you without warning. My compliments to your boss, whoever he may be, and tell him I'll find him out. His life, and yours, depend on the safety of Susan McSween. Now— it's your move!"

Billy's long speech contained the challenge which Campbell had been seeking all evening. Now that it had come, Campbell stood as though frozen in the moonlight. Seconds passed. Then Billy turned carelessly to Evans.

"The peace parley didn't turn out so well," Evans observed. "There'll be more trouble around Lincoln, so I'm on my way. Why don't you ride with me?"

"We won't do that," Billy said. "I promised the governor I would be a witness at Dudley's hearing. The governor is looking after Mrs. McSween, and I'm keeping my promise."

"Watch out for Campbell then. *Adios,* Kid," Evans said.

"*Hasta la vista,*" Billy called after Evans.

So parted, finally, the sometime friends. Billy and Evans had been reared in the same environment and had been destined to meet and clasp hands or clash many times in their young lives.[2]

---

[2] See Appendix II, Note B, Chap. XV.

Chapter XVI

THE Kid and his companions rode out of the village and sought Deputy Longworth. They had with them a gun which had been dropped beside Chapman's body. At the deputy's home, a mile east of Lincoln along the river, Billy reported the tragedy.

"We had no part in this," the Kid concluded, "and we couldn't have prevented what happened without starting a general fight. That's what they wanted, I think. Campbell killing Chapman, with all of us for witnesses, don't make sense."

Longworth was worried. He thought the incident signaled the outbreak of new trouble.

"I believe you, boys," he said, "but there are others who may not. You make yourselves hard to find and stay out of Lincoln for a time. Sheriff Kimbrell is at White Oaks and must be notified. I'll ride right in and take over."

Longworth made for Lincoln, and the other four went on to San Patricio. They separated there. Waite and Middleton held the opinion that there would be another local war, and, after some discussion, the two said goodby to the Kid and Tom O'Folliard and left New Mexico, never to return. The Kid and O'Folliard turned south in the direction of Alamogordo.

Daylight found Dolan riding rapidly to Fort Stanton. He was joined there a little later by Mathews, Van Sickle, and Campbell for a conference with Colonel Dudley. What was said at this meeting is not known, but, following it, Dolan and Mathews returned to Lincoln, leaving Campbell and Van Sickle at the post. Friends and former comrades-at-arms of Dolan and Mathews drifted into Lincoln, all heavily armed, and the town watched and waited.

The inquest into the death of Chapman was held in the late afternoon in the Tunstall store. Dolan and Mathews testified that, because of darkness, they had not been able to determine who had fired at Chapman.

"It may have been the Kid or one of his friends," Dolan suggested. "Where is the Kid and those who came with him? Where is Jesse Evans?" Answering his own questions, Dolan continued, "They ran for the hills, but Mathews and I are here, Waltz is at the store, Campbell and Van Sickle are at the post. Where are the others? The answer should be plain!"

Around the walls of the store, now bare of merchandise, ranged armed friends of Dolan and Mathews. Whether or not their presence influenced the jury, an open verdict was returned, concluding that the deceased met death from gunshot wounds inflicted by "person or persons unknown."

George Chapman found his final resting place in the brush-grown strip behind the Tunstall store where he was buried beside the unmarked graves of John H. Tunstall, Alexander A. McSween, and Harvey Morris. All the occupants of the little burying ground had fallen before blazing guns.

Sheriff Kimbrell and his deputy reported the occurrences of the night, and day, to Governor Wallace. Wallace was alarmed. Like Waite and Middleton, he anticipated another all-out factional fight.

Longworth related the Kid's version of the evening of February 18, and the deputy assured the governor that his investigations, and the statements of Juan Patron, confirmed Billy's account.

Governor Wallace issued orders with military promptness, hoping to forestall new violence. "Sheriff, you will immediately proceed to take Dolan, Mathews, Van Sickle, and Campbell into custody. Bring them to the post, where they will be held under military guard. Should you encounter resistance, a squad of cavalry will be placed under your command."

"Very well, Governor," Sheriff Kimbrell said. "I expect no trouble in making the arrests; but producing witnesses against these men will be the difficulty!"

"I understand there were five men, including Jesse Evans, who were present at Dolan's invitation. Any of those should be excellent witnesses."

"That's true," Sheriff Kimbrell acknowledged, "but those boys may not be easy to locate and hold for action of the grand jury."

"We will meet that situation when it arises," Wallace said decisively. "Meantime, we must take these men into custody."

Dolan, Mathews, and Campbell and Van Sickle were immediately apprehended and confined in the guardhouse at Fort Stanton.

Kimbrell made inquiries and learned that Evans, Middleton, and Waite had ridden over the border into Texas, although probably not together. Rumors were about that the Kid and O'Folliard had been seen in Fort Sumner, Roswell, Alamogordo, and elsewhere. The young men were using evasive tactics, and they told their friends they were fearful that enemies had implicated them in the murder of Chapman.

So vitally necessary to the case was the evidence of Billy the Kid that Governor Wallace resorted to a legal technicality and charged him as "accessory to the crime" and caused warrants to be issued for the arrest of Billy and Tom O'Folliard.

March 6, Governor Wallace sent a note to Fort Stanton relaying a tip that Billy and Tom were at Alamogordo, at the home of Pedro Peralta. Wallace directed that the two men be apprehended by a detachment of cavalry and brought to Fort Stanton, to be held in the matter of George Chapman. The note concluded with the order that, if Billy and Tom were not found at Alamogordo, they should be pursued until caught.

No secrecy surrounded the preparations of the military mission, since it was thought unlikely that Billy would hear of the proposed pursuit. However, a young Spanish-American employee at the post was observing carefully. The boy had a limited command of English, and he understood, mistakenly, that the Kid was wanted for murder; that a reward was being offered for his capture; and that an entire company of cavalry was being detailed to effect the arrest.

The boy mounted and rode eight miles to Lincoln, lathering his horse in his great haste. He went straight to Juan Patron.

"Many soldiers go to Alamogordo to get Billy," he told Patron, breathlessly. "They say he killed Chapman, and that the governor will pay much money to get Billy—maybe one thousand pesos, the soldiers say, and laugh. They—they say many things I do not understand," the boy finished lamely.

"You have done well," Patron said. "Find Manuel Avilla and bring him here at once; then return to the post and say nothing about coming here."

A few minutes later, Avilla reported to Patron.

"Manuel," Patron said to Avilla, "they are sending many soldiers to capture Billy. They say he killed Chapman and they will, perhaps, pay one thousand pesos for his arrest!"

"What shall we do?" Avilla asked.

"Take my best horse and ride to Alamogordo. It is nearly eighty miles, so go by the Sanchez ranch and get a fresh horse. Find Billy. Tell him what we have heard. He will know what to do, and he will tell you what you must do."

Avilla rode hard for Alamogordo and found Billy and O'Folliard at the Peralta home He delivered Patron's warning and Billy made a plan instantly. Perhaps he had expected the governor's move and had, without being conscious of it, anticipated the eventuality.

Speaking rapidly in Spanish, Billy said to his host, "Pedro, if the soldiers come to your house, tell them we were here but have gone, taking the trail to the southwest. We will ride a few miles in that direction, then circle back to the north. We will be seen leaving, and others will tell it, if they are asked."

"And you, Manuel," Billy said to the messenger, "return to Lincoln. Ride slowly and go by the Mescalero Reservation. You should meet the troop somewhere near Blazer's Mill. If you are questioned, say you have been on a visit to Alamogordo. Say you saw Tom and me, but we left for Las Cruces." Billy laughed. "That will give them another nice ride!"

Billy drew Avilla apart from the others. "Thank you for riding to warn us," Billy said, clasping Avilla's hand warmly. "And when you see Juan, tell him we'll be heading back for San Patricio."

A platoon, under command of Lieutenant Leffenwell, left Fort Stanton in the afternoon. Its pace was slowed by two heavily laden pack mules providentially included in the excursion in case the quest should be a long one.

As Billy had predicted, Avilla met the detachment near Tularosa. Avilla displayed no interest in the soldiers, but he was detained and interrogated by Leffenwell.

"I have been to Alamogordo to see my sister, who was very much sick. She is well, so I go home," Avilla said innocently. "*Si*—yes, I see Billy," Avilla answered another question. "With him is Tom O'Folliard. Some day ago they go to El Paso, or maybe across the border to Chihuahua. Billy make some more trouble?"

"That is not your affair, *muchacho,*" Leffenwell replied. He ordered the column to proceed and moved away, frowning at the prospect of a long ride past Alamogordo, in compliance with his orders to continue the search.

Safely back in San Patricio, only three or four miles over the mountain from Lincoln, Billy puzzled over Juan Patron's warning. What had gone amiss? Had not Deputy Longworth told the governor that Billy and Tom O'Folliard had no part in the Chapman murder? Had not he, Billy, been the first to report the tragedy? Wasn't it known that Tom and Billy had followed Longworth's advice to leave Lincoln at once? Billy had given his promise to appear as a witness in the hearing of Colonel Dudley. Why, then, was he being sought in this way?

Suddenly, Billy's mind suggested the answer. He was wanted as a witness in the Chapman killing! That must be it. He would write to the governor.

Exercising unusual caution, so as not to reveal too much, Billy set down, in a brief but comprehensive letter, such details as were pertinent to the case. He also included enough personal data to inform the governor of his identity as well as his reasons for remaining in hiding:

SAN PATRICIO, N.M.
March 10, 1879

Governor Lew Wallace
DEAR SIR:

I have heard that you will give 1000 dollars for my body which as I understand, it means alive as a witness. I know it is a witness against those that murdered Mr. Chapman. If it was so as I could appear in court, I would give the desired information, but I have indictments against me for things that happened in the Lincoln County War, and am afraid to give myself up because my enemys would kill me.

The night Mr. Chapman was murdered I was in Lincoln at the request of some good citizens to meet Mr. J. J. Dolan, to meet as friends so as to be able to lay aside our arms and go to work.

I was present when Mr. Chapman was murdered and know who did it and if it wasn't for those indictments I would have made it clear before now.

Please send me an answer telling me what you can do. You can send answer by bearer. I do not wish to fight any more and I have not raised an arm since your proclamation. As to my character I can refer you to any of the good citizens as a majority of them are my friends and have been helping me all they can.

Sometimes I am called Kid Antrim but Antrim is my stepfather's name.

Waiting your reply, I am,

Your obt. servant
W. H. BONNEY

The letter was dispatched by a trusted messenger to Juan Patron with a request that it be delivered to General Wallace at his headquarters at Fort Stanton.

Wallace seemed pleased by the content of Billy's letter, and he moved to avail himself of the implied offer. An exchange of notes followed, resulting in an arrangement for Billy to submit to arrest. The arrest was to be a *pro forma* affair, but to have every appearance of an actual capture by a posse of peace officers. In his own hand the governor penned a letter of minute instructions, arranging for a meeting between himself and Billy:

LINCOLN, March 15, 1879

W. H. BONNEY

Come to the house of old Squire Wilson (not the lawyer) at nine (9) o'clock next Monday night alone. I don't mean his office, but his residence. Follow along the foot of the mountain south of the town, come in on that side, and knock at the east door. I have authority to exempt you from prosecution, if you will testify to what you say you know.

The object of the meeting at Squire Wilson's is to arrange the matter in a way to make your life safe. To do that the utmost secrecy is to be used. *So come alone.* Don't tell anybody—not a living soul—where you are coming or the object. If you could trust Jesse Evans, you can trust me.

LEW WALLACE.[1]

The Kid arrived punctually and knocked on the door of Squire Wilson's modest adobe home, as had been arranged. Wilson admitted him while the governor waited in the shadows of the dimly lit room.

Billy entered cautiously and surveyed the interior. A rifle rested in the crook of his left arm, and he held a pistol in his right hand. The governor could see clearly the lithe, slender figure and the narrow, boyish face that always appeared to smile.

"I was asked to meet the governor at nine o'clock," the Kid said quietly. "Is he here?"

His Excellency stepped into the light.

"I am glad to see you again, Billy," he said. "Please sit down."

"Your note promised absolute protection, sir," Billy said warily.

"I have been true to my promise," the governor replied. He pointed to Squire Wilson. "This man and myself are the only persons present."

The Kid lowered the rifle and returned the revolver to its holster. He stepped into the light and took the chair Wilson placed for him.

Governor Wallace immediately presented his proposal that the Kid should testify before the grand jury, and also before the trial court, regarding the murder of George

[1]See Plate XIV in the Appendix.

Chapman. Then the governor suggested that, in return for his testimony in this case, the Kid might go free with a full pardon covering his former misdeeds.[2]

Billy remained silent for several moments before replying. "Governor," he said finally, "I will be killed if I do as you ask. I will never leave the courtroom alive."

"We can prevent that, Billy," the governor said. "You will consent to a prearranged arrest, when you are asleep or supposed to be unaware of the presence of the officers, so that your capture will appear to be genuine."

The Kid considered the plan briefly, then he smiled. "All right, Governor, I'll play the cards you've dealt. I've thought it over since I got your note. It don't sound too safe to me, but I'll do it. Just one thing—I want to pick the men who will make the arrest. We wouldn't want anyone who would give the plan away, would we?

"And then," Billy added, "I want to be handcuffed all the time I'm held. It will be real convincing that way, and I've got an idea I could shuck those cuffs if I really wanted to."

"How do you mean?" Wallace was puzzled.

"It's just that my wrists are large, and my hands are small. I can get them off," Billy said.

The governor and the boy sat for an hour discussing the details of the plan and weighing its potentialities. A chance listener would have been unable to detect the gulf separating their stations.

At the close of the conference the governor turned to a subject about which he had been curious. Wallace was, first, a soldier, and he had a soldier's interest in arms and shooting. So it was that he said, "Billy, I have often heard of your unusual proficiency with the revolver. Is there some trick to your kind of shooting? How do you do it?"

---

[2]See Appendix II, Note A, Chap. XVI.

"I practice a lot, Governor. I like shooting, and I've won a lot of bets that way. Often that was the only money I had."

"It's only practice, then?"

"Well, there's one more thing—I never think of it as a trick, but some people have said it's unusual. When I was a boy, I noticed people pointing with the first finger. When I lift my revolver, something seems to say 'point with the finger.' I think of my finger as going along the barrel, and it makes my aim certain. To *think* of aiming takes a second or more, and a second can be mighty important!"

The Kid smiled his boyish smile and rose to depart.

"We can both trust Juan Patron and Hijinio Salazar. I will send you a message by one of them. *Hasta la vista.*"

The Kid looked cautiously through the slitted door, and then went out silently, to disappear in the darkness.

Chapter XVII

IMPORTANT influences were at work to circumvent Wallace's determination to bring to justice those guilty of Chapman's murder. District Court Clerk Billy Mathews and James Dolan, who had been taken to Fort Stanton by Sheriff Kimbrell, were promptly released on bond by Judge Bristol. This was understood to be in compliance with orders from District Attorney W. L. Rynerson.

Colonel Dudley had been embarrassed because of his connection with Campbell and Van Sickle. His worry was ended on the night of March 19 when Campbell and Van Sickle escaped from the Fort Stanton guardhouse. The two were fortunate enough to "find" horses and arms in a ravine half a mile from the post, and they fled the territory, as had Jesse Evans, never again to be taken into custody.

Rumors of the escape came quickly to Lincoln. The residents did not immediately learn that the escapees had left the area, and there was widespread apprehension that more outrages might be expected. Children were kept indoors, women stayed near their homes, and the men of the town were grim and watchful.

Hijinio Salazar, the boy who had so successfully feigned death in the yard the last night of the battle at McSween's home hurried to confer with Patron. The loyalty of the Spanish-American population to the cause of McSween and to Billy the Kid has been well established, and Juan Patron was the man to whom Salazar and other young men turned instinctively for advice.

Patron listened thoughtfully as Salazar told of the escape of Campbell and Van Sickle.

"They may try to kill Billy. This he doesn't know, and he must be warned," Salazar concluded.

"Billy is more careful, lately," Patron said, "but he might be shot from ambush if he is not warned. Ride out to San Patricio and tell him what has happened."

Salazar found Billy at San Patricio. The Kid heard his report without comment. He was turning over a question in his mind. How would the escape of Campbell and Van Sickle affect the arrangement between himself and Governor Wallace? Billy knew he must have the answer to this question. If he wrote the governor directly, the plan might be betrayed, or Wallace might suffer personal embarrassment. He remembered his final remark to Wallace, made as he was leaving Squire Wilson's house.

"Hijinio, remove your saddle and wait here," he said. "I want you to return with a letter."

In a few minutes, Billy came from the little house. He concealed a letter between the folds of Salazar's saddle blanket which lay on the ground. Then he resaddled Salazar's horse.

"I don't want anyone to take this letter from you, Hijinio," Billy explained. "It's private and important. Deliver it to Squire Wilson. Let no one see you do so. Then follow his instructions. Do you understand?"

"*Si*, Billy," Salazar promised. "No one but the squire will get the letter from me." He mounted.

"*Gracias*, go quickly," Billy said. He slapped Salazar's horse smartly, and watched the rider out of sight.

Salazar reached Lincoln quickly. He surveyed Wilson's premises and approached the house discreetly. At the door he unsaddled and presented the note. Swiftly Wilson scanned the few lines addressed to him by Billy:

San Patricio
Thursday, 20th, 1879

Friend Wilson.

Please tell You know who that I do not know what to do, now as those Prisoners have escaped. to send word by bearer, a note through You it may be that he has made different arra[n]gements if not and he still wants it the same to Send William Hudgins, as Deputy, to the Junction tomorrow at three o'clock with some men you know to be all right. Send a note telling me what to do.

W. H. Bonney

P. S. do not send soldiers[1]

Wilson properly identified the person who was not mentioned by name to be the governor. He thought Billy's last caution, that soldiers were not to be sent, seemed superfluous.

Having been told he was expected to return with a reply, Salazar waited while the rancher read what Billy had written.

"Get a fresh horse from my corral," Wilson told Salazar. "I want you to ride to the post with a letter for Governor Wallace. Deliver it only to him. He will give you instructions."

Wilson merely enclosed the Kid's note in another envelope and addressed it to Governor Wallace. To insure against interception, he added, in a bold hand, "Official Business—Wilson, J.P."

At the governor's quarters, Salazar was challenged by the sentry. He displayed the envelope. "For the governor only," he said in Spanish, and repeated the formula until he was admitted.

The governor read the note and began at once to write a reply. His note was addressed directly to Billy:

[1]See Plate XV in the Appendix.

FORT STANTON, March 20, 1879

W. H. BONNEY

The escape makes no difference in arrangements. ~~I will comply with my part, if you will with yours.~~

To remove all suspicion of understanding, I think it better to put the arresting party in charge of Sheriff Kimbrell, who will be instructed to see that no violence is used.

This will go to you tonight. ~~If you still insist upon Hudgins, let me know.~~ If I don't get other word from you, the party (all citizens) will be at the junction by 3 o'clock tomorrow.

LEW WALLACE.[2]

Wallace's note contained a sentence in which he stated that he would comply with his part if Billy would comply with his. This line was deleted by the governor. What the sentence referred to and what his reason for deleting it was, can only be inferred. In view of the later development of Wallace's relationship with the Kid, it appears that the governor entertained at least one mental reservation.

The completed reply was enclosed in a heavy envelope and endorsed "Official Business." Wallace turned to Hijinio, who stood waiting, and asked, "You have seen Billy?"

Hijinio smiled politely. *"No comprendo, Señor,"* he said.

Wallace summoned his orderly to serve as interpreter and repeated the question.

"Yes, I have seen Billy many times, *Señor,*" Salazar replied eagerly.

"Is he now at San Patricio?"

"I do not know, *Señor.*"

"His letter says he is there," Wallace insisted. "And it has the date of today."

"I have not seen what is written, *Señor*. And, besides, I do not read English."

---

[2]See Plate XVI in the Appendix.

The governor hid a smile. Hijinio's evasions were transparent, and Wallace recognized him for a loyal and trusted friend of the Kid's.

"Very well, son," Wallace said gravely. "Deliver this envelope to Squire Wilson. He may be able to locate Billy, even if you can't remember where you saw him last. To have a poor memory," His Excellency added, "may be very wise."

"I thank the Governor for his understanding," Hijinio responded courteously. "After I was wounded at McSween's home, I now forget much that I see and hear. That is very bad, no?"

The governor laughed as he spoke to the interpreter, "Get this young rascal on his way before he succeeds in convincing me he has been truthful and is just simple. At least, he has proven he is a trustworthy friend to Billy!"

When the young orderly returned to the governor, Wallace said thoughtfully, "I have frequently wondered at the bond between the Kid and your people."

"I believe I can explain it, sir," the young Spanish American ventured. The governor's look of interest encouraged him, and he continued, "Formerly, as you know, this territory was part of Mexico. After the Civil War, many Anglos came, and some of them were very bad. They looked upon my people as an inferior race. Lands and other property were taken from my people, and many were reduced to poverty. All this is a little better now, but most of my people are very poor."

The orderly paused. He looked through the window at the grassy parade ground; the rolling, green-tinged hills rising beyond. He turned his large, melancholy eyes back to the governor's face.

"Very few Anglos respect our rights, our—our dignity. Not so, the Kid. He has recovered and returned property stolen from us. He has helped to bring a winter's load of wood for families who were unable to procure it. He has ridden to the home of a destitute family with a sack of food thrown over his saddle. Not to offend, he has laughed and asked the lady to prepare a meal for him, as a great favor. Then he has ridden away, grateful, leaving a quantity of food behind. He plays with our children, and they love him. He does not drink liquor. He likes to attend our *bailes*, and he is always courteous to our women, and he never uses language he would not speak before his mother."

The young man clasped and unclasped his hands. "Old and young alike respect him. He is fearless, generous, and considerate of the rights of others—and that is why he has and holds the loyalty of my people! Your pardon, sir, for expressing myself so freely."

Wallace inclined his head in a gesture of understanding. He dismissed the young orderly and resumed his interrupted work.

Hijinio Salazar rode directly to San Patricio and handed the governor's note to Billy. The Kid studied it carefully. He noted especially that the proposed arrest must be executed in such a way as to preclude any suspicion that it had been prearranged. Not only his own person, Billy realized, but also the governor's part in the operation, must be safeguarded.

The governor had promised fair treatment and, if need be, a pardon in return for Billy's testimony at Dudley's hearing and in the case of the murder of George Chapman. He must keep faith with the man who had the power to make him a free and useful member of society. To this end Billy had worked under the manly guidance of John H. Tunstall, and he had risked his life time and again in the hopeless cause of Alexander McSween.

Those helpful influences had been terminated by assassin's bullets, and Billy was outlawed. Now he had a new opportunity to achieve the status of good citizen, which he so much desired.

Billy formed a resolution. He would comply with the governor's plan for his arrest and, further, he would inform the governor of the activities of the outlaws in the area. If the governor could use the information to advantage, real peace might come to Lincoln County.

Billy allowed his mind to wander along the wooded trails and grassy plains he knew so well. He imagined, for a moment, that he knelt to drink from the clear, cold Ruidoso where it splashed through the tall mountains. He pictured great herds of cattle feeding along the sandy banks of the Pecos.

Then he wrote a letter in which he agreed to the governor's plan. This communication was much longer and more informative than anything he had written before:

San Patricio
Lincoln County
Thursday 20th, 1879

General Lew Wallace
Sir:

I will keep the appointment I made, but be Sure and have men come that You can depend on. I am not afraid to die like a man fighting but I would not like to be killed like a dog unarmed. [T]ell Kimbal to let his men be placed around the house, and for him to come in alone; and he can arrest us. All I am afraid of is that in the Fort we might be poisoned or killed through a Window at night, but You can arrange that all right. Tell the Commanding Officer to Watch Lt. Goodwin. [H]e would not hesitate to do anything. [T]here Will be danger on the road of Somebody Waylaying us to kill us on the road to the Fort.

On the Pecos, all that I can remember are the so called Dolan Outfit but they are all up here now; and on Rio Grande this man Cris Moten I believe his name is, he drove a herd of (80) head one year ago last December in Company with Frank Wheeler, Frank Baker, deceased, Jesse Evans, George Davis alias Tom Jones, Tom Hill, his name in Texas being Tom Chelson, also deceased. [T]hey drove the cattle to the Indian Reservation and sold them to John Riley and J. J. Dolan, and the cattle were turned in for Beef for the Indians. [T]he Beckwith family made their boasts that they Came to Seven Rivers a little over four years ago with one Milch Cow borrowed from John Chisum. [T]hey had when I was there [a] Year ago one thousand six hundred head of cattle. The male members of the family are Henry Beckwith and John Beckwith, Robert Beckwith was killed the time McSween's house was burned. Charles Robert Olinger and Wallace Olinger are of the same gang. Their cattle ranch is situated at Rock Corral twelve miles below Seven Rivers on the Pecos. Paxton and Pierce are still below them forty miles from Seven Rivers. [T]here are four of them: Paxton, Pierce, Jim Raymer, and Brick Powel. They had when I seen them last about one thousand head of cattle. [A]t Rocky Arroya there is another Ranch belonging to Smith who Operated on the Penaco last year with the Jesse Evans gang. [T]hose and the places I mentioned are all I know of. [T]his man Cris Moten, at the time they stole those cattle was in the employ of J. J. Dolan and Co. I afterwards seen Some of the cattle at the Rinconada Bonita on the reservation. [T]hose were the men we were in search of when we went to the Agency. [T]he Beckwith family were attending to their own business when this War Started but G. W. Peppin told them that this was John Chisum's War and so they took a hand thinking they would lose their cattle in case that he—Chisum—won the fight. [T]his is all the information I can give you on this point.

Yours Respectfully
BILLIE

You Will Never Catch those fellows on the road. Watch Fritzes, Captain Bacas ranch and the Brewery. [T]hey Will either go to Seven Rivers or to Jicarillo Mountains. [T]hey will stay around close untill the Scouting parties come in. Give a Spy a pair of glasses and let him get on the mountain back of Fritzes and watch and if they are there, there will be provisions carried to them. [I]t is not my place to advise you, but I am anxious to have them caught, and perhaps know how men hide from Soldiers, better than you. [P]lease excuse me for having so much to say. Tell Kimbal not to come before 3 o'clock for I may not be there before.

And I still remain Yours Truly,
W. H. BONNEY

P. S.
I have changed my mind. Send Kimbal to Gutieres just below San

Patricio one mile because Sanger and Ballard are or were great friends of Comels. Ballard told me yesterday to leave for you were doing everything to catch me. It was a blind to get me to leave.[3]

Billy dispatched the letter to the governor by the faithful, and now weary, Hijinio Salazar. It was, quite possibly, the longest letter Billy was ever to write, and he massaged his cramped fingers as he turned to the house to make his preparations for keeping a rendezvous with the men who were to arrest him.

---

[3]See Plates XVII, XVIII, XIX, and XX in the Appendix.

Chapter XVIII

LEW WALLACE, with the co-operation of Sheriff Kimbrell, had organized a group of citizens, including many who opposed the Dudley-Dolan-Turner faction, into a unit known as the "Lincoln County Mounted Rifles."

The Rifles were not a military company, but, rather, a stand-by posse, in which the governor reposed full confidence. They were "minute men" who waited, ready to serve upon call of the sheriff. From this group men were drafted to perform special missions. The system effectively precluded the infiltration of doubtful characters into quickly organized posses.

When Wallace received the Kid's last, and longest, letter, he summoned Sheriff Kimbrell and his deputy to the post. He briefed them on his plan for the prearranged capture of the Kid and O'Folliard.

"Tomorrow, you will take twelve men upon whom you can rely and proceed to the line camp on Gutierrez' ranch, a mile or so from San Patricio. Plan to arrive not earlier than three o'clock in the afternoon. You will find the Kid and O'Folliard there, and you will take them into custody. No one other than yourselves is to know the arrest has been planned.

"In your posse," Wallace continued, "there must be some of the Kid's friends. You can explain their presence by saying they are on hand to insure the protection of Billy during the return, if he is captured. Lend to your action every possible appearance of a surprise capture. Billy will play his role."

"Where shall I take the prisoners?" Kimbrell asked.

"Bring them to Lincoln and confine them in the jail, for the time being. Is it all clear?"

"It is understood," Kimbrell answered. "We will do as you direct."

The sheriff drew from his pocket the shabby notebook which contained the names of the Lincoln County Mounted Rifles. From this list he selected six and noted their names on a piece of paper, which he handed to his deputy.

"Longworth," he said, "please contact these men and tell them to meet you tomorrow at the junction of the Ruidoso and Bonito. They are to come a little after noon, drifting down separately so it will not look as if the Rifles are riding. They must not tell where they are going. I will gather the remaining six—that will make the twelve the governor wants. When we are all together, I will announce where we are going, and why."

The next day, March 21, 1879, twelve well-mounted, armed men assembled at the rendezvous at the appointed hour. As the last two arrivals rode up and dismounted, the whole group crowded around the sheriff and his deputy. There were six Spanish Americans in the party. The day was chill, and the horses moved about restlessly.

"Men," Kimbrell raised his voice to be heard over the creaking of saddle leather, "Governor Wallace has information that the Kid and O'Folliard are at the old adobe shack near Gutierrez' ranch. Our plan is to surprise them, take them, and escort them to Lincoln."

Silence greeted the sheriff's announcement. Then Chavez y Chavez came forward. This was the brave youth who, seriously wounded, had escaped from the flame-lit yard of McSween's home the night of July 19, the previous year.

"For what do you mean to arrest Billy and Tom?" Chavez inquired, in Spanish.

"In connection with the Chapman murder," the sheriff replied.

"But, *Señor,* they did not murder the law man. They came to Lincoln to make peace. I will not help to capture them. I will warn Billy, and fight beside him!"

In unspoken agreement, the other Spanish-American possemen moved to stand at Chavez' side. Some of the others muttered uncertainly.

The sheriff's mission and his authority were endangered, and there was tension in the party. Kimbrell was faced with the problem of making an explanation without disclosing the Kid's acquiescence in the plan. He lowered his voice, and the dissenters moved closer to hear what he said in fluent Spanish.

"I believe you all know I never side-step my official duty. I have been ordered to arrest Billy and Tom, and I shall do so. But most of us are friends of Billy, and so I will explain. The boys are not wanted as Chapman's murderers, but they saw the killings and so are named as 'accessories' in the warrants. You may see them."

Kimbrell held up the official documents. His eyes moved over the faces of the men.

"Now," he said, "it is my unofficial opinion that Billy and Tom cannot be charged with anything and are wanted as witnesses against the guilty parties. There are those, as you must know, who would have them killed because of what they know. I believe Billy and Tom are to be arrested and held for their own protection. I invited you, their friends, to serve on the posse to insure their safe arrival in Lincoln, if—" Kimbrell added, "*if* we capture them."

He had stated the circumstances in so far as possible, stopping short of revealing the part to be played by the

Kid. Long experience on the frontier had provided Kimbrell with a keen understanding of the mental processes of brave men. He would now turn his hole card face up.

"Men, Deputy Longworth and I will go to Gutierrez' place alone, if necessary. If the boys are there, we will arrest them. There is danger of an ambush on the return trip, but Longworth and I will protect the boys with our lives, even if you won't help us. We will see that all—or none—get through safely."

Kimbrell paused, for effect. "Now," he said at length, "if any of you want to withdraw from this mission, this is the time to do so."

Kimbrell's reputation for intergrity, courage, and action was recognized by his friends and by his enemies. He had spoken almost casually, without demand or appeal, and the response was all he had hoped. The rebels rejoined the posse, demonstrating their confidence in the sheriff's word. He expressed no thanks, but proceeded as if the interval of misunderstanding had not occurred.

"Unsaddle and water your horses," he directed. "We will remain here another hour to make our plans."

When the horses had been tended, the men again crowded around Kimbrell and listened quietly.

"Most of you know the old adobe line shack," he said. "It has only one room, one door, and a small window on either side. The door is the only exit. Billy and Tom may not be there when we arrive, so we may have to wait. We will approach from the rear. If the boys are inside, we won't be seen. I'll scout, and what we do will depend on what I find out. All clear?"

Sheriff Kimbrell timed the posse's action to conform with the Kid's instructions not to appear before three o'clock. Hidden in a narrow ravine near the house, the men dismounted and waited.

"Remain here and keep your horses quiet. I will return as soon as possible," the sheriff ordered as he rode away. From a small grove of jack pine, he saw the Kid and O'Folliard near the old corral at the rear of the shack. He gave a long low whistle. Both men replied similarly, but without appearing to be aware of his presence.

Rejoining the posse, Kimbrell reported, "Both boys are there, working on the corral. Tom," he directed, addressing Longworth, "take six men, spread out, and cover the right. The rest of us will take the left. Ride at a walk and, no matter what may happen, don't fire. I will move out alone and signal for a parley."

When the posse emerged from the trees, the Kid and O'Folliard, simulating surprise, rushed into the shack and closed the door. Kimbrell advanced on the building, his arm raised, palm outward, in the Indian sign of peace.

Opposite a small window, he drew rein and called out, "Boys, I hold warrants for your arrest. We have you surrounded, so come out quiet and make no trouble."

"Howdy, George," the Kid drawled. "It's comfortable here, so I guess we'll just stay inside."

"Don't make it hard on yourself, Billy. I mean to serve these warrants."

"Just what do those papers claim me and Tom have done?"

"It's about Chapman. You're not wanted for the murder, but as accessories."

"That word sounds a sight worse than murder," Billy laughed. "We'll stay right here!"

"Have it your way," the sheriff replied. "We can't spare the time, but I guess we'll just make camp and starve you out."

"I didn't notice a pack train with your army, General," Billy said. "But we have plenty of air-tights[1] and

---

[1] See Appendix II, Note A, Chap. XVIII.

a keg of water in here. We'll share, when your belts get slack!"

"Hell, Kid," the sheriff retorted, "you mavericks come on out. You can't protect your rear, and we'd hate to burn Gutierrez' shack."

"Tom and me have been burned out before, Sheriff, and we made a getaway. Looks like you learned your Injun tactics from Dolan and Dad Peppin. That's war Apache style, Sheriff—I mean, General."

Kimbrell was exasperated by the Kid's prolonged by-play. He well knew the boy was laughing at his discomfiture.

"Well, I'm coming in for a powwow," the sheriff announced, "so don't get funny with your guns."

Dismounting, Kimbrell hung his gun belt over the horn of his saddle. Now, unarmed, he stepped inside the door, closing it quickly behind him.

"See here, Kid, tie down that 'General' palaver and quit the double talk," Kimbrell growled, but his tone did not match his grin.

"We're sitting pretty in here," Billy said.

"Setting fire to this flea coop would make this party look plenty real, no?" the sheriff asked. "But look at your friends out there, Billy. If I tried to fire the roof, they would hog-tie me and Longworth and tell you to stampede. They don't know we're dealing this game from a stacked deck, and they're getting restless. Now, put these bracelets on, and let's go!"

Still laughing, Billy and Tom donned the handcuffs the sheriff had ready. As the sheriff threw open the door, they straightened their faces.

"The boys have decided to be reasonable," Kimbrell called, shepherding his charges outside. "Saddle their horses, and we'll ride."

When the captives arrived in Lincoln and learned they

were to be confined in the miserable *carcel,* they were resentful to the point of rebellion. They had not expected this, and they could not know the governor planned to have them detained there only temporarily to lend realism to the capture. They exchanged bitter glances. Should they submit, or make an escape? Since they were unarmed, there seemed no choice but to comply. Turning to the deputy, Billy voiced his protest, "Tom, I've sworn never to go in that hole again alive!"

"I don't see how any of us can help it, Billy. I don't want to put you in there, but those are my orders. I'm in a tough spot. Don't make it any tougher for me."

After a brief hesitation, Billy walked slowly into the jail, followed by O'Folliard.

"Tom," Billy said to Deputy Longworth, "we're doing this because we don't want to make trouble for you, but I'd give all I ever hope to possess if the one who gave that order was standing there in your boots!"

Wallace was well pleased when Sheriff Kimbrell reported the success of his delicate mission. The governor dispatched a note to the military so that the search party could be relieved of the quest for the fugitives. He also decreed that Billy and Tom should be held under guard a couple of days and then sent to the post.

A few hours after they had reluctantly entered the jail, the youths were removed to the house of Juan Patron where they were held with very few restrictions. This change cheered Billy. Besides loathing the filthy little jail, he had been distressed by the thought that the governor did not trust him, or, alternatively, that the governor did not intend to carry out his part of the agreement. Billy and Tom were happy and comfortable with kindly Juan Patron. They were guarded by Deputy Sheriff Longworth, to whom they had pledged on their honor not to escape. They knew and trusted Longworth, and he had had an example of their trustworthiness the night Chapman was killed.

In this relatively easy situation, Billy received friends who came to call on him with good humor. Always ready with a jest, Billy seemed to surpass himself at this time. He slipped a handcuff off when extending a greeting, saying, "I don't want to disgrace my friends by asking them to shake hands with a chained criminal!" or, "You don't get a chance to steal *my* jewelry!"

The atmosphere at Patron's home during the Kid's stay there resembled a party. In addition to his Anglo and Spanish-American friends, bright-eyed little children came bearing peppery delicacies prepared by their mothers for "The Keed." Apparently Billy commanded the sincere affection of the native population, as well as their loyalty.[2]

Little is known about the appearance of the Kid and O'Folliard before the grand jury when they gave evidence against those guilty of the Chapman murder. Such proceedings were most informal at that time in the territory. Stenographic reports and transcripts were not made. The grand jury simply heard and questioned the witnesses, and returned their findings to the court. The findings were then published.

In this case Dolan and Mathews were indicted for the murder of George Chapman. Upon motion of District Attorney Rynerson, they were immediately admitted to bail, pending trial. Eventually, having obtained a change of venue to Socorro County, through the influence of Rynerson and the Santa Fe Ring, both were tried and found not guilty.

Fugitive warrants were issued for Campbell and Van Sickle, but they were not taken, and no one was ever punished for the brutal murder of the young attorney.

[2] See Appendix II, Note B, Chap. XVIII.

Chapter XIX

NEARLY two months had now elapsed since the arrest of the Kid and O'Folliard. The youths had maintained faith with Governor Wallace. At no small risk to themselves, they had appeared before the grand jury. It was solely upon their evidence, since they were the only available witnesses to the tragedy, that indictments were returned against Dolan and Mathews, and fugitive warrants issued for the apprehension of Campbell and Van Sickle for the murder of Chapman. Their restraint had been light, and unrestricted fraternization with the friendly villagers was permitted.

Wallace, however, apparently had neglected, or forgotten, his pledge to the boys and had not ordered their release. During this period, His Excellency quite properly spent much of his time in Santa Fe, attending to official matters and conferring with General Hatch on the pending action against Colonel Dudley.

Tom O'Folliard had neither seen nor heard from his young Spanish wife in Fort Sumner since he had been taken into custody, and he was growing morose and restive. The Kid, on the contrary, maintained his customary buoyancy. He reposed full confidence in Governor Wallace's implied promise to exempt him from prosecution.

One afternoon O'Folliard sat silent for a long time, his head sunk on his chest. At last he turned to Billy and said, "Kid, I don't admire the way this game is being played, so I'm going to throw my hand into the discard.

We done all we promised the governor, and what's *he* done, except keep us hog-tied here in Lincoln?"

Billy made no reply, and O'Folliard continued seriously, "I'm getting worried about my wife, so I'm going to shed my hobbles and get back to Fort Sumner. What about you?"

Billy considered. He reasoned that he had fully complied with his promise to the governor, as agreed in the exchange of notes. He felt that the promise applied to the Chapman case, only. His pledge to Wallace and Mrs. McSween to appear as a witness against Colonel Dudley had been made voluntarily, and Billy had promised to present himself when summoned. There had been no condition that he should remain in custody until the Dudley hearing. Why, then, the continued silence of the governor? And what of the parole to Longworth? Torn between his promise to Longworth and his growing doubt of the governor's good faith, Billy was perplexed.

"Tom," he said finally, "we can't break out. We passed our word to Longworth, and he has treated us right. Maybe the governor has been busy and forgot us."

"I mean to deal square with Longworth, Billy," O'Folliard said earnestly, "so I'll just tell him all bets are off. I don't know what he'll do, but he can't claim I crossed him up.

"You see," he continued, "you wrote the governor you were willing to go before the grand jury. He promised, if you would surrender peaceful, he would throw them indictments into the discard—or, at least, it sounded like that. Because we are friends, I drew cards with you, but the governor never made *me* a promise, so I owe him nothing. Now, I got to look after my own scalp."

"Looks like you may be right, Tom," the Kid agreed. "But I can't go with you right now. I hear Dudley is due for trial real soon, so I'll just stay hitched till then, to show Wallace I mean to do right. You tell Longworth how you feel. He'll release you from your promise, but he may put you back in the 'kennel' again."

"Don't bet one white chip on that, Billy," O'Folliard said defiantly. "I'll have to be dead before they put me in there again, and it wouldn't matter then, anyhow!"

While O'Folliard was speaking, Billy was thinking. Suppose Tom landed in jail because of him? What then?

Billy formed a plan, and then he smiled cheerfully. "Tom," he said, "we don't know how Longworth will play his hand. He'll do his duty as he sees it. If he decides to lock you up, you'd be a fool to put up a fight and get hurt, and he'd take the pot, anyway. But maybe your string of luck hasn't run out yet." Billy winked broadly at his puzzled friend and walked away.

In the afternoon, Longworth dismounted before Patron's place and entered the building. It was his regular visit. He was accustomed to exchange banter with his charges a few minutes and then leave them, to continue with his work.

The Kid was seated at a table, idly playing solitaire, and O'Folliard watched him gloomily. Neither spoke as the deputy entered, and Longworth instantly sensed there was something amiss.

"You mavericks off your feed, or sick?" Longworth asked.

The Kid threw aside the cards. "You called the turn. Tom here is pretty sick, but he don't need a doctor. He's homesick. He's going back to Fort Sumner. It's lucky you dropped in so he can tell you *adios*."

Longworth was baffled. He was morally certain neither youth would violate his parole.

"I don't get my loop on this palaver, boys. So what about it?" Longworth asked, frowning.

"I been thinking," O'Folliard said. "The governor

never made me any promise like he did Billy, here, so I don't owe him nothing. I dealt myself in because Billy and me are pals. Now, I'm quitting."

"What you say may be so," Longworth said. "But the sheriff had orders to take both you and Billy into custody. That makes your arrest plenty legal."

O'Folliard argued that he knew of the prearranged plan and could have escaped before the arrival of the posse. He did not choose to do so, and thus, in effect, he had appeared voluntarily before the grand jury. That duty discharged, he believed he was now entitled to his release.

Longworth had a devotion to the law that was unshakeable. He was considerate of prisoners when that was possible, but if he met with trickery or resistance, he became a cold, uncompromising officer.

"You've made good your word, so far," he said coldly to O'Folliard, "and I guess you have the right to call all bets off and make a getaway *if* you can. But my orders are to hold you, so don't crowd me!"

Longworth thought a moment, then he continued, "Why not wait a spell, and I'll ask Kimbrell to write to the governor, suggesting you and Billy be cut loose so you can stampede back to your home range."

O'Folliard would not agree to the delay, and so Longworth removed a pair of handcuffs from his pocket.

"All right, you're calling the shots. Put these on, and we'll take a walk."

Billy saw that O'Folliard was to be taken to the jail.

"Wait a minute, Longworth," he said. "Why not deputize two boys from the Rifles to ride herd on him here? That jail is a rathole, not good enough for sobering up a drunk Apache. With one man for day, and one for night duty, you can keep him rounded up here."

While Billy spoke, O'Folliard edged toward the door.

The movement was observed by Longworth. "A good try, Tom," the deputy said, his pistol appearing almost magically in his hand. "Now take another step, and you will sure as hell be hurt."

Longworth turned to Billy. "You must think I've been grazing on loco weed. If I tried your idea, do you know what would happen?"

The Kid waited with disarming attention for the officer to answer his own question.

"Well, I'll tell you," Longworth said. "The very first night, the guard would hand over his gun, get himself hog-tied, and tell Tom to leave for the hills, *muy pronto* —and you know it! Your idea don't shine with me."

Longworth handcuffed O'Folliard and directed him to the door. Billy smiled. If the officer had agreed to his proposal, he would have been disappointed. He had another plan, entirely, and he had no wish to involve members of the Rifles, most of whom were his friends. As O'Folliard hesitated at the door, Billy said lightly, "Well, *hasta la vista,* Tom, old pal. Just remember, every deck has its joker."

The jail, or *carcel* as it was locally known, was a squat adobe structure of one dark room built over a murky dugout. The door was heavy planking set in a solid timber frame and secured by a massive cast-iron padlock. Ground water seeped through the rotten logs that formed the walls of the underground room. Tradition relates that water could be diverted from an adjacent irrigation ditch into this cellar, bringing fear and extreme discomfort to any unfortunate confined beneath the floor. This was the prison to which O'Folliard was brought.

As soon as O'Folliard and Longworth left the Patron home, the Kid set his plan in motion. He required aid, and he thought at once of loyal Hijinio Salazar. A small boy served as messenger, and, after dark, Salazar slipped into Patron's patio where he found the Kid waiting.

Billy told Hijinio that Tom O'Folliard had been removed to the jail, and why, and Hijinio saw the point at once.

"That is not good, Billy. Tom is in need of help, no?"

"Is that your idea, Hijinio?" Billy asked innocently. "Well, someone could—but I'm bound to stay here because of my promise to Longworth. You know about that?"

"But of course," Hijinio said. "I can help?"

"If you found Chavez y Chavez to serve as lookout, and if you got a crowbar and hammer from Vejar's smithy, and if Tom's horse was saddled and tied away from the road—"

"How?" Salazar inquired.

Billy explained that the hardware—hasp and staple—which held the massive padlock might be pried away from the wooden door, allowing the door to swing inward. Billy's eyes had rested on the lock as he was leaving the jail, nearly two months before, and he had observed that the space between the staple and the wood was sufficient to permit the insertion of a small bar. This piece of information he had kept to himself until now.

"If Tom should get safely away," the Kid said, "the staple could be replaced and no marks left. Then Longworth would have a headache figuring how Tom got through a padlocked door!" He laughed, then, serious again, he concluded, "If you can't pry the hardware loose, just break the lock with your hammer, as quiet as you can, and leave. The rest will be up to Tom. Now go—and good luck!"

O'Folliard was freed by means of Billy's first plan, found his horse, and made a hurried, silent departure. From a high point at a safe distance, O'Folliard turned and looked back at the sleeping village. It was to be his last glimpse of Lincoln.

Longworth had risen early. He was a decent human being, and he had not slept well. He kept thinking of O'Folliard in that filthy hole. He meant to try, when he took breakfast to his prisoner, to persuade Tom to abandon his determination to escape so that he could be returned to detention in comfort at Patron's.

The deputy could see from the dusty road that all was quiet at the jail, the heavy iron padlock securely in position. At Patron's house he dismounted and entered, carrying a small canteen. Billy was finishing his breakfast. When he saw Longworth, he became quiet in a sudden change from his high spirits of a moment before.

Longworth asked Señora Patron to fill the canteen with hot coffee for his prisoner.

"*Si, Señor,* and I make some hot *tortillas* for him. He is good boy. You bring him back soon?" the good woman said, busy at the stove.

"If I can, *Señora,* Longworth said, and sighed heavily. He turned to Billy. "Well, *muchacho,* still keeping your back bowed like a loco bronc in a blizzard?"

Billy looked sorrowfully at Longworth and made no answer.

"See here, Billy," Longworth said defensively, "you know I had no choice. I'll talk to Tom when I take him his feed. One night there may have changed his mind. He can be here in five minutes, if he will give me his parole again."

The Kid shook his head. "Not a chance," he said. "Tom is one stubborn *muchacho.* He'll wait and play for the breaks. Better watch out or he'll outsmart you."

Disdaining a reply, the deputy took the basket Señora Patron had prepared and left the house.

At the jail, Longworth dismounted, unlocked the padlock with a large key from his pocket, and went inside, closing the door behind him. The place was dark and odorous. The only light came dimly from a few slits near the ceiling.

"Put on the feed bag, Tom. I've brought your breakfast."

There was no answer, and Longworth looked about the room with eyes growing accustomed to the darkness. He opened the trap door to the basement. Surely, he thought, O'Folliard would not have taken refuge there! He went outside to examine the padlock. There was no evidence of tampering. The only other key was in the possession of Sheriff Kimbrell.

Well, there was no help for it—in some manner, Billy had released his friend. Longworth had been made a fool, and, if he could prove Billy's part in the affair, he resolved that lad should occupy the building just vacated by O'Folliard!

Longworth returned the basket of food to Señora Patron.

"Tom was not hungry?" she asked with motherly concern.

"He may be plenty hungry, by now, *Señora*. He escaped during the night." Turning to the Kid, he said angrily, "You broke him out. I don't know how, but when I find out—"

"Hold on, Deputy, you're throwing a pretty wide loop," Billy interrupted. "I'm glad Tom was able to shake off his hobbles, but I gave you my promise I wouldn't leave this place, and I haven't been away from here. I don't lie. A liar gets tangled in his own rope and hangs himself. If I had been near your dirty jail, I would admit it. That's the spread. Take it or leave it."

Longworth had no answer for this. He believed Billy

was truthful; still, Tom was gone. He went to inform Sheriff Kimbrell of O'Folliard's escape.

Señora Patron smiled as the door slammed, and Billy glanced at her inquiringly.

"Last night, I prayed to the Blessed Virgin to free Tom from the jail, and the Holy Mother has answered my prayer." The devout woman crossed herself, then she added, "With the help of Salazar and Chavez. You see, I chanced to overhear you and Hijinio talking in the dark!"

"We will keep this our secret, *madrecita?*"

"Naturally," Señora Patron replied. "Did you not see how industriously I made *tortillas* for the absent one? No one shall ever know from me!"

It was not learned exactly how the escape was managed, but the event was the talk of the village for a day. More than a few attributed the incident to the supernatural. How else could one escape from a securely padlocked jail?

Billy, when pressed to express an opinion, assumed a thoughtful mien. Perhaps the deputy had not secured the door? Perhaps he permitted his prisoner to escape? Or, possibly, a good friend had opened the door for Tom? But who? *Señor* Diablo, or another? *Quien sabe?* Billy was serene. He had not broken his parole.

Chapter XX

GOVERNOR WALLACE had come to feel, very deeply, that Colonel Dudley was not the proper officer to be in command at Fort Stanton, due to Dudley's entanglement in the unhappy affairs in Lincoln County, and particularly due to his marked partisanship of the Murphy-Dolan faction. In an official communication to General Hatch, commander of the Department of the West, with headquarters in Santa Fe, the governor requested that the colonel be removed from command at Fort Stanton, inasmuch as he had engendered the resentment of the law-abiding citizens of Lincoln County to the degree that law enforcement had become an impossibility.

General Hatch referred the request to the Secretary of War, and, in due course, Hatch was informed that neither he nor the governor had authority to remove the colonel. The War Department required that he first must be convicted upon specific charge by a military court.

Governor Wallace's action in making the request so outraged Dudley that he made reply through the columns of *The Santa Fe New Mexican.* This paper was anti-Wallace and usually voiced the sentiments of the Santa Fe Ring. Dudley charged His Excellency with slander, libel, defamation of character, and other crimes and misdemeanors. Concluding, the colonel declared that neither he nor any other officer at the post had committed a single illegal act since he had been in command at Fort Stanton.

This bitter exchange had occurred during the relatively quiet interval before the murder of Chapman, and the governor had dropped the matter for a time. When the Chapman killing aroused the community again, the governor called a public meeting which was attended by more than a hundred citizens representing every section of the vast county.

At this meeting the governor appealed for volunteer witnesses against those responsible for the crimes that kept Lincoln County in the grip of terror. Some of those present muttered that Dudley was responsible for the murder of McSween and those with him. Others accused him of connivance in the death of Chapman. But—and this was the insurmountable obstacle—only a few agreed to appear as witnesses.

The governor promised protection by the military, but this promise was scornfully refused. How, it was argued, could the military defend the citizens from assassination and ambush, or protect their scattered homes from night riders? And who could expect the military to defend witnesses who accused one of their number?

Those upon whom the governor could rely included Susan McSween, William Bonney, and one or two of the bolder citizens who had no families to place in jeopardy. Wallace expected that Billy the Kid would be a witness, and, like the good general he was, he decided to move to the attack with the forces at his command, limited though those forces were.

Wallace personally prepared the charges and specifications against the colonel and presented them to General Hatch. A Board of Inquiry was convened to consider the evidence that would disprove the charges or remand Dudley for trial before General Courts Martial. The inquiry began at Fort Stanton early in May.

Ranchers, cowboys, and even known outlaws drifted

to Lincoln, drawn by the proceedings. Tempers flared as pro- and anti-Dudley sympathizers exchanged compliments. No bloodshed resulted due to the presence of the Rifles, under the efficient command of Sheriff Kimbrell. The Rifles were reinforced by a general belief that, since this was a military proceeding, troops would be employed, if needed, to quell any violence.

General Hatch detailed five officers to the Board of Inquiry, three to serve as judges, one as Judge Advocate, and the fifth, designated Recorder, to function as prosecutor.

Colonel Dudley was represented by Judge Henry L. Waldo, then Attorney General of the territory of New Mexico, and by Lieutenant Poague, a junior officer stationed at the post. The sessions of the board were open, except when closed for arguments relating to the admissibility of evidence and other technicalities. Such intervals were frequent, for Judge Waldo brought all his talents to bear in a strenuous battle for Dudley.

Unlike the crude proceedings before grand juries, all evidence produced before the Military Board was laboriously recorded in longhand, so that it could be submitted for review to General Hatch and then forwarded to Washington for final disposition.

Following the murder of Chapman, Mrs. McSween had retained Ira E. Leonard, a well-known young attorney of White Oaks, to advise her. Leonard also assisted the recorder in presenting the evidence against Colonel Dudley before the board.

An air of expectancy pervaded the old stone barracks as Susan McSween entered, accompanied by her attorney, closely followed by three men whose side arms rested loosely in their holsters. These were Territorial Troopers, summoned from Santa Fe by Wallace to guard Mrs. McSween.

LINCOLN, NEW MEXICO

UPPER.—Road entering the village from the east. The building at the right is the old Tunstall store, established in 1877 and still serving for that purpose. The museum appears at the far left against the hill.

LOWER.—Road entering the village from the west. The large building on the right was the Murphy store, later the courthouse, and presently the Old Lincoln County Museum. There are no streets in the village—just this road, which extends, much as an elongated S, through its entire length. There has been little or no change in the village for the last three quarters of a century.

PLATE II

UPPER.—The Old Lincoln County Museum as it now appears after restoration. It was formerly the Murphy-Dolan-Riley headquarters, and it later became the Lincoln County Courthouse. Subsequently it was purchased by the state and is now one of New Mexico's most interesting landmarks. The window marked by a cross (x) is the one from which the Kid fired when he killed Deputy Bob Ollinger.

LOWER.—The Murphy-Dolan-Riley headquarters as it appeared in the seventies and during the Lincoln County War. Deputy Ollinger fell just beyond the old tree, which no longer remains. Deputy Bell was shot within the building as he attempted to escape down the stairway. He was not instantly killed and succeeded in reaching a side door entering into the west yard. There he fell dead in the arms of G. Gauss, the caretaker of the building.

PLATE III

LEADERS OF THE MURPHY FACTION

Seated, left to right: Colonel Emil Fritz and Lawrence G. Murphy. *Standing, left to right:* James J. Dolan and John H. Riley.

PLATE IV

Upper left: Alexander A. McSween. *Upper right:* Susan McSween. *Lower left:* Pat F. Garrett. *Lower right:* John H. Tunstall. John H. Tunstall was murdered on February 18, 1878, by members of the Murphy-Dolan-Turner faction. Alexander A. McSween was murdered by members of the same faction on July 19, 1878. Pat F. Garrett was assassinated at Las Cruces, New Mexico, on February 29, 1908. The circumstances of this latter crime are fully related in the Postscript. (The case was never satisfactorily solved.)

PLATE V

A VERY DOUBTFUL REPRODUCTION OF AN ALLEGED PHOTOGRAPH OF THE KID

Diligent search has failed to produce "the authentic photograph," as alleged.

PLATE VI

PHOTOGRAPH OBTAINED FROM A SPANISH-AMERICAN FAMILY FOR A CONSIDERATION

They valued it because the "Keed" was a member of the group. Among them he is still something of a family tradition. The other hard-looking characters pictured here are not identified.

PLATE VII

OLD PHOTOGRAPH NAMES SEVEN AS TEXAS RANGERS AND INCLUDES BILLY THE KID ON THE SIDE OF LAW AND ORDER

An old newspaper print showing the Kid as he was during the Lincoln County War

PLATE VIII

Upper. — The burial place at Fort Sumner of the three pals: Billy the Kid, Charlie Bowdre, and Tom O'Folliard. On a small footstone at the Kid's grave is carved a facsimile of a six-gun. Beneath it are twenty-one notches purporting to continue the legend (or fiction) that twenty-one men fell before the Kid's guns in the brief span of his twenty-one years.

Lower.—The torreon at Lincoln, a circular fortification constructed of adobe and stone, built about 1850 for the protection of the settlers from Indian raids. Later it became of strategic importance during the Lincoln County feud. The structure has three levels or sections, beginning with the ground floor. Then, eight feet above this, there is a floor, and an equal distance above this there is a flat roof surrounded by a four-foot breastwork or parapet for the protection of its defenders. All three levels are provided with loopholes at intervals around the entire circumference, thus permitting riflemen to fire in all directions. The upper floor and roof are reached by means of ladders passing through trap doors.

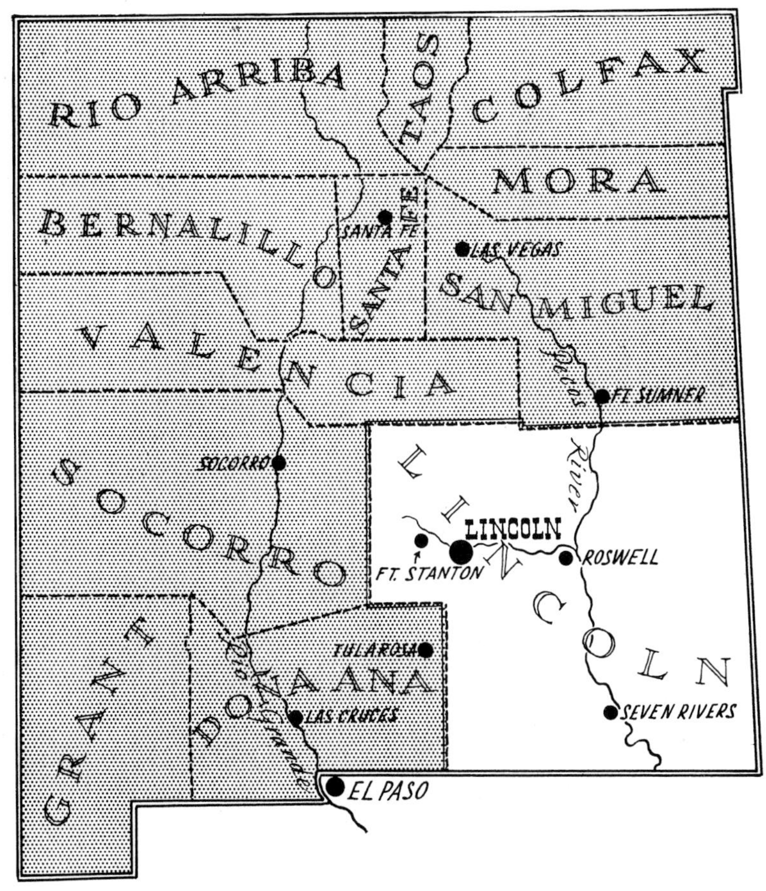

NEW MEXICO COUNTIES IN 1880

Reproduction of a map of the territory of New Mexico as it appeared in 1880. It shows that Lincoln County then embraced about one fourth of the entire territory, or an area equal to the combined area of several of our New England states. This vast region was subsequently partitioned into nine counties, some of which were named for early pioneers of New Mexico. New Mexico's constitution provides for two official languages, English and Spanish, and no other state in the Union has a like provision.

PLATE X

TORREON WATCHTOWER
From an old print

PLATE XI

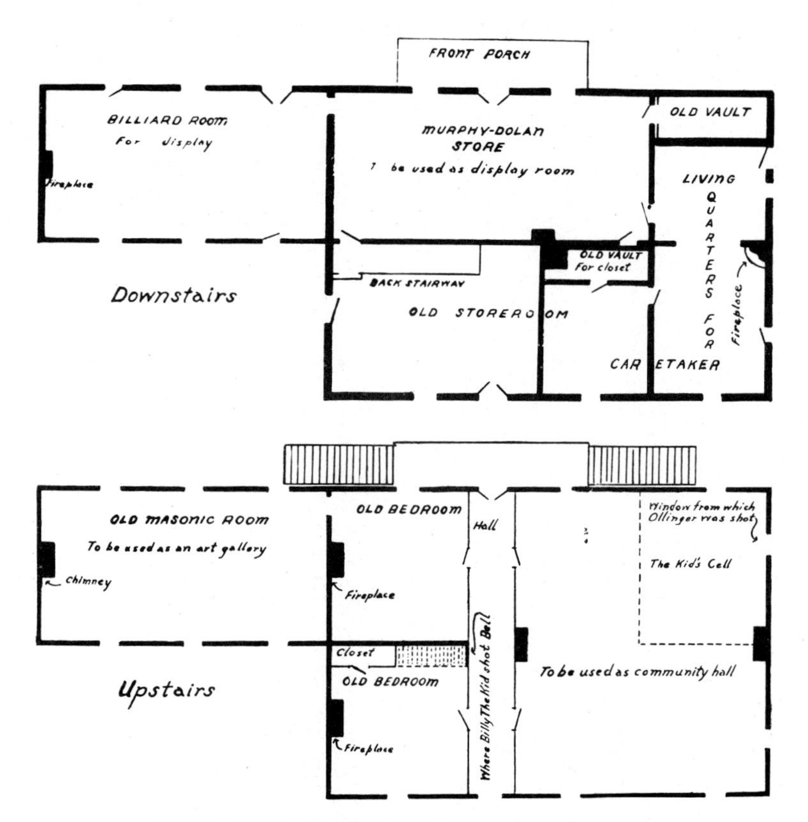

FLOOR PLAN OF THE OLD MURPHY BUILDING

The legends in heavy type indicate the uses to which the rooms of the building were put when it was the Murphy-Dolan store. Those in light type show how the building was converted for museum purposes.

PLATE XII

MARKER AT THE GRAVE OF KATHLEEN BONNEY ANTRIM,
MOTHER OF BILLY THE KID

At Silver City, New Mexico. The elements have nearly destroyed the inscription

PLATE XIII

Susan was calm and poised. Her composure gave no hint of the grief and strain she had endured since the murder of her husband and the destruction of her home.

When she was escorted to the witness chair, her guards took up strategic positions in the room so that no movement among the spectators could escape their eyes.

Colonel Dudley was seated at a table with his counsel, Judge Waldo and Lieutenant Samuel S. Poague, of the Fifteenth United States Infantry.

Susan McSween centered her gaze upon Dudley. Her eyes were brilliant in the ivory pallor of her face, but her expression was inscrutable. Her unwavering gaze caused Dudley a certain amount of discomfiture.

The recorder, a serious young captain of cavalry, had been ordered to the post to assume the role of prosecutor. He addressed the witness courteously, establishing her name, place of residence, and the fact that she was the widow of Alexander A. McSween.

"Will you state the date of your husband's death and the circumstances?" the recorder asked.

"The nineteenth of July, 1878. It was in Lincoln." Susan paused.

"Please continue, ma'am, if you are able," the recorder said.

"My husband was murdered while he and others were endeavoring to escape from our burning home."

"Do you know the origin of the fire, and, if so, will you please state?"

"My home was fired by a group of men under the command of Sheriff Peppin, Deputy Sheriff Marion Turner, James J. Dolan, and others," Susan said clearly.

"Are you acquainted with Colonel Dudley, the respondent in this proceeding?"

"I know *who* and *what* he is!"

"A reply I find puzzling, madam. Will you be good enough to explain?" the recorder asked.

"I know him to be Colonel N. A. M. Dudley, United States Army, now suspended from command of this post, a character assassin and a disgrace to the service he represents.

Judge Waldo was instantly upon his feet, voicing a vigorous protest. Dudley's habitually flushed face assumed a deeper hue.

"I desire to enter an objection to the observations of the witness and demand that this statement be stricken from the record," Waldo said.

"Your objection is well taken, sir, and it is so ordered," the Judge Advocate ruled. "I adjure you, madam, to be more circumspect in your replies. Proceed, please."

"Mrs. McSween," the recorder resumed, "will you please tell the court what transpired in Lincoln on the day and night of July 19, last, at which time your husband and others lost their lives and your home was destroyed, beginning with the arrival of Colonel Dudley in the village with his troops and continuing until his departure on the following day?"

Calmly, unemotionally, Susan McSween related the incidents of those last tragic hours, telling the stark and bitter truth, as she saw it.

During the narration, her gaze continued to rest upon Colonel Dudley, who sat with eyes averted.

At the conclusion of her recital, the recorder addressed counsel for Colonel Dudley. "We have no further questions. The witness is at your service for cross-examination."

Judge Waldo, always astute, believed any attempt to impeach or shake the testimony of Susan McSween would be futile, and might react against his client. He decided to exercise diplomacy.

"Gentlemen," he addressed the members of the board, "I am aware this proceeding has been a most trying ordeal to this witness and has occasioned her no little mental and physical stress." He bowed deeply to Mrs. McSween. "Therefore," he continued, "in the circumstances and in respectful deference to the witness, we waive the privilege of cross-examination."

However, Waldo had neglected to confer with Lieutenant Poague, and, before the Judge Advocate could dismiss Mrs. McSween, the young officer arose.

"With the court's permission, I desire to address one or two questions to this witness."

"Very well, you may proceed," the Judge Advocate said.

"It is not true, madam, that on the evening you allege you visited General (referring to the colonel by his brevet rank) Dudley's tent, and in the presence of witnesses, you made numerous and vicious threats against him?" Poague asked.

The recorder was about to interpose an objection on the ground that the question was not within the scope of proper cross-examination, but Leonard made an almost imperceptible gesture of negation. Attorney Leonard sensed that the young lieutenant was courting disaster.

"You confuse terms, sir," Susan said, permitting herself a half smile at the young officer. "I made no threats against him, to whom you refer as 'General.' To the contrary, I made him the *promise* that, should I survive that terrible night, I would devote my every energy and what might remain of my fortune to effect his personal ruin and destroy his career for refusing to intervene to prevent the certain death of my husband and of his loyal defenders. That *promise* I still hope to redeem."

"A distinction without a difference, madam," Poague retorted, in a lame attempt to be facetious. "Now, one more question, if you please. It is true that you have, in the presence of various witnesses, expressed the hope that General Dudley would be assassinated, or otherwise meet with some violent death?"

"To the first part of your question, I can truthfully state that at no time have I expressed the wish that he should be assassinated. To the second, I freely admit that knowledge of his death 'otherwise,' as you suggest, would afford me personal satisfaction, and I have so stated."

Here was admission of bitter antagonism directed at his commander, and the lieutenant proposed a make the most of it.

"Tell me, madam," he inquired caustically, "have you ever suggested publicly the method by which, in your opinion, the demise of the general should be accomplished?"

The question, though again manifestly irrelevant to all cross-examination procedure, elicited no objection from the recorder or from Attorney Leonard. They both felt Susan McSween was coming off well in this exchange.

"I have believed this respondent merited death, but not by assassination. I would have him tried by a General Courts Martial, found guilty, and sentenced to the firing squad. This would seem to me justice for an accessory to arson, pillage, and several murders. Does that satisfactorily answer your question, sir?"

As the officious and now frustrated young subaltern resumed his seat at the counsels' table, the angry look of his commander boded him ill.

At the conclusion of Mrs. McSween's testimony, the recorder requested a recess until the following morning. This was granted.

The governor called a conference in his quarters. Attorney Leonard, the recorder, and Sheriff Kimbrell were present. The governor was in excellent spirits.

"Gentlemen," he said, "Mrs. McSween was a good witness. This is evidenced by the fact that Waldo declined to cross-examine. He made it seem like a chivalrous gesture, but I thought it obvious he feared she might damage his client further. And the lieutenant seems to have overreached himself.

"However," Wallace continued soberly, "we anticipate that Dudley's witnesses will contradict Mrs. McSween's statements. We must have corroboration. The only witness we can count upon is William Bonney, known as Billy the Kid. I believe this boy is in your custody, Sheriff?"

"That is true," the sheriff assented.

"Then bring him to the guardhouse here at the post and confine him. This will insure his presence."

The sheriff stared at the governor with undisguised surprise. "That will be impossible, sir," Kimbrell said. "The boy is a voluntary witness in this case—and, besides, to confine him here would endanger his life!"

It was the governor's turn to look surprised. "Are you questioning my authority?" he demanded.

"I respectfully decline," said the sheriff softly, "to bring the boy here. But I promise to produce him in court when so directed."

Kimbrell's tone was quiet, but he was firm in his resolve to protect the life of his prisoner. He had not believed the governor had authority to require the prisoners held in custody after their testimony before the grand jury, but, recognizing the wisdom of the plan, he had followed the governor's orders. Now, the sheriff was ready to produce the boy in court, but not to place him in the hands of his enemies.

After a tense silence, Attorney Ira Leonard said to Wallace, "I find myself constrained to agree with the sheriff, sir. To bring Bonney here would multiply the opportunities for his enemies to kill him. Further," Leonard cleared his throat and continued, as if reluctantly, "I am of the opinion there presently exist no grounds upon which he may lawfully be held in restraint."

"I disagree," said the governor promptly. "The Kid was taken into custody pursuant to warrants charging him as accessory to the Chapman murder. This should be sufficient authority to detain him until his status is adjudicated."

"I could find myself in harmony with Your Excellency's hypothesis," Leonard said, "if the facts bore out your contention."

"Please explain," Wallace said.

"Certainly, sir," Leonard replied. "I have investigated and find that, for reasons unknown to me, those warrants were not actually served. In this, I believe Sheriff Kimbrell will bear me out. Dr. J. H. Blazer, who was foreman of the grand jury which investigated the Chapman murder, informed me no evidence was found to implicate Bonney or O'Folliard. To the contrary, the jury found Bonney had attempted to intervene to protect Chapman, but was restrained by Evans. Patron testified that Billy had, earlier, prevented Patron's murder by Campbell, the killer of Chapman. I understood both boys were fully exonerated."

Leonard had warmed to the plea. He had risen, and he paused to study the faces of the men in the room, measuring their responses, reacting to them as to the members of a jury. He faced the governor.

"It is true, sir," Leonard continued, "that there are indictments pending against the Kid, among which is one charging him with the murders of Sheriff Brady and his deputy, Hindman. As you know, sir, I have endeavored to prevail upon Judge Bristol to dismiss those indictments as he has dismissed indictments against many of the Kid's enemies, so that the boy, too, might take advantage of the terms of your wise and generous Proclamation of Amnesty. In this I have, unfortunately, failed."

Leonard dropped his head upon his chest. When he raised it, he spoke briskly. "However, as you know, there is a great difference between a pending indictment and the actual issuance of a warrant for the arrest of the accused. No such warrants are in possession of Sheriff Kimbrell! I understand the boy is willing to appear as a voluntary witness in the present proceeding, at great risk to himself. I submit, sir, that Bonney is not now lawfully detained, and is entitled to unrestricted liberty!"

"Brilliantly argued, sir," the governor said drily. "Very well, what assurance have I that Bonney will appear when required?"

"A double assurance, sir," Kimbrell said quickly, "his promise, made to you and to Mrs. McSween some weeks ago, and my pledge to see that he is present."

"One or both should be a sufficient guarantee," the governor said, "but—" he smiled, "I suggest that, in the event of failure, Lincoln County may require a new sheriff!"

Leonard chuckled at the governor's little joke, but Sheriff Kimbrell frowned. He was not amused by the inference of a possible lack of integrity or efficiency on his part. He directed a steady gaze at the governor and spoke with dignity.

"If the Kid should not be available when called, for any reason, my removal will not require action on your part. My resignation will be in the hands of the Board of County Commissioners. Good afternoon."

Kimbrell went out of the governor's quarters, left the post, and rode toward Lincoln with a troubled mind. He had been holding the Kid and O'Folliard unlawfully! In the past weeks, he had had moments of doubt when he thought that might be the case, but it was a shock to have it confirmed. Had the governor been acting in good faith? What were the Kid's enemies doing? These and other questions would require some answering, Kimbrell thought.

As he came into Lincoln, Kimbrell decided he would not tell Billy that Leonard thought he should be released. It was only a short time, now. Perhaps Billy was safer in confinement. At least, the boy would not go to the guardhouse at the post. After he appeared before the Board of Inquiry—the sheriff shook his head in perplexity as he dismounted in front of his office.

The next day, a sergeant of cavalry drew rein at the sheriff's office. Taking a document from a dispatch case, he said, "I have an envelope which I am to hand to the sheriff, personally."

"I am the sheriff," Kimbrell said. He opened the envelope and read a formal note from Governor Wallace requiring him to produce the Kid May 3, at ten o'clock in the morning.

Kimbrell passed the note to Longworth. "The governor is mighty legal, since yesterday," he said ruefully. "I guess we'll ride down to Patron's and talk to Billy."

"Will there be any reply to the note?" the sergeant asked.

"No. Well, perhaps there is." Kimbrell found paper on his desk. He scrawled four words: "Order received. Kimbrell, sheriff." He sealed the paper in an envelope and gave it to the sergeant. "Please hand this to the person who detailed you to deliver the message to me. It will confirm your discharge of the mission."

"Thank you," the sergeant smiled. "This means I won't be questioned when I return. I think you must have been a soldier." He placed the envelope in his dispatch case and left the office.

Kimbrell and Longworth found Billy playing poker at Patron's house. When the officers came in, Billy hastily gathered up the cards. "This game is closed," he said in an exaggerated whisper. "Stampede, *amigos,* here comes the law!"

When the other players had gone out, laughing, Kimbrell said, "Billy, I have just received an order from the governor."

"Well," Billy said cheerfully, "has he decided to loose my hobbles and deal the game like we agreed?"

The sheriff handed the governor's note to the Kid. As the boy read, his happy expression was replaced by a frown.

"I don't quite get this," he said. "It says for you to produce my 'body' in court tomorrow. A body is something plenty dead!"

Kimbrell recalled the misery he had suffered because of the Kid's clowning at the time of the prearranged arrest. He saw an opportunity for retaliation.

"I'm damned sorry, Billy, but an order is an order! If I don't comply, it will mean my job. A body, generally speaking, means something plenty dead — you're right about that!"

Kimbrell spoke with downcast eyes. Now he stole a glance at Billy, who was looking angry as well as puzzled. His reaction satisfied the sheriff, who looked up and smiled.

"Relax, Billy, it's just that His Excellency was using some of his education when he wrote that note. By 'body' he means you—in person!"

The Kid grinned at the sheriff. "You had me worried, George. I don't get all the fine points of legal talk. I guess I'll be free after I tell about Dudley and the night of the fight?"

"I believe so," the sheriff said. If there was doubt in his voice, Billy did not seem to notice it.

"You have a good friend in Ira Leonard, son," Kimbrell added. "And in me and Tom, here. Be ready to ride in the morning."

Chapter XXI

KIMBRELL exercised every precaution to conduct Billy safely to the post. In the party, besides the sheriff and Billy, were Deputy Tom Longworth and two members of the Rifles, Luke Dutra and Sam Corbett. Two rode in advance, two to the rear, with Billy in the center of the hollow square.

All this care evoked the Kid's amusement. "Looks like a guard of honor," he said. "Will I get the twenty-one-gun salute when I get to the fort?"

"If those gunmen have outguessed me," the sheriff said grimly, "you'll be lucky if you don't rate *one* gun before we get there—one you don't want. Today you're about as popular as a case of smallpox."

About a mile from Lincoln, Sheriff Kimbrell led the party away from the main-traveled road and took a brushy, half-hidden trail at the edge of the Bonito River. The travelers complained bitterly and profanely about the rough going.

Whether or not the precautions had been necessary, the little party arrived safely at the post. The five men rode smartly across the parade ground to the old barracks where, in the conference room, they were joined by the military recorder and Ira Leonard.

Word of the Kid's arrival was passed about the post. When the board reconvened, the big room in the barracks was crowded to capacity with off-duty soldiers and curious civilians. The atmosphere was charged, and there were whispers that a plot was in the making designed to prevent the Kid from giving evidence. Possibly because of this, a provost guard, under command of a sergeant, had been detailed to keep order.

At the right of the long counsel table were the recorder, who acted as prosecutor, and Leonard, with Governor Wallace seated between them. Judge Waldo, representing Dudley, sat with his client on the opposite side of the table. Lieutenant Poague was absent. In his place there appeared W. L. Rynerson, United States District Attorney. Judge Waldo and Rynerson were well known as members of the powerful Santa Fe Ring, and the ring seemed to be coming forward publicly in support of Dudley, or in opposition to Governor Wallace, or, more likely, both.

The Judge Advocate, speaking for the Board of Inquiry, addressed the attorneys, "Gentlemen, recesses have been requested more frequently than appears necessary. The officers comprising this Board are desirous of returning to their commands as soon as possible. They therefore request that this hearing be expedited with all reasonable diligence. If you are ready, please present your next witness."

The door leading from the anteroom into the big room opened, and Sheriff Kimbrell and Deputy Longworth conducted the Kid to the witness stand. The boy surveyed the spectators with interest. A whisper ran through the crowd and some epithets—"traitor," "renegade," "assassin"—were uttered in low voices.

The Kid turned his smiling gaze on the governor, but His Excellency was occupied with documents before him on the table. When the room was quiet, the recorder began his questions.

"Will the witness please state his name, age, and place of residence?"

The preliminary questioning elicited the information that the witness was William H. Bonney, sometimes called

William Antrim, or Billy the Kid; that he was nineteen years of age, and sometime resident of Lincoln County. The recorder plunged almost at once into the business at hand, inviting the witness to state his whereabouts on the night of July 19, 1878, and the reasons for his being there.

Billy looked serious, for the first time since he had entered the room. He straightened his slim shoulders and spoke clearly and slowly.

"Me and some others were at the McSween home. We went there to escape capture by a posse of about forty men, led by Deputy Sheriff Marion Turner. We believed we could protect our lives better there than in the open."

"What led you to believe the posse was attempting to take you into custody?" the recorder asked.

"Dolan, Turner, and the others claimed we were guilty of the murders of Sheriff Brady and his deputy, Hindman, and Frank Baker, Morton, and Buckshot Roberts."

"How did you manage to evade this large posse and return to Lincoln?"

Judge Waldo entered an objection to this question on the ground that the circumstance was irrelevant. However, the officers of the Board of Inquiry seemed very much interested in the tale and in its narrator, and the Judge Advocate ruled that the witness should proceed. He added that, should the answer subsequently appear to have no bearing upon the matter at hand, the Court would entertain a motion to strike it from the record. Billy was instructed to reply to the question.

"We were told by friends that the posse was coming for us. We had a little food and water and thought we could hold out for a while, but we held a powwow and decided it would be best to go to Lincoln."

"You succeeded in avoiding the posse and made your way to Lincoln?"

"Yes, sir. There were six of us. We circled east toward

the Pecos, leaving on purpose a trail a blind man could follow. Then we rode a while on rocky ground. Every half mile or so, at a rocky arroyo, one rider dropped out and headed for Lincoln. This way, our trail got dimmer and dimmer until there were no tracks at all."

"When you were all in Lincoln, how many persons were in the McSween home?"

"There were six men, sir. Tom O'Folliard, Jim French, Doc Scurlock, Harvey Morris, Hijinio Salazar, and me. There was also Mrs. McSween, Mrs. Shield, and Mrs. Ealy."

"Mr. McSween was absent from home then?"

"Yes, sir, when we arrived he was still away. He had been hiding out to save his life. He returned the same day with some of his friends."

"And what day was that?"

"July 15, sir."

The questions continued, and the recorder established that, after the arrival of McSween and his party, eleven men and three women had been in the McSween house. Billy estimated the sheriff's forces at forty men or so, without objection. He said that McSween had other friends in town besides those in his home. Turner, the witness recounted, posted riflemen about the McSween house to prevent the escape of the party, and invited those inside to surrender.

The members of the Board of Inquiry sat forward, attentively following while the recorder led Billy to describe events leading to the arrival in Lincoln, July 19, of Colonel Dudley with his troops. Billy denied personal acquaintance with Dudley, but stated that he knew him by sight and recognized him, seated at the table.

"Did you see this officer on the day and night of July 19, 1878, and, if so, under what circumstances?" the recorder asked.

"I saw him in the afternoon, but not during the night.

He came into Lincoln with a platoon of cavalry, a cannon, and a baggage van. He placed the troops across the street, and trained the big gun on the McSween home. No one fired at this time."

"Please continue."

"Dudley sent his orderly to ask the governor to come out to talk—"

Judge Waldo was instantly on his feet. He had permitted the interrogation and the narrative of the witness to proceed more or less informally up to this point because he had noted the great interest of the officers of the board, and he had sensed that his technical objections would be largely disallowed. Now he thought he had an opportunity to bring out something which would prove damaging to Wallace in some way, or to Billy's veracity.

"Are we to understand," Waldo demanded, "that Governor Wallace was also quartered in the McSween home?"

"No, sir, Governor Wallace was not there. If I recollect correctly, sir," Billy said, smiling at Waldo, "he wasn't governor then, and I don't think he was in this territory. I was referring to Mr. McSween. You see, sir, we often called him 'Governor'—sort of a nickname, you might say."

"Judging by Governor Wallace's *great interest* in this case, I thought he just might have been there," Waldo said sarcastically. "And, hereafter, please refer to the individuals in your testimony by their correct names, titles, or ranks, as the case may be!"

"If the learned counsel is satisfied that His Excellency was not among the defenders, and has no further questions," the recorder observed pleasantly, "the witness will continue."

"We thought the soldiers were there to restore order, and so we all went out in the road. Colonel—uh, General Dudley told the governor—Mr. McSween, I mean—

if there was any more firing from his house, he—Colonel Dudley, that is—would order the cannon into action and level the house to the ground.

"The governor," the Kid continued, finally deciding to ignore Waldo's instruction as to the use of names, "said he would obey if the cease fire order was given to the sheriff's men, too, as we were defending ourselves."

"And what was Colonel Dudley's reply?"

"He said he didn't have authority to tell Peppin how to run his business, and that he and the troop were in town to protect property and women and children. He left men with the cannon and posted others along the road. He went to the Torreon and ordered Don Martin Chavez and some other friends of ours there to leave town at once or take the consequences. They went and left us with only the party in the house against the sheriff's forty men, not counting the soldiers."

"And how many were then in the house?"

"Ten fighting men. I don't count Mr. McSween or the ladies."

"Why don't you include McSween?" Waldo interposed.

Billy turned away from the recorder and answered Waldo directly. "The governor wasn't armed. He never would touch a gun all through the trouble. Said he would rather die than take a life. He was armed, as he thought, with his Bible.

The recorder asked, "May the witness proceed?"

"Proceed," Waldo said.

"Well, we found out we made a mistake, leaving the house unguarded. When we all went out to hear what Colonel Dudley had to say, someone came in the back and soaked everything with coal oil. They piled some brush against the west wing and set it on fire. There was already smoke and flame when we went back in the house."

"Who did this?" the recorder asked.

"Well, we saw Jack Long and old man Pierce running for cover out back."

"These were members of the sheriff's party?"

"Yes."

"And the whole house burned up at once?"

Billy hesitated to answer, picturing the McSween home as it had been. The house was large, of native architecture, and carefully constructed. There was no hall or passageway, but rather a succession of rooms, each of which had an exit to the yard. The rooms were spacious, the thick adobe walls painted with dazzling white *jaspe*,[1] the massive beams hand-hewn. The McSween house had seemed, to the homeless boy, solid, luxurious, and permanent. It was to this house that he and his friends had come, partly to find sanctuary for themselves, and partly to protect Alexander McSween.

"No," Billy said slowly, "not all at once. It—" he cleared his throat, "it burned for hours, room by room."

"What happened after you discovered the fire?"

Billy told of Sheriff Peppin's men, stationed about the house and firing sporadically, and of the appearance of soldiers outside. He related that McSween had sent a note to Dudley, asking the reason for the soldier's presence, and Dudley's reply that, if a shot were fired, the military detail would return the fire.

"Were other notes exchanged between Colonel Dudley and Mr. McSween?"

"Yes, sir, there was another. The governor wrote Dudley offering to surrender himself, if the colonel would promise him safe conduct to the post, and would let the rest of us leave the burning house without shooting at us."

"And there was a reply?"

"A note came back. It wasn't signed. It said he didn't

[1] See Appendix II, Note A, Chap. XXI.

have authority to interfere with the duty of the sheriff, and he was in Lincoln to protect the women and children. He'd told us that before, but we knew that nearly all of them had left when that bunch of Rio Grande outlaws rode in to help out Peppin's bunch."

Leonard, seated at the counsel table, glanced at Waldo, but Waldo allowed the reference to "Rio Grande outlaws" to pass without challenge.

Billy described Mrs. McSween's appeals to Dudley, as she had related them to those in the house, and then the recorder drew from him a description of the final hour in the burning house and of the escape. During the description of these moments of high drama, no one stirred, and Billy's words were closely attended. When he had finished, there was a sound in the big room like a long sigh.

The recorder consulted his notes.

"Then the casualties were Mr. McSween, Harvey Morris, Vicente Romero, Francisco Zamora, and Ignacio Gonzales killed; Chavez y Chavez, Hijinio Salazar, and Tom O'Folliard wounded," the recorder read from his notes, "while French and Scurlock escaped untouched. What of yourself?"

"Well, sir, as I told you, O'Folliard and I came out at the end, meaning to cover the governor from the rear. After I killed Bob Beckwith, I ran for the gate. There was firing, all right, but nobody hit me. Not fifty feet away from the gate I came through, I saw three of the soldiers. They had their rifles right on me, and as I ran past them I expected a shot in the back. None came, but just as I dropped down to the river, I heard three rifle shots. They must have held their fire until I was out of sight. I don't think the soldiers liked the job, and I don't think any of them did any real aiming that night."

"There is but one more question. This is very important," the recorder said. "Please consider carefully before you answer. Did Colonel Nathan A. M. Dudley at any time during the day or night intervene to prevent bloodshed, looting, or the destruction of the McSween home?"

The Kid turned a steady blue gaze on Dudley, and replied, "No, sir, he did not. As far as I know, he supported Dolan, Turner, and Kinney's men in every way possible!"

In the buzz of excitement which followed this unsolicited and unexpectedly forthright statement, the board called a brief recess.

"General," Waldo murmured to Dudley, "this outlaw makes a surprisingly good impression. And he corroborates the McSween woman. If I cross-examine, I may not be able to improve the situation. Have you a suggestion?"

It was District Attorney Rynerson who replied, "I believe, Waldo, our best approach is to discredit this witness and the other McSween partisans."

"You are right," Waldo said. "And since you know all the facts about the indictments involving these bandits, I believe you should continue."

When the Board of Inquiry reconvened, Rynerson came forward and stared at the Kid for perhaps half a minute. Billy returned the stare with a quizzical half-smile.

"Is it not true," Rynerson began, "that the nineteenth of July last, and for some days prior, you and others were barricaded in the McSween home resisting by gunfire arrest by Sheriff George W. Peppin and his deputies?"

"We were defending our lives and that of McSween from a mob," the Kid replied spiritedly.

"Were you not ordered to surrender by peace officers?"

"Yes, sir, but we believed we'd live longer if we fought it out!"

"Then you refused commands by those in authority to cease fire and surrender?"

"Yes, sir, but if we hadn't refused, we would have all been shot down, just as five of us were."

Rynerson shrugged and turned to address the members of the board.

"In spite of the justifications this witness adds to each answer," Rynerson said, "it should be self-evident that the incident complained of was wholly brought about by the individuals in the McSween house declining to submit to arrest by the legally constituted authorities who were endeavoring to perform their official duties. Admission by this witness that demand for surrender was duly made, and refused, clearly demonstrates that General Dudley cannot be held responsible for the developments which resulted from the failure of this outlaw and his companions to surrender. If they had done so, peace would have been restored at once."

Feeling that he had scored, Rynerson tacked off in a new direction. "Cross-examination of this witness would produce no fruitful results and would be an imposition upon the patience of this court. To aid the court in evaluating his testimony, we propose to prove him a person of ill repute—a murderer, a cattle thief, consort of outlaws. I will now ask the witness a single question. Is it not true that you killed a man—"

Leonard rose and interrupted sharply, "Sir, if you mean to show this witness a murderer you must do so by means of additional witnesses or collateral evidence. It would seem that the district attorney should know that, under the Constitution, before this board, as elsewhere, a witness is privileged to refuse to give testimony which might tend to incriminate or degrade him. In the United States and her territories, no man may be required to testify against himself. Let us be charitable with the district attorney for his ignorance on this point of law." Leonard looked at Billy, seated in the witness chair.

"On the other hand," Leonard continued mildly, "my witness will answer this and other questions of learned counsel"—Leonard inclined his head in Rynerson's direction—"provided he is allowed to make any explanatory statements he sees fit. We all know the killing of a human being is homicide. However, this falls into various categories, or degrees, including one designated 'justifiable.' Because we believe extenuating circumstances surround the alleged crimes of this witness, we not only decline to object, but we *challenge* counsel to continue this line of questioning, subject to our provision!" Leonard sat down.

The Judge Advocate remained silent for a moment, then directed Billy to answer Rynerson's questions if he pleased, adding that he would be privileged to make any additional statements he wished.

Rynerson was in an awkward position. He must now proceed with his line of questioning or lose face. But he still believed he could demonstrate Bonney to be a person of bad character.

"Is it not true you killed a man known as Joseph Grant during a drunken brawl in a saloon in Fort Sumner?"

"There was no drunken brawl—"

"But you *did* kill Joseph Grant?"

"Yes, sir."

"In a saloon?"

"Yes, sir."

Rynerson waited expectantly. Billy remained silent, his expression unreadable.

"Well," Rynerson said, "we await your statement. You were free with explanations when you testified for the recorder. Mr. Leonard has won for you the privilege of making such statements in connection with my questions. We are *eager* to learn how you are going to explain murder!"

"Well, I never drink," Billy said quietly, "though I often go to saloons with my friends. This Grant boasted he came over from the Panhandle of Texas just to kill me. I didn't know him, but my friends told me about him. When we met, I tried to avoid trouble. When he went for his gun, I threw myself sidewise and drew. He missed. I didn't. The peace officers said I was justified."

"Is it not true," Rynerson asked, "that indictments have been returned, charging you with the murders of Sheriff William Brady, Frank Baker, William Morton, and Robert Beckwith, and that warrants have been placed in the hands of peace officers ordering your arrest on charges of theft of cattle from John S. Chisum?"

Leonard was on his feet before Rynerson had finished. "That is *quite* a question, sir! Perhaps counsel is also ignorant of the law governing the introduction of evidence—that only the best may be presented. The indictments and warrants, if there be any such, clearly fall within this rule."

Rynerson was flushed now, at a second imputation that he lacked knowledge of legal procedure.

"I welcome instruction from so learned and distinguished a barrister," Rynerson said, bowing low to Leonard, "and, in anticipation of the point so brilliantly raised, I have here certified copies of the indictments and warrants in question."

Rynerson handed the documents from the table to the Judge Advocate, who glanced at them and passed them to Leonard. Rynerson waited patiently for Leonard to complete his examination.

"We do not question that the indictments remain in effect," Leonard said, "but the present validity of the warrants is doubtful. They are directed, I note, to George

W. Peppin, a former sheriff. Endorsements appear, 'Returned. Service not made,' signed by Peppin. As Peppin is no longer sheriff, I believe the warrants ineffective. I have ascertained that no alias process has been issued, directing Sheriff Kimbrell to arrest this witness. Clearly, then, no warrants now exist for his apprehension."

The legal byplay had an underlying current of real bitterness, which indicated that feeling still ran high on both sides, but it was incomprehensible to the Kid and to the spectators, who had lost interest in the proceedings. It was not obvious that Ira Leonard's purpose was to provide Billy with a public opportunity to make explanations concerning his alleged crimes. Leonard liked the boy and was acquainted with the circumstances surrounding most of his acts, and the attorney, rather naively it would seem, believed that if the Kid's story were known, he would be substantially vindicated.

The boy glanced at Wallace, hoping to read in the governor's reaction, a clue as to the meaning of the exchange between Rynerson and Leonard, but the governor was preoccupied. Doubt, confusion, and Billy's old devil —mistrust—filled the boy's mind. Then the voice of the Judge Advocate claimed his attention.

"Does witness desire to answer counsel's—uh—multiple questions? He need not do so, as we have explained before."

Leonard nodded encouragement, and Billy began to speak thoughtfully.

"I didn't fire a shot at Brady. A few of us came into Lincoln to see Mr. McSween. We heard he was in danger. We just got in when we saw Brady, Hindman, Peppin, and Billy Mathews coming down the road. They were armed, and it looked like they were coming for us."

The onlookers who, only a moment before, had been inattentive, were listening now.

"We got behind an adobe wall," Billy continued, "and we were just waiting there. Someone fired, then there was lots of firing. I tried to get Mathews, but someone brushed my arm, and I missed. After Mathews and Peppin went around a corner, I tried again. I wanted to kill Billy Mathews. He led the posse that killed Tunstall, and I wanted to get him. When I thought they were gone, I exposed myself to get my rifle back from Brady and was wounded.

"The governor, and all of us, felt pretty bad about the gunfight. The boys didn't know Brady was only going to open court. It didn't look that way to us. And then, since there *was* shooting, I felt bad about missing Mathews. I didn't shoot at Brady or Hindman, either. If I had," Billy said firmly, "I would say so."

Rynerson rocked back on his heels with an air of satisfaction. "Do you not know," he asked, "that if one member of a party engaged in some unlawful act, though he may not actually have perpetrated the crime, he becomes a *particeps criminis,* or accomplice, and is equally guilty?"

For the first time, the Kid showed signs of strain. He had had a long session as a witness, and he showed weariness and anger as he answered.

"I didn't know it for sure, Mr. Rynerson. And, if it is so, you are head lawman of this county, so why haven't you prosecuted Turner, Dolan, Boyle, and the others for the murder of those boys at McSween's house; and why isn't Dudley as guilty as they are; and what about the posse members that killed Mr. Tunstall? Or does that rule apply only to friends of Mr. Tunstall and Mr. McSween?"

Rynerson spoke as quickly as he realized the intent of Billy's questions, but not quickly enough to prevent its being finished. "May I remind the witness that he is here to *answer*, not to *ask* questions!"

"It appears the witness has propounded some questions," Leonard said from the counsel table, "to which the citizens of this community have long desired the answers. Should he proceed?"

Rynerson nodded, and Billy told of the deaths of Morton and Baker, freely acknowledging that he shot them while they were fleeing from the posse of which he was a member. "I have already told how I killed Bob Beckwith," Billy concluded.

"Then you admit having murdered four men, Grant, Morton, Baker, and Beckwith, not including Sheriff Brady?"

"No, sir," Billy said gravely, "I said I *killed* them, and I told you how it happened."

Rynerson selected a document from the papers before him. "I have copies of warrants for your arrest, based upon affidavits of John S. Chisum, charging you with theft of an undetermined number of cattle from his range."

"I know of the warrants and of the reward Old John offers for my capture—but he don't say *how much* he will pay!" Billy grinned, and a ripple of laughter stirred the spectators.

"I took a few cows in payment of wages due me and some others—and without asking, either. Me and Fred Waite, and Doc Scurlock had been working for Old John for about three months. After roundup, he told us to get off his range. We asked for our time, and he told us we didn't have any coming as we had been rustling his cows. Well, we hadn't been, but when he told us that, we collected enough jingle bobs[2] to pay us off."

---

[2] See Appendix II, Note B, Chap. XXI.

"How many cattle did you 'appropriate' in this manner, and to whom did you sell them?"

"About twenty or twenty-five head," Billy replied ingenuously, "and we sold them to Mr. L. G. Murphy. His outfit was never too particular about the brands they bought. This was before I went to work for Mr. Tunstall."

"Were those the only cattle you drove from Mr. Chisum's range?"

"No, sir," Billy replied quickly. "We took a lot more."

Here the Judge Advocate asked a question. "If you had liquidated your claim for unpaid wages, why did you take more cattle?"

"The first cows we took didn't rightly belong to Old John," Billy said. "When he brought his cows over from Texas, he gathered assorted brands on the plains. These were scattered in his herds, and he didn't even bother to rebrand them. Some of his riders quit because they didn't want to get caught nursing a bunch of 'strangers.' They thought they might get in trouble."

"That may be as you say," the Judge Advocate said, "but I am unable to see any justification for your having taken additional cattle."

For the first time in the long day, the Kid showed embarrassment and obvious reluctance to reply. Leonard whispered to the Kid, and, finally, the boy said, "To tell you why, sir, I'll have to go back quite a ways."

"Very well, let us hear the story."

In a hesitant manner, Billy explained that, when the differences between the Tunstall-McSween and Murphy-Dolan factions had begun, it became necessary for every man to choose his side. Chisum, he said, volunteered to help McSween with money and supplies, but not with men. To McSween, Billy said, Chisum expressed his anxiety that the "Seven Rivers Gang" should be broken up so that the Chisum herds would be safe along the Pecos.

When McSween had occasion to appeal for help, Billy said, Chisum failed to make good his promise.

The Judge Advocate interrupted with a question. "What was the source of your information regarding this agreement between Mr. McSween and Mr. Chisum?"

"I was present and heard their conversation."

"Please continue."

"After the fight, when the governor was killed, some of us were hiding out over near the Pecos. We believed Chisum had given Mr. McSween the Indian double cross. The others lost their property and their lives, and Old John got what he wanted without putting out a thing. We gathered up about a hundred of Chisum's Texas-branded cows and sold them to contractors at Tularosa."

"And who helped you in this enterprise?" Rynerson asked.

Billy sat, frowning in deep thought. "I seem to have forgot," he said finally, "except to remember they were all Anglos."

"Have you also 'forgot' how much money you received for these cattle, and what you did with the proceeds?"

"I remember the cows brought a little over ten dollars a head. As there were some rejects, we got about a thousand dollars—"

"With that sum of money in hand, no doubt you and your companions did not find it necessary to work for some time?"

"We got rid of the money right away," Billy admitted.

"By gambling, no doubt," Rynerson said.

"No."

"How, then?"

"I'd rather not answer that, sir," Billy said to the Judge Advocate, "and I wouldn't, except he makes it sound like we lost it gambling. We had a meeting. We took half the money and divided it among the parents of Romero,

Francisco Zamora, and Ignacio Gonzales. They were three of the boys killed at McSween's. Harvey Morris was killed that night, too. His mother is a widow in Dodge, and we knew he sent her money. We took the rest of the money to Roswell, and Ash Upson sent her a letter, telling about Harvey's death and the money."

"Very touching, if true," Rynerson said. "No doubt you would have us believe you follow in the footsteps of Robin Hood of Sherwood Forest, stealing from the rich to give to the poor!"

The boy was puzzled by the literary allusion. "No, sir," he said earnestly, "I never follow any man's lead. I don't know Mr. Hood or where he rides, but if he just rustled a few cows to help out a widowed mother, I hope the sheriff's posse will never cut his trail!"

The Judge Advocate suppressed a smile. "Does counsel wish to question the witness further?"

"No further questions," Rynerson said.

The Board of Inquiry conferred briefly, and then the Judge Advocate spoke to Dudley's chief counsel.

"Judge Waldo, although we have heard a great deal of irrelevant testimony, nothing has been forthcoming to contradict the statements of this witness. The finding of indictments and the issuance of warrants constitute no proof of the commission of a crime. Such proof requires the verdict of a court of competent jurisdiction. Had this witness been *convicted* of a felony, his credibility would be subjected to careful scrutiny, but such does not appear to be the case."

The Judge Advocate continued with an analysis of Billy's testimony and reiterated that his testimony was corroborative of that of Susan McSween and would be admitted and duly recorded. When he had finished speaking, the hearing of the Board of Inquiry was recessed.

Chapter XXII

THE KID rode back to Lincoln in the twilight. He was thoughtful and silent, and his friends rode quietly beside him. At Patron's house, kindly Señora Patron was concerned at the boy's subdued mood and troubled countenance. When she had left the room to prepare coffee for the riders, Billy turned to Sheriff Kimbrell.

"George," he said, "I'm all through. I withdraw my promise not to leave. You can't say I crossed you up. I've done all I promised, and today I thought Governor Wallace didn't even know me. I won't count on him to order my release. I'll just shift for myself."

"Very well, Billy," the sheriff replied, "but just promise to wait until we can have a talk tomorrow. One day won't matter, will it?"

Billy tried to read his expression. Finally, he shrugged. "I don't know what you have in mind, but—well, why not? I'll wait."

At dawn, the sheriff and Deputy Longworth came into the Patron kitchen. Billy was at breakfast. Kimbrell laid the boy's rifle upon the table. Beside it, he placed Billy's pistol and holster and a well-filled cartridge belt. Outside the kitchen door, Juan Patron got off Old Grey, leaving the reins trailing. Strapped behind his own saddle, Billy saw a roll of new blankets. All this was done in silence. Patron came in through the kitchen door, and Kimbrell spoke for the first time.

"Billy, your legal hobbles are off—and they have been for some time. We found this out a couple of days ago. Nothing has held you here but your word to me. I believed it best not to tell you this until after you testified.

"Last night," the sheriff continued, "Tom and Juan and I had a long palaver. We don't think His Excellency is going to take any steps on your behalf—not now, anyway. We think there are political reasons we don't know about that make it so he can't."

Billy waited. "I'm not long on handing out advice," Kimbrell said, "but Tom and Juan agree with me that Rynerson will be more anxious than ever to get you. You'd be smart to leave Lincoln for now. Go to Las Vegas, or, better still, go over into Texas. Rynerson will get those warrants straightened out, and it will be up to me to serve them. Don't put me on that spot. My term of office will soon run out, and I hear Pat Garrett is pining for the job. Do you know Pat, son?"

"I know him," Billy grinned. "He plays a good game of poker, and he drinks too much, and I've heard it said he has a quick eye for a lonesome maverick. He must be wanting to change his character to play sheriff."

Billy stood up and buckled on his gun. He finished his coffee standing and picked up the rifle.

"I'll be all right, George," he said, shaking hands all around. "You and Tom and Juan have dealt me a good hand. I won't forget."

At the door he turned. "Juan, I know I should say good-by to *madrecita,* but, somehow, I cannot. Will you tell her for me—and thank her? I'm sure she will understand, and—well, *hasta la vista, amigos.*"

Billy left, then, and quickly. He paused only to say a word to Old Grey, then mounted and rode away without looking back. Thus the Kid took the trail that led to his death.

Chapter XXIII

THE recorder, acting as prosecutor, was able to present one or two courageous witnesses who furnished additional corroboration for the testimony of Susan McSween and the Kid. Governor Wallace, who was to be the last witness, was expected to round out the case against Dudley.

Judge Waldo assumed the full burden of the "defense," not relying upon the young lieutenant and Rynerson, who had not been especially successful with Mrs. McSween and Billy.

As each question was put to Governor Wallace, Waldo interposed deferentially, before the governor could reply, "Was Your Excellency personally present when the incident occurred?" or, "Did Your Excellency overhear the conversation to which reference is made?" Waldo smiled at the governor's negative replies, then asked the court that the governor not be allowed to reply when his answer must be based upon hearsay, and so inadmissible, evidence. In these requests, Waldo was sustained, and justly so. It became apparent almost immediately that Wallace could add nothing to the case against Dudley.

Both Wallace and Leonard recognized the American judicial principle which denied weight to secondhand evidence, but both believed very strongly in the truth of the information they had, and they had entertained a slim hope that the governor might be allowed to testify in support of the eyewitnesses. This hope proved vain.

Governor Wallace was followed by Colonel Dudley's "dress parade." Dudley testified first and related that, at the urgent solicitation of Sheriff Peppin, he had reluctantly stationed soldiers in Lincoln to protect the lives and property of its citizens against the outlaws quartered in the McSween home.

The outlaws, Dudley stated, were resisting arrest by force of arms, endangering the safety of the women and children of the village. Dudley concluded with a firm statement that he had no authority to interfere with the activities of the peace officer and had performed an unwelcome duty thrust upon him by circumstances beyond his control.

There was nothing new here. Dudley was merely restating the position he had maintained with laudable consistency from the outset.

A number of soldiers, both commissioned officers and enlisted men, followed Dudley to the witness stand. Each of them vigorously supported the statements of his commander.

Other witnesses made up the "rear guard." They were as vociferous as they were numerous, and they included Peppin, Dolan, and Turner. They characterized Governor Wallace as the persecutor of Dudley and described Dudley as a brave and efficient officer, and a gentleman. They particularly praised the military diplomacy of Dudley in persuading Don Martin Chavez to withdraw from support of the McSween forces in Lincoln.

The Board of Inquiry, after deliberation, exonerated Dudley of all misconduct. However, in a somewhat contradictory spirit, they added a statement that nothing was found to the discredit of Governor Wallace's honor, integrity, or motives. The Board of Inquiry stated that, in its opinion, His Excellency had been mistaken or misled in his opinion that, in the years 1878 and 1879, the civilian populace of Lincoln and environs had been antagonistic to the accused officer.[1]

---

[1] See Appendix II, Note A, Chap. XXIII.

Chapter XXIV

LEAVING Lincoln behind, the Kid rode leisurely eastward along the old wagon trail to Roswell.

He drew rein where the Rio Bonito joined the Ruidoso to form the Hondo, a small stream making toward the Pecos River Valley below. Billy dismounted and allowed Old Grey to graze along the river while he sat on a sun-washed boulder to think and to plan his future.

Billy, always a realist, needed time to face facts and decide on a course of action. Literally, and figuratively, he was at the crossroads this May morning. Eastward along the trail lay Roswell and Fort Sumner. There were friends in that direction, it was true, but that was the logical area for Billy to be sought and, quite possibly, found. Without the championship of Governor Wallace, which appeared to him to have been lost in some manner, Billy knew he was again outlawed. And Kimbrell had indicated that was so.

To the southwest was a fainter trail following the Ruidoso through a narrow valley, over the mountains, past Blazer's Mill, and down on the other side. That way lay fewer friends but wilder country, and perhaps greater safety.

In times of crisis the Kid reacted quickly, with perfect co-ordination of physical and mental faculties, but with no immediate danger confronting him he hesitated, weighing the advantages of two trails beckoning in opposite directions.

Fort Sumner, offering friends, gambling, and gay *bailes* lasting from dusk until dawn, although promising danger, seemed enticing to the boy who had not yet passed his twentieth birthday.

To the southwest, relative safety called to his reason and maturity, even though hardship and loneliness would be the better part of his life.

In the end the man triumphed over the boy. Resolutely Billy left his place in the sun, mounted Old Grey, and rode up the shadowy valley. He would go southwest —to Alamogordo, perhaps on to El Paso, and across the Rio Grande into Mexico.

He passed the ridge where, only a few months previously, he had encountered Jesse Evans and his followers while Billy and his friends were protecting the Tunstall horses. Near Blazer's Mill, the scene of the fight with Buckshot Rogers, Billy stopped again. He wondered whether he should go on to the mill for food and a night's lodging. He knew Dr. Blazer had refused to take sides in the trouble, and that Blazer was a completely honest man and if he were asked if Billy had passed that way, he would tell the truth. So it was that, supperless, the Kid rolled up in his blankets a little way off the trail.

At dawn, Billy was up. He made a meager breakfast from the small provisions given him by Juan Patron and mounted, still bearing southwest.

A mile or so beyond his camp, he saw something that caused him to rein the big grey to a halt. Crossing the trail was the unmistakable sign of a small herd which had passed late the day before. Billy studied the tracks. Had it been a band of Apaches returning to the reservation with cattle stolen in a raid? Billy discarded that theory when he observed that the drovers had ridden shod horses. It had been a small herd—twenty-five cattle, he estimated, and four riders.

The fact that the tracks crossed the trail and did not

follow it in either direction greatly diminished the possibility of a legitimate drive.

The sun was barely up, the morning was fresh, the boy was in no hurry. He resolved to follow the tracks and satisfy his youthful curiosity as to who had crossed the trail, and why.

Billy followed along for about two miles to a point where the trail turned down a steep bank into a narrow, rocky arroyo. Apparently the cattle had watered at the little stream within the canyon. A quick search of the ground on both sides revealed that the herd had been driven along the rocky canyon. Billy touched the big horse lightly with a spur, and Old Grey moved forward with a loose rein.

Less than a hundred yards along, Grey began to edge into the desert willow that bordered the canyon. Billy dismounted and left his horse ground-hitched. He moved cautiously forward until he sighted a hidden draw, or box canyon, leading off at an angle from the gorge. Across the narrow entrance, there was a rude barricade of rocks and logs. The small herd was securely confined within.

Billy observed the weather-beaten appearance of the logs and the permanent way in which they were arranged, and he deduced at once that this lonely place had been employed before as a cache by enterprising rustlers. Billy saw no one, but a whiff of smoke came to him. He returned to Old Grey and quietly led the animal around a clump of jack pine. In a small, open spot, four Mexicans moved about a small fire. They seemed to be preparing breakfast. One of the four was a boy about sixteen. Four saddled horses stood near. Four rifles rested upon bedrolls, out of reach, Billy saw at once, of those around the fire.

The whole story was clear to Billy, wise in the ways

of the West. Here were four men who had rustled a small bunch of cattle—and he intended to challenge them. Although it would be four against one, he had surprise in his favor, and the situation exhilarated the boy after his weeks of enforced inaction.

Billy looped the reins of his mount over his arm. He thrust aside the screening branches and stepped into the clearing, saying quietly in Spanish, "Good morning, gentlemen. May I join you for some coffee?"

Three men jumped to their feet, hands instinctively moving to their holsters. The fourth, the boy, remained seated and motionless, showing surprise rather than fear. Billy smiled, but his eyes showed no friendly humor. He had not drawn and only stood easily, awaiting some further hostile move by one of the men around the fire.

Suddenly, one man lifted both hands above his head, exclaiming, "It is the Kid!" The others followed his lead, raising their hands.

The Kid ordered the youngster to arise and join his companions. "Now, you," Billy said to the man who seemed to be the leader, "lower your left hand, unbuckle your gunbelt, and drop it!" A similar order was given to—and promptly obeyed by— the other three.

"Thank you, my friends. Now, we understand each other." Billy's smile was warmer now.

He invited the four to seat themselves with their backs against a log, and he picked up their weapons. He removed the cartridges from the revolvers and from the rifles, and tossed the ammunition into the brush. Then he sat down cross-legged beside the fire, appropriated a can, and poured coffee into it from the steaming pot. At no time had he raised his voice or touched his revolver, but his eyes had never strayed from the silent men now seated against the log.

"Don't like to make you feel undressed, gentlemen,"

he said in a friendly tone, "but if you'll just remove those knives from your boot tops and toss them over here—be careful, so you don't cut yourselves!"

Three long, bright knives were tossed. The young boy did not move.

"Your knife, boy, and make it quick," Billy said.

"I have no knife, I swear it by the Holy Virgin," the boy protested.

The rustlers exhibited growing uneasiness. The unhurried nonchalance of the Kid puzzled them. Billy knew what he was doing. He wanted the additional advantage of dealing with uncertain men.

After a long silence, the leader of the rustlers spoke. "I cannot know what you mean to do. Will you take us to the sheriff? Or to those who own the cows? Or will you shoot us here and take them for yourself?" When there was no immediate reply, the speaker shrugged hopelessly. "For us, it matters little," he said, "but will you let the small one go free? He is my brother, and young."

"Your *brother?*" Billy's blue eyes darkened, and he stared at the speaker. "You wanted him shot from the saddle, or hung, if you were caught? That you would bring the child on such a raid proves you are so low you could walk under a snake's belly standing up and never muss your hair!"

The men lowered their eyes, shamed by the scorn in the Kid's voice.

"Come here, son," Billy directed the boy. The appellation was incongruous, coming from one only two or three years older, but no one smiled. "Place those guns in the holsters and hang the belts from my saddlehorn. Now, the rifles—tie them securely to the other side!"

The Kid examined the knives, lying on the ground beside the fire. They were of the finest steel and workmanship. He admired the knives and had an impulse to keep them, but he gave another order.

"Throw those on the coals. Only renegades use knives."

When that was done, Billy faced the most difficult part of his problem.

"I don't trust any one of you," he said to the leader. "You three mount and ride in advance. The boy stays with me. Haze the cattle out into the main canyon. If anything goes wrong—" Billy looked significantly at the boy. "Well," he finished, "I guess you understand."

The men moved quickly to do his bidding. It seemed to Billy that all of them were fond of the boy and would do nothing to prejudice his safety.

In a moment the small herd of cattle passed the barricade, in a hurry to reach the water. Billy scanned the brands. There were only two, P-A and H/J. Those brands were registered to Hugo Juber and Pablo Analla, two cattlemen with small ranches near Puerto. Both men and their brands were known to the Kid. For the first time he drew his rifle from its boot and rested it menacingly on his arm.

"So you buzzards raided those small ranches owned by men of your own people. Very brave! You didn't have the courage to lift cattle from Chisum or Dolan. Move those cows onto the trail, and fast, if you want to keep on living!"

When they neared the trail, Billy halted the party. "Those cows are going back to their home range," he said in a voice that admitted no doubt of his determination.

"You," he ordered, addressing the leader, "will ride point. You two on each flank, and the young one will ride drag with me." He shifted the rifle for emphasis. "Now, move," he snapped.

"The boy will go free?" the older brother asked.

"If you and your friends follow orders, he will come to no harm," Billy replied.

"But if we should meet a party hunting these cattle, we might be shot, or hung, and the boy—"

"Shut up, and take your place at point," Billy said. "If it happens as you fear, I promise there will be only three hangings!"

The cattle moved with little urging through what remained of the morning. Their homing instinct drew them toward the lowland range where they had been calved and grazed.

A little after noon, a number of horsemen approached the little herd from the east. They moved slowly, as if following a trail. The Kid ordered the drive stopped.

"This is it, men," he said to the rustlers. "Those men are trailing this herd. If you don't want to hang, do exactly as I say. As soon as they see you, raise your hands high. Leave the rest up to me."

There were eight horsemen on the trail of the herd. From a distance they believed Billy and the rustlers were running a small drive in their direction. When they were near enough to discern the brands, they deployed to surround both the men and the cattle. Only then did they recognize the Kid, calmly sitting the big grey horse, a broad grin on his face. The Kid ordered the prisoners to lower their hands and remain quiet. He rode forward boldly.

"*Buenos tardes,* Hugo, and you, Pablo. I've brought in a few cows from my rancho, and you can have them plenty cheap. How about five dollars a head, just as they grade?"

"What do you mean?" Analla asked. "And why were those *hombres* reaching for the clouds when we rode up?"

"They were afraid your boys might get notions and try a little long-range rifle practice. You may have noticed they've all shed their guns. Have someone ride herd on the outfit, and come over here for a palaver."

Billy rode aside into the shade off the trail, and Analla and Juber followed him. There he told the two ranchers the story of the discovery and capture of the rustlers. Both men were glad to recover the cattle, and they muttered threats against the rustlers. Juber summoned two of his riders, and four ropes were quickly thrown over a sturdy limb. The Kid maneuvered Old Grey under the dangling loops. His hand rested on his gun.

"Look, *compadres,* you have your cattle back. These men are my prisoners, and one among them is only a boy. I have given my word he will not be harmed, and he will not."

Analla and Juber exchanged questioning glances. They were thoroughly honest, small cattlemen, and they followed the unwritten law of the range when dealing with rustlers. Still, they recognized the Kid's determination, and they sensed that he was making no idle threat.

Analla broke the silence. "Go and bring the boy," he directed one of his men. "What is your name, son?" Analla asked, not unkindly.

"My name is Hermano Fontez," the boy replied in Spanish. "I am sixteen years old and a little more, I believe."

"Where is your father?"

"He was killed by Indians when I was young."

"And your mother," Analla's voice was stern, "does she know you ride a rustler's trail?"

"My mother is with God. She died when I was but ten years old. I have only my brother."

"You believe in God, my son?" Analla asked.

"But of course, sir. My mother told me of the Holy Madonna, the Blessed Child, and all the Saints. She was beautiful and wise."

There was something appealing in the modest simplicity of the boy's replies. He was small in stature, and he stood very straight. His battered hat was in his hand, and he looked directly at Analla with clear, brown eyes. Analla was childless, and he had a tender heart. The rancher stood quietly for some minutes, his dark face serious and thoughtful. Then he laid a hand on Hermano's shoulder.

"My boy, would you like to come to my ranch and learn from books, and become a cattleman someday?"

The boy's face lighted, then quickly became sad. "Such would be my wish, sir, but I must obey my brother," he said.

Analla asked that the older brother be brought to the group under the trees.

"We will learn if he is worthy of this loyalty," Analla said to Billy.

Analla made his proposal, and the older brother listened quietly. When Analla had finished, Fontez spoke to the boy. "You have heard, little brother. Do you wish to go?" The boy nodded.

"It is well," the rustler said. "Now, listen. Always respect and obey Señor Analla in all things. Work hard. Be honest. In the presence of the Señora Analla, be always courteous. Respect her and serve her. In time, she may love you as a son."

Fontez cleared his throat. He was maintaining his dignity, but his voice roughened with emotion.

"The Holy Virgin has guided you here, my brother. Perhaps this is due to the intercession of our sainted mother whose spirit watches over you. Go with God!" Making the sign of the cross, Fontez turned his back on the boy and rode toward the herd.

The boy watched his brother with tears in his eyes. He wiped them away before he turned to face Analla.

Billy had been listening to the conversation, wondering, as he often did, at the depth of religious feeling displayed by the rustler and the boy, and usually to be found even in the most desperate Spanish American. His thoughts turned to his own well-loved mother. He had seen a boy rescued, by some unfathomable act of Providence, from a life of banditry. How similar had once been the promise of his own future! If Tunstall had lived—but he had not. The Kid sighed deeply and tossed away the cigarette which was burning his slender fingers.

Hugo Juber had followed the conversation of his friend and neighbor, Analla. When he heard the boy choose to go home with Analla, Juber directed his man to remove the ropes from the limb and re-coil them on the saddle. There would be, he declared, no hanging.

"Well, you've had your way, Billy," Analla said cheerfully. "I leave those *bandidos* with you as your prisoners, but," Analla's eyes turned to the boy, "I may be the real winner, after all. Why don't you ride over to my ranch?"

"Thank you, Pablo," Billy responded, "but I cannot now go to your ranch. I should bring you trouble, for I have enemies. When real peace comes, we will meet again."

Billy removed the best rifle and revolver from the weapons of the rustlers and presented them to Hermano.

"Care for these well, son," he said, "and use them only when you are in the right. Good-by, and go with God."

The Kid watched Analla, Juber, Hermano, and the riders start the herd moving along the trail to the east. Then he turned to the three rustlers.

"There are your guns," Billy said. "Pick them up and ride."

Fontez stepped forward. "Those ropes caused us greater fear than many guns have done. We will not return to stealing cattle, but will ride back to Mexico to become honest *vaqueros*. One day I will return to see that all goes well with my brother. Thank you."

"*Adios*," the Kid replied soberly. He touched Old Grey with a light spur and turned south again.

Chapter XXV

IN THE late twilight, Billy located a sheep camp just off the trail. He turned to approach the rude tent, pitched near a brush sheepfold.

Two men appeared from behind the tent, covering him with their rifles. Billy recognized them as Basques.[1]

Traditionally, cattlemen and sheepmen were mortal enemies. In practice, it was not uncommon for a practical-minded cowman to run a small flock of sheep on parts of his range unfit for cattle grazing. So it was with Don Miguel de Lana, whose ranch this was, on the lower Rio Penasco.

The Kid lifted his hands high and rode forward. Speaking English, he identified himself as a peaceful traveler seeking hospitality and having no designs upon the flock.

The Basques did not understand. Billy repeated his remarks in Spanish, and then the herders smiled widely in the fading light, laid aside their rifles, and offered him boiled mutton, rice, and hard bread. After the meal, they sat around the coals of a little fire, talking. Señor de Lana was in need of *vaqueros,* they told him, for much work, a big roundup. Did the stranger want a job?

Well, why not? Billy had no money and no plans. He made camp with the herders, and, at dawn, was in the saddle, following directions to de Lana's headquarters.

At sunset he came to the ranch house. Don Miguel listened courteously as the Kid, in fluent Spanish, made known his desire for work. Don Miguel did not ask his name, and Billy did not tell it.

---

[1] See Appendix II, Note A, Chap. XXV.

Don Miguel gave his answer in a hearty voice, using the curious mixture of Spanish and English still peculiar to New Mexico. "Very well, *muchacho,* if you can handle a *caballo* and a rope, go down to the bunkhouse and my *segundo* will put you on the payroll. He's an Anglo."

"Thank you, *Señor,*" Billy said. He was happy as he unsaddled Old Grey and turned him into the horse corral. Fortune was smiling, he thought. On this remote ranch he should be safe, and he liked Don Miguel.

Inside the long, low bunkhouse, a man was at work, writing in a book at a rude table. He looked up and registered astonishment as he recognized the boyish figure in the doorway. The foreman was Charlie Bowdre!

"Kid," he roared, "where the hell did you come from?" He rose and grasped his old companion by the hand.

"Well, Charlie," the Kid drawled, "glad to see you're still alive. I thought sure you'd been hung long before this. Don Miguel says for you to put me on your swindle sheet. He said, me being a top hand, to make it double pay!"

"Like hell, he did," Bowdre retorted. "You'll go on the sheet, but if you earn more than your fodder, or stay very long, I doubt! You tell the old man who you are?"

"He didn't ask."

"That's good, Billy." Bowdre lowered his voice and glanced at the open door. "He knows there's a reward out for you. He likes a peso or two, if they come easy. Looks like he won't have to do any hunting. You've saved him a heap of time and saddle sores!"

"Maybe you'd better scratch out that name," the Kid said in a troubled voice. He made an uneasy movement toward the door. "I was heading for Texas. Seems like I never stopped here. I just thought I did—I'm still riding!"

Bowdre broke into a good-natured laugh.

"Forget it, Kid. De Lana is all right. You're as safe here as you would be in jail. I know, for he helped me out plenty. I'll tell you how, after we put on the feed bag."

The de Lana family had held their lands long before the ceding of the territory to the United States after the Mexican War. With the coming of the Americans, the de Lanas had suffered many injustices. To Don Miguel, the last of his line, there remained only a limited holding of what had once been an empire. And because he grazed a few sheep in the hills and on the rocky barrens of his range, he was held in ill favor by neighboring cattle ranchers with larger spreads who did not need to follow this practice.

When the two men went to the ranch house for supper, Bowdre called his employer aside. "Don Miguel," he said, "this man is William Bonney, better known as the Kid. We are old friends. Will you let him stay?"

The old man smiled. "But of course, Carlos. I knew him at once." And to Billy, he said, "You are welcome, my boy. I have heard much of you. Don Martin Chavez and I have long been friends. He has told me of the happenings in Lincoln. He regrets that he and his followers were forced to leave you there. As for you and Carlos, feel pride in having opposed the forces of evil. Few strangers pass this way. You will be safe." Don Miguel bowed slightly. The lamplight gleamed on his silver hair. "*Mí casa es suya,*" he said simply.

"My house is yours—" Thus spoke a Spanish gentleman, descendant of a proud people whose courtesy and gentility have not been surpassed. He spoke, not as to an employee, but as to an honored guest.

Bowdre and the Kid did not go at once to the bunkhouse after supper. Instead, they wandered away from the house to a wooden bench placed among some gnarled old apple trees. They sat in silence for a time, then Billy said, "Charlie, someway I can't drop my loop on Señor de Lana. It don't seem he ought to be on this rocky ranch. He is kind and good—more like a padre strayed away from some old mission."

Bowdre smiled in the darkness.

"Well, yes, Kid, he is plenty mild and gentle. I recall something that made me plumb ashamed. We delivered a bunch of steers down in Tularosa. It was a hot, dirty drive, and Don Miguel took us hands to a bar for some cold beer to wash the dust out of our throats. A big Anglo came in and pushed up to the bar. He shoved in right between the boss and me."

Bowdre paused to roll and light a cigarette.

"I was timid, like always," Bowdre drawled on, "and moved over, but Don Miguel didn't seem to notice. This made the big fellow peevish. 'Move over, you damned greaser,' he says, 'and give a man room according to his weight,' but the boss was deaf, dumb, and blind.

"Well, I thought the old man was scared, and I guess the bully had the same idea. As you know, I am mighty shy in a gun fight"—there was irony in Bowdre's voice—"but I thought it was about time for me to draw cards in this game. Don Miguel shook his head at me, him reading my purpose. About then the big man took a long draw on his cigarette and blowed the smoke right in the boss's face."

Bowdre was a good storyteller. He paused for dramatic effect.

"You've seen a rattler uncoil and strike, Kid? Don Miguel half turned and said, real quiet, 'Draw, you gringo polecat!' Before that *hombre's* gun cleared his holster, the boss was ready, but he didn't shoot. He just pistol whipped[2] that bravo twice across the face, and that was all. The boss picked up the *hombre's* gun, shucked the shells, and handed it to the barkeeper, saying, real polite, 'Please give the American gentleman his gun when he wakes up, and express my sympathy for his unfortunate accident.' Then we finished our drinks and went."

"He was mighty fast, then?" Billy asked.

"Fast!" Bowdre said. "I've seen some forked lightning that was a hell of a lot slower than his draw. He's stood off more Indians, singlehanded, than any man in the territory. You couldn't *hire* a scalp-hunting Apache to ride across the far corner of his land. And that's the *hombre* you said seems like a padre drifted off his home range! Hell, Kid," Bowdre finished, laughing, "you sure did read his pedigree wrong!"

Billy joined in the laughter.

For some time the men remained silent, each busy with his own thoughts. It seemed strange to them both that Fate should bring them together on this isolated ranch after the lapse of a year following the fight at the McSween home. Bowdre seemed far older than Billy, although he was not yet twenty-two.

"Charlie," the Kid finally inquired, "I'm wondering how you happen to be riding for Don Miguel and how you got to be his *segundo*."

"By accident, Kid. I was working for a little spread down in La Mesa country, holding down a line camp. One day, a half-baked constable from Mesquite rode up. He had a star on his bosom the size of a saucer, and he said he had a warrant for my arrest, and I was to come along quiet and peaceful. I was plenty surprised and asked him whose cows I was supposed to've been stealing.

" 'That would be deuces,' he says, real important, 'but

[2] See Appendix II, Note B, Chap. XXV.

this warrant is aces, and spells murder; the deceased, Buckshot Roberts.' "

"What did you do?" Billy asked.

"I never did like small-town constables," Bowdre said smugly," and I didn't admire this one in particular. My gun was in the shack. Like a fool, I'd left it there because everything looked so quiet. I moved my horse alongside him, close, and said, 'Officer, this has got me scared plenty, but I'm glad they sent a real he-man to round me up instead of a posse. Will you read me the paper, as I ain't educated?'

"Well, Kid, that law-man was real accommodating. As he used both hands to open his fancy, spotted-calfskin vest to get the writ, I just reached over and lifted his gun from the holster. Then he howled like a lonesome old timber wolf with the toothache and a skinful of wood ticks."

Bowdre laughed, recalling the scene, and Billy laughed, too. The situation appealed to the Kid's sense of humor.

"What became of the constable?" Billy asked.

"Well, I herded him down to the line shack and buckled on my own gun. I took the shells from his and wadded up the barrels and chambers with scraps of the warrant. I told the Shorthorn just to shoot his writs the next time he made an arrest! I tied him with my hobble rope and told him he could find his horse and gun at the ranch when he got loose. It was only eight miles, and the walking wasn't bad.

"Well, that *hombre* handed me a line of lingo that was sure educating. I listened real patient, then I took his star to remember him by.

"Up at the ranch I explained to the boss how come, drew my time, and high-tailed it. In a couple of days, I met up with Don Miguel, and I've been with him ever since.

"You know, Kid," Bowdre said, after a long silence. "Sometimes I'm sorry I had to kill old Buckshot. He was a real fighting man. He stood off thirteen of us, like an old grizzly at bay. Why the hell he wouldn't surrender, I'll never know."

"If he'd gone back to Lincoln," Billy said, "Dolan and Peppin would have helped him get away. They claimed our posse was illegal. I guess he was just scared he wouldn't get there alive, like we were once or twice, Charlie."

"I had him covered," Bowdre said. "I didn't touch the trigger until the old longhorn started shooting. I only shot once and got him in the middle. I'm sorry about that; I wanted to wing him. But that didn't stop him. He nearly killed Middleton, busted George Coe's hand all to hell, got me in the side, parted your hair, and killed Dick Brewer."

"Remember, you carry *two* of his brands, Charlie."

Bowdre swore colorfully and at length. "Yes," he said finally, "one where he got me in the shoulder that time he bushwhacked you and me, and the other in my side where he hit me at the mill. Buckshot cashed in, but he sure licked the hell out of us first. Well, if he has found a better range, I'm wishing him plenty of good grazing."

"That rides double with me, Charlie," the Kid said. "Buckshot Roberts was a real man."

Then, "Charlie," the Kid said, "there is one thing I find hard to tie down. Sheriff Kimbrell says Pat Garrett is fixing to run for sheriff of Lincoln County. Me and Pat have got along good, whenever we've met. If he's elected, he'll take his orders from Rynerson, and then what? More war, sure as hell—a private war this time, with us caught in the middle."

"You may be right," Bowdre admitted.

"Rynerson is anxious to rope me and O'Folliard in," Billy said. "He claims we killed Brady, and he wants you for killing Buckshot. Some of the other boys are wanted for siding with McSween, but I hear he means to get me special."

"A lot of the boys have left the country," Bowdre said.

"Most of them went to Texas," Billy put in. "Frank and George Coe stampeded. George is still keeping under cover, but they caught up with Frank near Santa Fe and have him in jail, I heard.[3] If we were smart, Charlie, we'd pull our picket pins for a while."

"Well, I think we're safe here for now," Bowdre said. "If that long-legged old pelican gets hisself elected sheriff, I'm wondering who they'll put to watching him. Well, he ain't elected yet, and we won't climb no trees tonight. We have plenty of branding to do tomorrow so we better hunt the hay."

The routine at de Lana's, as at any well-regulated cattle ranch, was conducted with military precision. Before daylight the cook pounded on an old dishpan and called out, "Roll out, you coyotes. Come and get it or I'll feed it to the *other* hogs," and that greeting served as the cowboys' alarm clock.

Already the wrangler had ridden out to bring the day's *remuda* from the horse pasture. The cowboys gathered about the horse trough where the morning ablutions were quickly accomplished. After breakfast by lantern light, each man roped the mount he meant to ride for the morning's work. De Lana's men had four horses assigned to each. This was referred to as a man's "string." During roundup, the work was particularly strenuous for both horse and rider and required a change of mounts twice during the morning and again in the afternoon.

---

[3] *The Independent,* (Mesilla, New Mexico, May, 1879). See Appendix II, Note C, Chap. XXV.

From dawn until dark, the work went forward. Supper was served, as breakfast had been, by lamplight.

The Kid loved a roundup, and he was carefree as he worked, apparently unmindful of possible peril. He attracted the notice of Don Miguel because of his dexterity with rope and branding iron, and for the great care he gave the horses in his string.

After roundup, Billy stayed on with de Lana's outfit, and only one incident occurred to disturb the routine. One day a *vaquero,* attempting to rope a wild steer, missed his loop. He was angry and began to abuse his horse with quirt and spur. The Kid rode over and suggested that he leave the animal alone.

"You care for *your* horse, *muchacho,*" the hand retorted. "This is my business," and he struck the horse again.

Billy raised his voice, "Stop it, you damned cholo, the horse has more sense than you. He knew you missed your loop, and he stopped short, the way he was trained to do."

The *vaquero's* only reply was another vicious cut to the horse's jaw with his heavy quirt.

Billy crowded his horse forward, dragged the man from the saddle, and threw him to the ground. His eyes, smoky with anger, caught the motion of the man's hand toward his holster.

"Don't draw that gun unless you mean to shoot," Billy said in a tone of quiet menace. "It's dealer's choice. You call the play!"

Don Miguel, sitting his horse a little way off, had been watching the altercation quietly. Now, sensing that gunplay might result, he spurred quickly forward to a place between Billy and the cowboy.

"You, Pedro," Don Miguel said, assuming command, "unsaddle and turn your horse into the *remuda.* Rope another and return to the house. You will receive your time tonight."

"*Señor,* it was nothing," Billy said earnestly. "Pedro was angry when he failed to rope that loco steer. The fault was partly mine. Won't you reconsider?"

Don Miguel studied Billy's face. "Very well," he said at last, "it shall be as you wish." He turned to Pedro. "You cannot know how near you were to death," he said, and rode away. Don Miguel shared Billy's contempt for a man who abused an animal, and he was not ill-pleased with the little scene. He smiled with satisfaction at his own part in it.

The fall roundup was finished and the gathered cattle started on the trail for Alamogordo. The big herd moved slowly along the rough trail. The night herders were particularly vigilant for marauding Apaches.

At the end of the trail Billy had to make a decision. When the cattle were delivered, the extra hands were paid off and dismissed. The proceeds of weeks in the saddle usually went quickly for *aguardiente*[4] and for bangles for the seductive native daughters of the plaza.

The regular employees returned to their camp at the edge of the village. Fall chill was in the air, and they gathered near the chuckwagon around the cook's inviting fire of pine knots. Don Miguel, Bowdre, and the Kid sat apart, smoking.

"*Señor,*" Billy said thoughtfully, "these past weeks have been fine and free for me. It was you who made this possible. But I am under a cloud. I believe I must go to White Oaks to get advice from Ira Leonard. As long as those indictments are against me, I'll be hunted."

"So?"

"All I ask," Billy continued, as if talking to himself,

[4] See Appendix II, Note D, Chap. XXV.

"is peace and the chance to live like other men. If I don't take some action, I may be outlawed the rest of my life."

De Lana tossed a cigarette into the fire. He rolled and lighted another.

"I think I understand your problem, Billy," he said. "But perhaps you would be wise to return to the ranch where you have been safe and just wait for a while. It may be the governor will be able, in time, to do something for you. You are welcome at the ranch."

In the long silence which followed, the fire died.

Presently, de Lana arose and spread his bedroll. "We have a long ride before us tomorrow. Now let us rest."

In the dark hour before dawn, the Kid saddled Old Grey and, without taking leave of his sleeping friends, quietly took the trail leading to White Oaks.

Chapter XXVI

THE KID rode slowly along the old military and freight route that led north from El Paso on the Mexican border. He arrived in the small plaza of Tularosa, above Alamogordo, just as the sun was rising. He turned Old Grey into the livery stable feed corral and found breakfast in the kitchen of a little hotel facing the still-slumbering plaza. He was resaddling when a rider turned into the feed yard. Billy had heard no one coming, and his hand dropped to his holster. The newcomer laughed as he raised his arms in mock fright.

"Howdy, Kid," he said. "Just pick up your hand and rest your arm."

The boy was Billy Wilson, well known to the Kid as a restless, carefree, adventuresome lad who managed to live just inside the law.

The boys greeted each other warmly and exchanged guarded questions. When Wilson learned the Kid was going to White Oaks, he volunteered to ride along. He was, Wilson laughingly explained, "hunting a job." White Oaks had experienced a mining boom and was a sizable settlement.

Wilson reported a pertinent piece of news. "Kid, I hear some young braves have jumped the reservation and are raising hell. Several troops are out from Fort Stanton, scouting for them. I hope we don't meet up with them war whoops!"

"We'll go directly north," Billy said decisively, "straight to Three Rivers, then cross-country to the mountains.

We ought to be able to miss the troops *and* the Indians, if we look sharp. Let's get riding!"

Young Wilson and the Kid arrived in White Oaks after dark the following day. The long ride had been without incident. They left their horses, still saddled, behind a deserted shack and went at once to the home of a friend, Rufino Lucero.

However, their entrance into the village had been observed. Lew Ordway, who was sleeping off his liquor in the shack, was awakened when the boys left the horses. Stealing a glance through the paneless window, he recognized the Kid. Immediately Ordway saw a chance to become a hero. He would give the alarm, and perhaps someone would reward him with a bottle! Ordway slipped down the street to the town's most popular saloon.

At Lucero's house, the Kid and Wilson were made welcome. "You are in some trouble," Lucero said. "How may I help you?"

A single candle illumined the small, neat room and flickered on the low ceiling. Billy's smile was brilliant and reassuring in the dim light.

"No, Rufino, no trouble—at the moment. But you can help me. Do you know the house of Ira Leonard, the attorney?"

"I know it, yes."

"Will you go at once and tell him I am here? Ask him where and when I can see him. Let no one see you go or come, if possible. Now, make haste."

Billy had slipped into Spanish, and Lucero understood him at once. Lucero went out.

Señora Lucero brought food, and, before the guests had finished eating, Lucero came in as silently as he had gone. "Señor Leonard has gone to court in Lincoln. The *señora,* his wife, say maybe he does not return for three day, or more."

This information disappointed the Kid. He considered briefly, then he said, "Thank you, my friend. It cannot be helped. I will go to Lincoln and see him there."

Lucero protested, "The danger is great. There are those there, and here, who seek to do you harm. I will take my horse and ride with you!"

This loyal offer touched the Kid. "My thanks, good friend, but you must think first of the *señora*. There may be an accident. I ride alone."

"Are you meaning to leave me all unprotected in this hostile town?" young Wilson spoke up. "I'll just come along for my own protection."

Billy laughingly approved Wilson's decision. The boys made their farewells to Lucero and went out into the darkness to reclaim their horses.

Meantime, Ordway's information had been received with excitement at the saloon. He was given the bottle he had hoped for, and promised another if he would lead a party to the quarry.

"I don't know where they went," Ordway protested, "but I can show you their horses."

A mob was quickly organized with the purpose of securing for White Oaks the honor of capturing, or, better still, killing the Kid. As the Kid and Wilson neared the shack behind which they had left the horses, a voice from the shadows said, "Throw down your arms. You're covered."

Aware that they made obscure targets in the night, Billy and Wilson made a dash for the horses. Sensing their purpose, the leader yelled, "Down their horses, men, and then we'll have them." A volley from the hidden gunmen left both animals dead upon the ground.

The boys retreated to the protection of the shack. From there, they fired at the gun flashes of their attackers. This firing was ineffective on both sides.

By constantly changing direction and taking evasive tactics, Wilson and Billy succeeded in gaining the open. The members of the mob became confused and stopped firing. They had no stomach for a fight in the darkness where it was impossible to identify friends.

Afoot, and anticipating a daylight search for them, Billy and Wilson traveled west to the lava beds, the better to hide their trail. Then, for two days, they bore east and north through incredibly rough country. Billy grieved for his horse, Old Grey, and Wilson could not console him. At the end of the second day, they arrived at the Greathouse Ranch and Trading Post.

The White Oaks citizens had not been idle. Scouting parties of horsemen searched the countryside in all directions. Just as interest in the search was waning, a rancher rode into White Oaks and told of seeing two men afoot. He reported their position, and a council was held by the townsmen. It was agreed that the Greathouse Ranch and Post would be the logical objective for the fugitives. A party of fourteen, under Tex Hudson, a local saloonkeeper, immediately started in pursuit.

The December weather turned bitterly cold, and, when the party arrived at the Greathouse post the next afternoon, snow was falling.

The men left their horses out of sight and out of range, and quietly surrounded the building, erecting barricades and shelters as best they could. Then they held a "council of war" to devise the best method of attack.

Greathouse was a mountain of a man, and not lacking in courage. He had observed the activity of the men outside. After a time he threw open the door and, with arms elevated to show his empty hands, stepped into the open and roared a demand to know the reason for the raid on his post.

"We want the Kid," came the reply. "Send him out, and *you* won't get hurt."

"The hell with you," Greathouse retorted. "That being so, just come in and take him. I don't see anything holding you ground-hitched out there!" With that challenge, Greathouse backed into the building and closed the door.

At once, a volley of shots was discharged at the structure. The one large window in front was shattered from its frame, and bullets thudded into the heavy door. After that, there was silence.

Steck, Greathouse's German cook, was terrified by the shooting. He attempted to steal from his cabin to the main building, and was captured. He admitted to the White Oaks party that Wilson and the Kid were inside, along with Dave Rudabaugh. Rudabaugh, a former peace officer, was wanted in Las Vegas for murder.

The capture of Steck offered a means of communication with the opposing force. Tex Hudson, leader of the White Oaks party, wrote a note to the Kid, asking him to come out for a parley, promising he would not be harmed and could return to the house if he chose. The frightened Steck delivered the note.

Billy was amused. "Hah," he said, "I wouldn't get twenty feet from the door before I'd be filled full of lead. He must think I'm dumb not to smell that bait."

He turned to Steck. "Tell that *hombre* I'm plenty warm and comfortable in here. If he wants to talk, he can come in out of the cold. Tell him he will be as safe here as if he was hiding behind his bar in White Oaks."

The German shook his head in negation. He did not care to leave the building again.

Both sides waited quietly for a time, except for an occasional shot from outside.

The besieged men inside the building conferred in the afternoon. They hoped to delay a concerted attack until after dark, when their chances of escape would be improved. Greathouse believed himself to be in little danger, so he agreed to take the message Steck had declined to deliver to Hudson. Making the peace sign, Greathouse strode out through the snow to the nearest barricade, where he found the self-appointed leader.

"Hudson," he said, "the Kid doesn't trust you *or* your promise. He said for you to come in to talk things over. You'll be safe if you leave your gun behind. I personally guarantee it."

"Well, I don't—" Hudson began.

"He said," Greathouse interrupted, "if you don't have the guts to come in, just send one of your boys that does have."

Hudson was furious. Anger choked him for a moment. "You go back and tell those damned outlaws this game is dealer's choice," he sputtered, "and *I'm* dealing. If they don't come out, and pronto, we'll fire the house and get them like rats when they have to run!"

James Carlyle, a young blacksmith from White Oaks, pushed forward and spoke to Hudson. "Tex, I know the Kid, and he keeps his word. I'll go in. Maybe it won't do any good, but then, maybe it will. I don't like to see anyone get hurt if we can work it out some other way."

Hudson did not agree.

"See here, Hudson," Greathouse said, "Carlyle will be safe. I'll stay as hostage. If he's hurt, you can shoot me."

Carlyle unbuckled his gun belt and handed it to a friend. He walked steadily across the open space and into the house. Inside, Carlyle spoke directly to the Kid. "Howdy. You men sure led us one hell of a chase. Why don't you come out now, hands high, and no one will get hurt? We're fourteen out there, and it sure looks like the deck is stacked."

"Well, Jimmy," Billy said, "welcome to our camp. You look mighty cold and miserable to me." Billy called to the cook, "Here, you, Steck, bring hot coffee and some of your bullet-proof biscuits and the usual scorched bacon."

"You're a good Injun, Billy," Carlyle said. He drank the coffee and ate with appreciation.

"What happened to Greathouse?" the Kid asked.

"He offered to stay as a hostage," Carlyle replied. "He said if anything happened to me, they could shoot him."

"He knows damned well he's safe." Billy laughed. "Now, I'll answer your question. You asked me to go out and surrender. You know that mob out there isn't a proper posse, and I don't think it's my *surrender* they're after. But even if they don't shoot me, they'll take me straight to Rynerson, and he's promised to hang me."

To Wilson and Rudabaugh, Billy said, "It's me they want, boys. If you want to walk out, I wish you luck. I'm staying."

Wilson shook his head. "Like hell, I'll go," Rudabaugh said. "If they didn't shoot me on sight, they'd send me back to Vegas. In Vegas I'd last about as long as a bottle of redeye at an Apache war dance. I'll live longer if I stay."

Carlyle was troubled. There appeared to be no way of forestalling bloodshed. He walked over to the shattered window and waved to his comrades to show that he was all right.

"Jimmy," Billy said, as Carlyle crossed the room, "I went to White Oaks to see Leonard, the lawyer. He promised to help me. He wasn't there, and Billy Wilson and I were leaving town quietly when that mob jumped us and killed our horses. If a plan I have pays off, no one should get hurt."

"What's your plan?" Carlyle asked.

"Well, after dark we'll all go out in a bunch," Billy said. "You'll be with us, Jimmy. When we're clear, we'll turn you loose. I hate to do it, Jimmy, but it's a sight better than to chance some unnecessary killing, mine included!"

"Looks like you're holding top cards," Carlyle said reluctantly. "I only hope no joker shows up in the deck."

The light, feathery snow had stopped falling. The men in the house waited for the early, cold December dark. In the leaden twilight, they heard a shot from the barricades.

"My God," Carlyle exclaimed, "they've shot Greathouse, the fools!" He looked wildly around the room.

For a frozen second, Billy, Wilson, Rudabaugh, and Steck stared at him. Perhaps their faces seemed menacing to Carlyle. Possibly he feared they would shoot him in instant reprisal. In any event, Carlyle, almost at once, leaped through the shattered window and ran, angling away from the house. He had not gone a dozen steps when a volley came from the barricades. Carlyle pitched forward, and a crimson stain spread on the snow. He was dead.

Minutes later, Greathouse came into the house. He was unharmed and greatly distressed. Carlyle's death had been a tragic mistake, he explained. One of the men of the besieging party had accidentally discharged his weapon while handling it with half-frozen hands, a rather common mishap. This was the shot Carlyle had heard.

"Billy," the big man continued, "the light is bad out there. When Jimmy broke to one side instead of running direct to his pals, someone yelled it was you, and they cut him down. Damn them, that mob came here for murder. Mistaking their victim doesn't make it any different."[1]

---

[1] See Appendix II, Note A, Chap. XXVI.

The besiegers had been without food or shelter in the freezing weather for eighteen hours. Hudson observed discontent and discomfort among his followers, and decided to withdraw and make camp for the night. He directed that the Greathouse horses should be driven off to leave the Kid's party afoot. The White Oaks men then withdrew to the Hocradle ranch a few miles distant, planning to capture the men in the morning.

A little after midnight, Billy and his friends went to the small ranch of Seth Spencer. There they obtained food and a few minutes' rest, but there were no horses for them. Daylight found them traveling as fast as possible. Antón Chico, on the Pecos, was their destination.

The White Oaks men, reinforced by some Hocradle riders, returned to the Greathouse ranch where they learned the quarry had fled. They buried Carlyle's body, set fire to the house, and then followed the plain trail to the Spencer ranch. When they found the men gone from the Spencer place, they fired Spencer's house and outbuildings.

Hudson's men and their horses were nearing exhaustion. Tempers were at the breaking point, and a brief conference brought a decision to abandon further pursuit. The tired party returned to White Oaks.

A few days later, Billy, Rudabaugh, Wilson, and Greathouse were in Antón Chico. They were all well mounted, and it was understood their horses had been provided by the embittered Greathouse. From Antón Chico, Billy led the men to Las Canaditas, where they were joined by Tom Pickett, Charlie Bowdre, and Tom O'Folliard. It was a happy reunion. Bowdre and O'Folliard reported the newest rumors to Billy. He was now widely believed to be the leader of a band of renegades and outlaws, and credence was given to the story that he had murdered James Carlyle.

Billy sat down at once and wrote to Governor Wallace denying any such leadership of a "band of outlaws" and relating the circumstances of the incidents at the Greathouse ranch:

FORT SUMNER
Dec. 12th, 1880

Gov. Lew Wallace
DEAR SIR

I noticed in the Las Vegas Gazette a piece which stated that, Billy "the" Kid, the name by which I am known in the Country, was the Captain of a Band of Outlaws who hold Forth at the Portales. There is no Such Organization in Existence. So the Gentleman must have Drawn very heavily on his Imagination.

My business at the White Oaks at the time I was waylaid and my horse Killed, was to See Judge Leonard who has my case in hand. [H]e had written me to Come up, that he thought he could get Everything Straightened up. I did not find him at the Oaks and Should have gone to Lincoln if I had met with no accident. After mine and Billie Wilson[']s horses were killed we both made our way to a Station, forty miles from the Oaks kept by Mr. Greathouse. When I got up next morning the house was Surrounded by an outfit led by one Carlyle, Who came into the house and Demanded a Surrender. I asked for their Papers and they had none. So I Concluded it Amounted to nothing more than a mob and told Carlyle that he would have to Stay in the house and lead the way out that night. Soon after a note was brought in Stating that if Carlyle did not Come out inside of five minutes they would Kill the Station Keeper (Greathouse) who had left the house and was with them. [I]n a Short time a Shot was fired on the outside and Carlyle thinking Greathouse was Killed jumped through the window, breaking the Sash as he went and was Killed by his own Party they thinking it was me trying to make my Escape. The party then withdrew.

[T]hey returned the next day and burned an old man named Spencer's house and Greathouse[']s also.

I made my way to this Place afoot and During my absence Deputy Sheriff Garrett Acting under Chisum[']s orders went to the Portales and found nothing. [O]n his way back he went by Mr. Yorby[']s ranch and took a pair of mules of mine which I had left with Mr. Bowdre who is in charge of Mr. Yorby[']s cattle. He (Garrett) claimed that they were Stolen and Even if they were not he had a right to Confiscate any outlaw[']s property.

I have been at [Fort] Sumner Since I left Lincoln making my living Gambling. [T]he mules were bought by me the truth of which I can prove by the best Citizens around Sumner.

J. S. Chisum is the man who got me into trouble and was benefitted Thousands by it and is now doing all he can against me. There is no Doubt but what there is a great deal of Stealing going on in the Territory, and a great deal of the Property is taken across the Plains as it is a good outlet. [B]ut So far as my being at the head of a Band there is nothing of it. [I]n Several Instances I have recovered Stolen Property when there was no chance to get an Officer to do it.

One instance for Hugo Juber Postoffice Puerto De Luna. [A]nother for Pablo Analla Same Place. [I]f Some impartial Party were to investigate this matter they would find it far Different from the impression put out by Chisum and his Tools.

Yours Respect.
WILLIAM BONNEY[2]

Some weeks later, a postscript to the tragedy was added by one Buck Saunders. He told of the death of Carlyle:

Me and two or three other fellows were ordered to go out and plant Jimmy. We found him frozen plumb stiff. When we turned him over, we saw he had been hit in the chest by several bullets. If Billy had killed him, the wounds would have been in the back because he was running like hell to get away from the post.

When we came back, we told Hudson what we seen, and he got hostile. He said to forget it, for we didn't see nothing like that, and we must have been feeding on loco weed or been plumb snow-blind. Him being a nervous *hombre* with his gun, we just clean forgot to remember any more. Now that I'm stampeding out of this here Territory for Texas, I'm telling you for certain, the Kid didn't kill Jimmie Carlyle.

Shortly after the meeting of the Kid, Bowdre, Wilson, and O'Folliard, the quartet separated. Dave Rudabaugh had already gone to avoid apprehension by peace officers

[2] See Plates XXI, XXII, XXIII, and XXIV in the Appendix.

who sought him for the murder of a Las Vegas deputy sheriff.

Bowdre found work as foreman of the small cattle ranch of I. J. Yorba. O'Folliard and Wilson joined a trail herd heading north. The Kid went to Fort Sumner, as he had thought of doing many months earlier. It was at Fort Sumner that he was to meet Pat Garrett again.

Chapter XXVII

PATRICK FLOYD GARRETT was born June 5, 1850, in Alabama. When he was still a child, the Garrett family moved to Claiborne Parish, Louisiana. The West beckoned to nineteen-year-old Pat, and 1869 found him in Texas. There he worked as a cow hand and buffalo hunter. In 1878, he came to Fort Sumner, territory of New Mexico.

Garrett stood six feet four inches in his stocking feet, and, in his usual costume of tall-crowned sombrero and high-heeled boots, he presented a notable figure. His long body was lean and spare, and the citizens of Fort Sumner invariably referred to him as *Patricio largo*—long Patrick.

January 14, 1880, Father A. Redin united in marriage Garrett and Polinaria Gutierrez, according to the rites of the Roman Catholic Church. The honeymooners were snubbed in Fort Sumner, particularly by the women, because of his first marriage. The rumors were that the first Mrs. Garrett, a young belle of Fort Sumner, had sickened and died of grief, saddened to the last hour of her brief life that her marriage had been performed by a justice of the peace and not by the padre. The matrons of Fort Sumner never knew of any reason why the civil ceremony could not have been subsequently solemnized by the Church.

Garrett worked at Fort Sumner as a hand on the ranch of Pete Maxwell. Something occurred that caused Maxwell to dispense with his services, and Garrett opened a small restaurant. In time, a saloon was added, and it was in the saloon that the first meeting of Garrett and the Kid took place.

From the very first, the older man struck a note of easy comradeship with the boy. Garrett and Billy were a study in contrast. Garrett was sometimes surly and morose, Billy was always gay. Garrett was exceptionally tall, Billy of less than average height. Garrett sometimes drank to excess, Billy never touched liquor. Garrett's luck at cards was as bad as Billy's was good.

For a time the two men were inseparable companions and often gambled together. At the end of an evening, Billy might count the profits and hand half to Garrett, with the exasperated admonition, "Pat, you should either quit *whisky* or *poker!* Tonight you bet your stack on a pair of jacks. Quit being such a damned fool!"

When Billy returned to Fort Sumner, it appeared that the last reverberations of the Lincoln County War had been heard, but some of the supporters of the late Alexander McSween came to feel they were the victims of systematic persecution. Many of the Spanish-American partisans of McSween, Billy the Kid, Bowdre, O'Folliard, and Frank and George Coe were among the sufferers.

Over in Texas, the cattleman's association offered a bounty for the capture or death of many known "undesirable citizens." Ninety thousand dollars was the sum appropriated for the project, and the announcement of the amount had an unprecedented effect. More than three hundred desperadoes emigrated promptly and sought refuge in New Mexico, Arizona, and Colorado.

The territory of New Mexico attracted most of the *emigrés.* Its vast, sparsely settled areas furnished an ideal haven for fugitives, and Lincoln County became infected as by a plague.

John S. Chisum's great herds, roaming one hundred and fifty miles along the Pecos, were subjected to unusually heavy raids because of this increase in the outlaw population. From the Chisum range to the boundary of Texas was a distance of less than a hundred miles in places, and rustlers knew of Texas buyers who purchased the stolen steers and hastily drove them to rail points in the North.

Old John was moved to action. He called a meeting of the large operators at Roswell, and the Lincoln County Protective Association was organized. This group selected Pat Garrett as their candidate for sheriff, and he was elected late in 1880.

Garrett had had no previous experience as a peace officer, and the whole of Lincoln County waited to see how he would perform his duties. Added incentives in the form of reward offers may have made the job seem more attractive to Garrett. Chisum, as we have already noted, had offered a reward for Billy the Kid. This offer was verbal, its terms were vague, and, as far as can be learned, no figure was named. Its very existence subsequently escaped the memory of "honest John." Governor Wallace, however, had caused to be published in the *Las Vegas Gazette* the following notice:

> $500 REWARD
>
> Notice is hereby given that Five Hundred Dollars reward will be paid for the delivery of William H. Bonney, alias "the Kid" to the sheriff of Lincoln County.—Lew Wallace, Governor of New Mexico.

The Kid's friends and many others opposed the election of Garrett and took a dim view of Garrett's campaign statement that he would capture the Kid—kill him, if necessary. It appeared that Garrett was going to quite a lot of trouble to get into the position of hunting down his former friend.

Billy knew that Garrett had turned against him and

promised his capture or death, if elected. Quite naturally, Billy did what he could to prevent Garrett's election. George Curry, who later became one of New Mexico's most illustrious territorial governors, related this incident:

"As a very young man, I was running the Block cattle spread in Lincoln County. One day, a smiling young fellow rode up to the ranch house, and we had a feed together. He said he was heading to a dance at a village some miles distant, and suggested that I accompany him. I regretfully explained my boss had instructed me to go out and see some voters about the election to be held on the following day, and to get them to work for Pat Garrett who was a candidate for the office of sheriff.

" 'Do you know Garrett?' the stranger inquired. 'No,' I replied, 'but I hear he is a pretty good man.' 'Do you think he will be elected?' I was asked. 'I don't know, but I was given plenty of whiskey,' I answered. 'And that will sure carry this precinct.' "

Later in the day, the future governor learned his guest had been William H. Bonney. That day and night, the Kid had campaigned against Garrett, and the precinct voted overwhelmingly for Garrett's opponent in the election, George Kimbrell, the incumbent.

"That Kid," Governor Curry said, with a smile at the conclusion of his story, "would have been a good man to have in your corner in a hot political fight. He certainly had the art of persuasion!"

W. L. Rynerson, the district attorney, was a powerful supporter of Garrett, and, after the election, he ordered Garrett to capture or kill the Kid, O'Folliard, Bowdre, the Coe cousins, and others for their participation in the Lincoln County War. Rynerson did not manifest a very great interest in the apprehension of other outlaw elements of the county.

In the chaotic time that had immediately followed the Lincoln County War, Rynerson had secured possession of the Tunstall ranch on the Rio Feliz. He learned that the rustling fraternity was no respecter of persons, and his range was repeatedly raided until his herd had diminished to the vanishing point. Rynerson petitioned the commandant at Fort Stanton for aid.

That officer, remembering the troubles of Colonel Dudley, replied, "You should know, as a former soldier and as an attorney, that the military has no jurisdiction in your case. No state of emergency exists, and even if it did, I should require orders from the War Department before acting."

As his losses continued, Rynerson's fury increased. He had viewed the troubles of others with what the victims had sometimes felt was disinterested complacency. Now, rustling had assumed a far different complexion.

Rynerson decided to bypass the local peace officers and pursue an independent investigation. He sent Jim Barcus, a well-known outlaw, to the Pecos, Rio Feliz, and Seven Rivers sections to discover the sources of the depredations. Barcus returned to report three weeks later.

"Well, Mr. Rynerson," Barcus drawled, "out in the hills you seem to grade pretty low since you stole the Tunstall ranch."

"Hold that kind of talk, Barcus," Rynerson said angrily. "I stole nothing. I simply paid delinquent taxes and received a tax deed to the property. I filed claims on the water rights, which Mr. Tunstall had neglected to do, without which the ranch would be worthless. I took no action that would not be sustained by the courts. Just one thing more—see to it that you don't repeat around here the unwarranted remark that I 'stole' the Tunstall ranch."

Barcus smiled. "I'm sure glad to hear the deal was

legal," he said sarcastically. "But it seems you and me are about the only ones that believe it!"

"Just give me your report, Barcus. How about the cattle?"

"Well, I rode around like a saddle bum, not looking for a job, special. I put on the feed bag and talked a heap with them nesters, squatters, and small cattlemen. Most of them believe you rolled Mr. Tunstall's pappy off his blankets and stole his spread from under him, him being still in the old country. Them back-country folks are plumb hostile, not knowing, like you and me, that you got this ranch *legal* and *honest.*"

Barcus was enjoying the impatience of his employer. He rolled and lighted a cigarette while Rynerson drummed a foot. "Now, about the rustling," Barcus said slowly. "Those nesters and small ranchers all claim they ain't lost no steers, but they hear you and Old John Chisum have been raided plenty. One old mosshead said he seen the Kid and some riders near your ranch, but they didn't have no cows at that time. That's the facts—just figure it out. Could be you'll add it up to what I'm thinking."

Rynerson knew the Kid's antagonism for himself and for John Chisum, and Rynerson had heard Billy tell the story of his raids on Chisum before the Board of Inquiry.

Billy viewed Rynerson's acquisition of the Tunstall ranch as an usurpation and justified raids on Rynerson on that basis. Considered in the light of ethical behavior, Billy's action may not be approved or condoned—but Billy was outlawed, unable to secure honest employment, and with a price upon his head!

Barcus' report reinforced Rynerson's opinion that Billy must be eliminated.

"Barcus," he asked, "how would you like to bring the Kid in—or, better yet, just put an end to his rustling? There is a substantial reward posted for the job, to which

I will add a like amount. Chisum has said he'll match the reward offered by the governor. That makes a sweet pot, if you win it."

"I reckon you must've heard I ain't gun shy," Barcus said with a wry smile. "But then, you ain't heard I crave to commit suicide. Any *hombre* that gives the Kid a chance in a hundred to draw will find out he was too slow. No one will get him unless he gets himself dry-gulched, which," Barcus added, "I hope don't happen."

Rynerson wanted action. If the Rio Feliz ranch were not to go under, something must be done. He sent a courier to Roswell with a suggestion that Garrett come to see him at the first opportunity. Garrett answered the summons promptly.

"Garrett," Rynerson said at once, "you were elected to office on the pledge that you would rid this county of outlaws and cattle thieves. Well, you haven't!"

"What do you mean?" Garrett asked. It was an unnecessary question, for Garrett could see Rynerson meant to tell him what was on his mind.

"My ranch has been raided and raided repeatedly, and I have sustained severe losses," Rynerson said. "I have been informed that my ranch and Chisum's are the prime targets of these raids. I want this stopped, and I want you to direct your time and energy and the resources of your office solely to the capture or elimination of the rustlers. If you capture the Kid, I will see that he is hung. If he is not taken alive, the county will be spared the expense!"

"Mr. Rynerson," Garrett said, "there is more rustling along the Pecos than in the rest of the county. Those Texans are handing out plenty of grief over along the line, and when cattle are moved across the border they, and the rustlers, are out of my jurisdiction—as you know. Also, this is a mighty large county, and I need a full company of rangers to police it. With the few deputies I have, I'm doing all I can."

"The point is," Rynerson replied coldly, "you are responsible for law enforcement in the county. If you cannot fulfill the duties of your office, it may become necessary to replace you with an officer who can. You may recall a former sheriff was removed from office."

Garrett remembered that Rynerson and Bristol had effected the removal of Sheriff Copeland and secured the appointment of George Peppin, and Rynerson's implied threat brought a quick retort from the sheriff.

"I have met all legal requirements to qualify for this office, and my bondsmen have been approved. Samuel B. Axtell is no longer governor, and I am confident Wallace will not order my removal except on the ground of my incompetence—which would have to be proved."

The sheriff had relieved his mind, and now he assumed a conciliatory tone. "I don't want trouble between your department and mine, and I know about your losses. I'll take some extra measures, and—well, I'll do whatever I can."

"Thank you," Rynerson replied. He seemed mollified.

"I'm not convinced that Billy is the only one responsible for the raids," Garrett said. "I know of some cases when he was blamed for things he didn't do. And I don't have a rustling warrant for him. However, I'll try to serve the one charging him with the murder of Brady. It's my duty to serve it, and I'll sure try to. If I can, it will be in *your* interest *and* in the interest of the county."

Immediately after this conversation, Garrett left Lincoln for Fort Sumner, three days' journey away.

Chapter XXVIII

BILLY the Kid, Tom O'Folliard, and Charlie Bowdre, mindful of Garrett's campaign promise to capture or kill them, had joined forces for their mutual protection.

The three young men had fought together for a cause they believed in, and they had seen their comrades die in the struggle which had failed. That a certain *esprit de corps* held them together in this new peril was the natural result of the trials they had endured in common.

Garrett sought, and obtained, an appointment as deputy United States marshal. He also secured deputy sheriff commissions from surrounding counties. In this fashion he greatly extended the scope of his legal jurisdiction.

The wit of Billy the Kid, who acted as "general" of his party, proved a match for the wily Garrett. The sheriff traced down every clue from White Oaks to Las Vegas, seeking the quarry. He found none who would betray the Kid, and many of Billy's loyal friends gave false information to cover the trail and confound Long Pat.

One morning Garrett and a small posse stopped at a little hut and inquired if the young man who greeted them had seen Billy or his friends in the neighborhood.

"*Si*, Señor Sheriff," came the prompt reply. "Yesterday in Fort Sumner I have seen the Kid in the plaza."

"You're a damned liar," Garrett snapped, "for yesterday I was there all day."

"Ah, well," the young man conceded graciously, "perhaps it was another day. I am sorry I cannot assist the sheriff."

It was Garrett's plan to surprise the Kid and the others. He knew that hunted men take desperate chances, and Garrett, quite sensibly, did not want himself or any of his men killed.

The sheriff received some bits of information from which he gathered that the Kid's party was at or near the Wilcox ranch, ten or twelve miles south of Fort Sumner. He evolved a strategy which he hoped would be successful, and enlisted the aid of a reckless young man named Darley.

Darley was outfitted with a pack mule laden with camp equipment and instructed to go to the Wilcox ranch, learn if the Kid was there, and contact him, if possible. He was to learn what he could and, more important, convey a certain piece of information.

Darley got an early start and made a wide search. He was successful and rode up to the Kid's camp about noon. He was seen from afar and challenged and ordered to dismount when he rode close. Bowdre removed Darley's gun while the Kid questioned the stranger.

"Where are you from, *muchacho,* and where are you going?"

"I reckon that ain't none of your damned business," Darley replied with a convincing show of resentment.

"Maybe you're right," the Kid assented, "but I'm waiting, and I'm listening."

"I'm heading south from Mora County where I been riding—looking for a climate more suited to my clothes."

"Looks like you drifted off the trail," the Kid said suspiciously. "How come?"

"Do you own all this country? I didn't see no signs reading 'No Trespassing.' Don't a man have a right to keep away from the main drag if he don't want to meet up with no shenanigans? Why do you ask—you have this range roped off?"

The Kid studied the stranger for some seconds. Darley's story, and his outfit, were convincing.

"All right, *muchacho,*" Billy said finally, "come in the cabin, and we'll put on the feed bags."

Darley unsaddled his horse, then removed the pack from the mule. He hobbled both animals and released them to graze on the sparse grass near by. The Kid watched with approval. Here was a man who tended his animals' needs before his own. Darley rummaged in his pack and removed some air-tights to contribute to the meal. Then he filled a great tin cup with ground coffee from a bag.

There was little conversation at table. Darley seemed quite reticent, and no opportunity presented itself for him to question the Kid. When someone asked Darley if he had been in Fort Sumner his reply was simply, "Yes." Had he seen or heard anything of Pat Garrett? Darley seized the chance to follow the second part of Garrett's instructions.

"Listen, *compadres,*" he said belligerently, "you seem to be asking a hell of a lot of questions. But as I'm drifting along *muy pronto* I don't mind telling you, if that long-necked old gobbler had been around Sumner and seen me, I wouldn't be *here* now."

Darley was plainly inferring, as he had earlier, that he, too, was an outlaw. He continued, "If you're pals of Pat's, I heard tell him and some of his riders stampeded mighty fast for Roswell day before yesterday. He heard about some rustlers down there, I guess." Darley rolled and lighted a cigarette with satisfaction. He had completed the most important part of his mission.

"*Muy gracias, amigos,*" Darley said, when he had finished smoking. "Now I'll hit the trail."

Billy arose and returned Darley's gun from which he had removed the cartridges. Darley saddled up and departed, leisurely riding due south.

At midafternoon, he made a detour and hurried to Fort Sumner to report to the sheriff. Garrett was jubilant. He was sure the Kid and his companions would come into town, and he made plans to receive them.

At the outskirts of Fort Sumner, Tom O'Folliard's young wife occupied rooms in the abandoned military hospital, and it was here that Garrett expected the men to come first. He stationed his men near the building, and, himself, took a post with two deputies inside the building.

A light snow had fallen, and the night was bright with moonlight. About nine o'clock, a sentry called cautiously that several horsemen were approaching. Garrett believed it was the Kid's party. His strategy had succeeded! Garrett and the two deputies seized their rifles and went out into the shadows beneath a high porch. There they waited, Garrett in front, Lon Chambers behind him, and the third man at the rear.

Garrett had surmised correctly. Tom O'Folliard, eager to reach his home, was riding some distance ahead of the others. He was easy to identify in the bright light, and, as he neared the porch, from the shadows came the command, "Halt!" immediately followed by a single rifle report.

An agonized cry escaped the youth, and he doubled over, clutching his saddlehorn to keep from falling. He was ordered to raise his hands, and he answered that he could not, for he was helpless. O'Folliard was carried into the house and laid upon the floor. He died after a little while.[1]

After the single shot which took O'Folliard's life, firing by the posse became general. The party of horsemen turned and fled after a momentary hesitation, realizing they had been led into an ambuscade by the camp visitor.

---

[1] See Appendix II, Note A, Chap. XXVIII.

Later, Billy reasoned that the location of the camp was known to Pat Garrett, and so he decided to take his men to an abandoned shack at Stinking Spring to wait for daylight before riding into the hills.

Billy made two errors in calculating the situation. First, he assumed the pursuit would not commence until dawn. Second, he counted on the snow, which had commenced falling again, to obliterate the trail. But the snow soon stopped, and the posse was ordered into the saddle to follow a dim but discernible trail an hour or so behind the fugitives.

Just before dawn, the posse halted in a ravine about a quarter of a mile from the old cabin at Stinking Spring. It was bitterly cold as the sun rose. Garrett ordered the men to leave their horses and move forward, taking care to remain concealed by the brush. All was quiet.

When it was light, Garrett saw only three horses standing at the doorless entrance, their long saddle ropes leading into the house. Unless two of the riders had left the party, Garrett reasoned, two of the animals had been taken inside. A figure emerged from the house with feed bags.

"That's the Kid," Garrett whispered.

A rifle report broke the white silence. The man before the cabin staggered a few steps toward the posse and pitched forward. It was Charlie Bowdre who lay dead in the snow.

Two of the horses, frightened by the firing, broke and ran. The third horse was hit by a rifle shot and fell, blocking the doorway. Garrett believed it would be impossible for any of the fugitives to dash through to safety, and he shouted a demand for immediate surrender.

After a long silence, Dave Rudabaugh came through the door, unarmed, hands high. He stood in the open and said it had been decided that the position of the men in the house was hopeless, and all would surrender if a pledge were given to conduct them to Santa Fe and not to confine them at Las Vegas. The promise was made, and Rudabaugh returned to the house. Almost at once, the four youths came out and walked to the waiting posse.

The Kid stopped beside Bowdre and gazed down at the crumpled body of his friend and comrade. Then he faced Garrett. The boy's face was cold, his eyes dark and smoky.

"I saw that shot, Pat," he said evenly. "I was about to follow Charlie out to help with the horses. I have known many brave men in this territory, but I have seldom seen the brand of 'bravery' I just now witnessed—the shooting down of an unarmed man with no surrender demand or word of warning."[2]

Billy joined his companions, now surrounded by the posse. The horses were brought from the cabin, and the extra mounts of the posse came up. Bowdre's body was lashed across a saddle, and the cavalcade began a slow return to Fort Sumner.

The villagers were in sullen mood as news of O'Folliard's death and the manner of its accomplishment became known. When the returning posse entered the plaza and it was learned that Bowdre was a second victim, an ominous silence settled on the crowd which had gathered. Anger against the posse grew as sympathy spread for the grief-stricken young Spanish-American widows of the victims. Perhaps only the number of the armed posse members prevented bloodshed.

Garrett confined his prisoners in an old army barracks building which was surrounded by a low adobe wall. He posted guards at vantage points and made arrangements for the removal of his charges to Santa Fe.

A double funeral for O'Folliard and Bowdre was held

---

[2] See Appendix II, Note B, Chap. XXVIII.

on the following day. The crude coffins of rough lumber, draped with blankets, were borne in procession on a buckboard. Behind this conveyance was an ancient, one-horse carryall in which rode the village priest and the two grieving girls, neither of whom was yet twenty years old. Horsemen, wagons, and walking mourners straggled along at the rear. The village was deserted as most of its small population went along to the abandoned military cemetery, just north of the village proper.[3] O'Folliard and Bowdre were buried side by side.

Billy the Kid watched from the window of the improvised prison as the funeral party passed slowly across the plaza. He betrayed no emotion, but, as though unconsciously, murmured, "*Adois mi compadres. Hasta la vista.*"

During the passing of the mourners, Garrett and his men had stationed themselves along the wall outside the building which housed the prisoners. Garrett feared a demonstration, or an attempt to free the prisoners. When he felt this danger had passed, he went into the building. The Kid remained at the barred window. He was handcuffed and shackled with leg irons. He turned from the window to give Garrett a long look.

"Well, Pat," he said, "you provided the people of Fort Sumner with a fiesta they will long remember."

Garrett made no reply.

"When your spy reported we were holed up at the Wilcox ranch," Billy said conversationally, "why didn't you come after us, instead of plotting an ambush, Apache-style? If Tom had not been so anxious to see his wife that he rode ahead, you might have shot us *all* down without warning. You might have anyway, if someone hadn't got excited and fired too soon!

"Jim East told me how Tom died," Billy continued,

---

[3] See Appendix II, Note C, Chap. XXVIII.

"and I hear Bowdre was killed because you thought he was me. Neither of those boys had a chance to surrender. Remember, Pat, the governor offered no reward for those boys—only for *my* capture—or death. When you get that money, on each dollar will be the blood of Tom and Charlie. It will be blood money, Pat!"

Garrett was silent, studying the Kid. He was trying to understand this new Billy, so different from the carefree boy he had known.

"The cards haven't all been dealt," Billy said. "I may follow Tom and Charlie, and that will give you three of a kind."

The boy's voice was an expressionless monotone. He spoke slowly, pausing frequently, and the effect was menacing.

"I know these people, Pat. They are kind and gentle, but they hate treachery. They haven't always been well-treated by Anglos, but they accepted Tom and Charlie when they married the girls. They will call down curses on you. They will pray that you meet the same fate you dealt to those they loved. I'm not a religious man. I know little of these things. And I'm not superstitious, either, but I would hate to be in your boots. I'd rather face a blazing six-gun than—"

Billy broke off the sentence. He seemed to come to himself, losing his absent manner. He looked intently into Garrett's eyes; then he turned and hobbled away. The chains shackling his legs clanked along the stone floor.

Garrett commandeered a wagon and a team of mules from the local feed yard to transport his prisoners. Before the party left Fort Sumner, the Kid asked to see James East. "Jim," he said, "bring me paper and something to write with." Awkwardly, moving both of his hands together, Billy began to write. When he had finished, he handed the paper to East.

"This is a bill of sale for my horse, Jim. Looks like I won't be riding him for a spell. He's a fine horse. Take good care of him. And, Jim—thanks for what you did for Tom."

"Well, Billy," East said, "I'll take care of the horse on one condition, which same being, when you shake off your hobbles, we just light a match to this here bill of sale, and the horse is again yours."

"Thanks, Jim, we'll play it that way, but look out for old Pat. He holds he has authority to confiscate property belonging to outlaws, which he says I am one. He took a span of mules I left at the Yorba ranch, and I had bought and paid for them! Well, that bill of sale will tie a knot in his rope if he tries to claim the horse."[4]

The Kid and Rudabaugh were brought from the building handcuffed together. Behind them, Wilson and Pickett also were handcuffed together, and all four were wearing heavy leg irons. The weather was bitter, and the wagon offered only low sideboards and scant straw bedding for comfort. The journey from Fort Sumner to Las Vegas, the nearest rail point, was long and tiresome, over an old freight road with deep ruts. As the wagon jerked and lurched, the prisoners were tossed about, and their wrists were chafed and lacerated by the handcuffs.

Stewart, Mason, East, and Garrett escorted the party, and they, too, suffered in the cold. They frequently dismounted and led their horses for relief.

The afternoon of December 25, the group arrived at Puerto de Luna and stopped at the ranch home of George Douglas, a local peace officer.

The weary prisoners were allowed to warm themselves,

[4] See Appendix II, Note D, Chap. XXVIII.

and, after a hot meal, they were confined in a storeroom under a single guard, who was relieved at four-hour intervals.

The Kid's irrepressible good humor had returned. He greeted his guards with a cheery "Merry Christmas," and was ready with suggestions that the guard on duty should take a nap, give Billy a gun to ride herd on the outlaws, and other nonsense.

For Billy, yesterday belonged to the past; today, he lived as he found it; and tomorrow would bring what it would! He had seen men die, some of them before his own guns. He respected bravery in enemy or friend, and he admired, without fully understanding it, moral courage—the only arms of McSween and Tunstall in dealing with the forces which had opposed them.

On the contrary, he despised cowardice and treachery. He was fiercely loyal and followed through. Morton and Baker paid with their lives for the death of Tunstall, and Bob Beckwith fell before Billy's gun within minutes after McSween died.

Self-assured and nerveless, Billy was as unhurried and deliberate under fire as in target practice. He was courageous, but seldom foolhardy. He was a fair strategist and an expert at calculating odds with speed and assurance. Assurance—perhaps that was the key to the character of the boy. Once he had decided upon a course of action, he proceeded, confidently. If events proved him wrong, as they sometimes did, he never looked back, secure in the knowledge that he had done what seemed best at the time and under the circumstances. He wasted no part of his physical or mental resources on vain regrets.

So it was that Billy was laughing as the escort continued on to Las Vegas with the prisoners. The party arrived in Las Vegas the afternoon after Christmas Day. Word of their arrival had preceded them, and a mob had gathered, demanding that Dave Rudabaugh be surrendered to it. The lynching of Rudabaugh for the murder of a peace officer appeared inevitable, but hasty action by a group of sober-minded citizens forestalled violence, and the prisoners were safely confined in the local jail. Guards were posted, and a night of tense waiting followed.

Sheriff Garrett intended to make good his pledge to convey the prisoners to Santa Fe in safety, and, after a sleepless night, he demanded his prisoners on the morning of December 27. Billy the Kid, Wilson, and Pickett were delivered to him, but the surrender of Rudabaugh to Garrett was opposed by the local authorities on the premise that he had been convicted of murder and was under sentence of death. Garrett argued he was holding all the prisoners by virtue of federal warrants. These warrants, he insisted, superseded the jurisdiction of the local authorities. After a time, Rudabaugh, too, was released to Garrett's custody.

The prisoners were placed in a closely guarded carryall and hurried to the station and into a waiting coach, only to be confronted by a new mob, demanding Rudabaugh. Garrett hastily stationed guards at the doors of the coach with orders to shoot to kill, if need be. The mob had detached the engine from the train, and the engineer had been forced to move it some distance up the track. The shouting crowd grew in size and courage. Rifles and revolvers were flourished defiantly.

Garrett went to the platform and addressed the mob calmly, "Men, as deputy United States marshal, it is my duty to deliver my prisoners to Santa Fe. This I mean to do. If you rush this car, I will release and arm the prisoners so they may defend themselves. We will fire from the windows. If there is trouble, it will be of *your* making."

Garrett backed into the coach and locked the door.

"That's telling them, Pat," Billy called. "Just loose these bracelcts and give me a gun. If they see you and me on that platform, they'll scatter like a covey of quail. We can lick a crowd twice that size with no help. When the party's over, you can chain me up again—that's a promise, Pat."

Billy looked out the window eagerly, but the mob was breaking up, and, as he watched, the rail yard cleared. There had been no recognized leader, and the gathering had proved ineffectual in the face of a firm stand by Garrett. The engine was attached to the train, and the crisis was over.

Chapter XXIX

BILLY, although confined in the ancient Santa Fe jail, was cheerful. He believed the governor would take action in his behalf. To his unlettered mind, the wording of His Excellency's letter: "I have authority to exempt you from prosecution if you will testify to what you say you know," meant that he was to receive executive clemency.[1] Had he not appeared, at great personal risk, as a witness against the murderers of Chapman and against Colonel Dudley?

Billy was not physically comfortable. He was chained to the wall of the dungeonlike prison and furnished with a jug of water and a cot.

On January 1, 1881, Billy sent a brief but courteous note to His Excellency, requesting an interview:

SANTA FE
Jan. 1st
1881

Gov. Lew Wallace
DEAR SIR
I would like to See You for a few moments if You can Spare time
Yours Respect.
W. H. BONNEY[2]

The Kid, however, received no answer.

January and February passed. No word came from the governor, nor was any action taken to bring Billy to trial pursuant to the indictment and warrant charging him

[1] See Appendix II, Note A, Chap. XXIX.
[2] See Plate XXV in the Appendix.

with the murder of Sheriff Brady. In desperation, under date of March 2, 1881, he wrote once more to Governor Wallace, a curt, demanding note, which, like its predecessor, was unanswered:

SANTA FE NEW MEXICO
March 2nd/81

Gov. Lew Wallace
DEAR SIR

for the *last time* I ask, Will you keep your promise. I start below tomorrow Send answer by bearer

Yours Respt
W BONNEY[3]

Again on March 4, Billy addressed another letter to the governor. In it he combined appeal and defiance:

SANTA FE IN JAIL
March 4th 1881

Gov. Lew Wallace
DEAR SIR

I wrote you a little note the day before yesterday, but have received no answer. I Expect you have forgotten what you promised me, this Month two years ago, but I have not, and I think You had ought to have come and Seen me as I requested you to. I have done Everything that I promised you I would, and you have done nothing that You promised me.

I think when you think the matter over, you will come down and See me, and I can then Explain Everything to you.

Judge Leonard Passed through here on his way East, in january and promised to come and see me on his way back, but he did not fulfill his Promise. [I]t looks to me like I am getting left in the Cold. I am not treated right by Sherman. [H]e lets Every Stranger that comes to See me through Curiosity in to See me, but will not let a single one of my friends in, not even an Attorney.

I guess they mean to Send me up without giving me any show, but they will have a nice time doing it. I am not entirely without friends.

---

[3] See Plate XXV in the Appendix.

I Shall Expect to See you Sometime today.

Patiently Waiting

I am Very Truly Yours Respect—

WM. H. BONNEY[4]

His faith in what he believed to have been a pledge had diminished to the vanishing point. He had received no replies to his notes. Why? He could discover no answer. At one point, he reasoned that the governor did not desire to have his earlier negotiations with Billy the Kid revealed. Billy began to feel he was fighting for his liberty—his life. He wrote again, bringing pressure of the only kind he had at his command: "Come to the jail. I have some papers you would not want displayed."

To the governor, this smelled of blackmail, as indeed it was. He reacted instantly and resourcefully. His Excellency gave to the press copies of the letters arranging a meeting between himself and Billy to plan the *pro forma* arrest. He added a statement, fully explaining the circumstances. When the letters and the story were published, Wallace sent clippings to the Kid.

Late in March, the Kid's jailer greeted him one day with a cheerful grin. The guard had not relished the custody of the youth, and he was happy to be free of the responsibility.

"Well, Kid, pack your war bag. I'm told you're due to take a *long ride*."

The inference was not lost on Billy, but he was undismayed. In fact, he was delighted at the prospect of action.

"Lincoln is a pretty good town, and I have friends there," Billy said. "And besides, no place could be worse than this rathole you ride herd on."

"Could be," the jailer answered, "but I hear you're

[4] See Plates XXVI and XXVII in the Appendix.

going to Mesilla, and the jail there was made to pen up drunk Indians and Mexicans. However, you being special, maybe they'll graze you in the Drover's House."

Mesilla! This information caused the Kid deep concern. He knew there was a great deal of feeling against him in Doña Ana County. Why was he being taken there? What could he do to prevent it?

Billy frequently said, "If there is one chance in a million, I'll take it." He saw one, now, and seized it. He addressed a final note to the governor, in a last appeal for His Excellency to come to see him in the jail.

There was no reply. The "chance in a million" had not paid off.

During his confinement in Santa Fe, the Kid's enemies had not been idle. They had been working to insure his conviction for the murder of Brady. The death of that officer had occurred nearly two years before, and the public had lost interest in it. The Lincoln County conflict had produced so many tragedies that plunder, arson, and murder were commonplace.

Now the life of Billy was demanded, due to his having taken part in the warfare.

The boy had aroused the bitter hatred of Dolan, Mathews, and many others because of his part in the war, and more especially because of his evidence given before the grand jury and the Military Board of Inquiry. The alleged crime, the murder of Brady, had been committed in Lincoln County, but it was evident to those who wanted to see him convicted that a conviction-minded jury would be difficult to impanel there. Without knowledge or consent of the accused, a change of venue was obtained, and Doña Ana County, seat of the heaviest opposition to Billy and the cause for which he had fought, was selected for the trial.

Billy made the long journey from Santa Fe to Mesilla by rail, wagon, and horseback. In Mesilla, Billy was placed in jail under heavy guard. He was arraigned before Judge Warren Bristol to plead, and he stated that his plea was "not guilty."

"Are you represented by counsel?" the Court inquired.

"No, sir. I have no money to pay a lawyer, but I believe Judge Leonard will help me when he returns to the territory."

His Honor appeared to be considering, and the district attorney interposed an objection.

"We would respectfully point out to the Court that this defendant has had ample time to provide himself with counsel of his own choosing. He was taken into custody by the sheriff of Lincoln County nearly four months ago. The date of Ira Leonard's return is problematical. Therefore, we desire to resist such an indefinite postponement."

Judge Bristol announced his decision. "The Court is constrained to agree with the position of the district attorney. This defendant has long been aware he was to face trial and has neglected to provide himself with counsel and now states he is without resources to do so; therefore, it becomes the duty of this court to appoint competent counsel to defend him.

"It is the order of the Court that Albert J. Fountain and J. B. Bail, two very eminent members of the territorial bar, be, and they hereby are, appointed to represent this defendant in the matter before the court."[5]

The court recessed until the following day.

J. B. (Billy) Mathews and G. W. (Dad) Peppin were the only available witnesses legally competent to testify for the prosecution. They, of course, had personal knowl-

---

[5] *The Fort Worth Star* (Fort Worth, Texas). See Appendix II, Note B, Chap. XXIX.

edge of what had occurred on the April day, two years before.

Skilfully led by the district attorney, each witness told his story; Mathews first, beginning with the letter from Judge Bristol (the same Judge Bristol who was presiding at the trial) stating that, because of the unstable situation in Lincoln, he felt it would be advisable to postpone the spring term of court until a later date.

Then Mathews told of the walk from the Murphy building to open and close court in the old adobe building which served as school and courtroom.

"Were you then a peace officer?" the district attorney asked.

"No, sir, I was then clerk of the court, and it was necessary for me to be present. As we neared the old Torreon, we heard a single shot. Hindman fell in the road and died soon after. Then there was a volley of rifle fire from behind the wall. Brady was struck by several bullets and fell dead."

"Please continue, Mr. Mathews," the district attorney directed.

"Deputy Sheriff Peppin and I were not hit, and we ran around the corner of an adobe building near by."

"Did either of you return the fire?"

"Not then. While we were hiding, I saw the Kid—the defendant—jump the wall and run to Brady's body. He stooped and picked up the rifle. I fired at him once from the corner of the building where I was hiding. The bullet struck the sheriff's rifle and glanced, wounding the defendant."

"You fired only once? Why did you not fire again?"

"The defendant had located my position. He ran back to the protection of the wall and kept firing at the corner where I was. I couldn't expose myself to shoot again."

"I will now ask an important question," the district attorney said gravely, "and please consider carefully before answering. Did you observe or recognize any other member of the party during the attack, besides this defendant?"

"No, sir, I did not. There must have been quite a crowd. The post surgeon from Fort Stanton certified that Sheriff Brady had received nine wounds, and Deputy Hindman one. The only one of them I saw and recognized was William Bonney."

The district attorney gave his permission for cross-examination of Mathews by defense counsel.

Fountain and Bail conferred briefly, then cross-examined Mathews perfunctorily, until one final question.

"I will now ask you this question," Fountain said. "Please take time and consider carefully before you answer. Did you *personally* see the defendant fire any of the shots that claimed the lives of Sheriff Brady and his deputy?"

"Well, all of those men were hidden behind the wall, and—"

"One minute, please. I require a direct answer to the question. State whether or not you actually observed the defendant, William H. Bonney, fire any of the shots that took the lives of one or both of the peace officers."

"No, sir. At the time of the shooting I did not know the Kid was in the party, and I did not see him fire at the officers."

"That will be all."

Peppin could add little to the evidence given by Mathews. He corroborated, in substance, what Mathews had said. Under cross-examination, Peppin, too, admitted he had not seen the defendant fire at either of the victims, nor had he noticed Billy before he leaped the wall to reclaim his rifle from Brady and exchanged shots with Mathews.

When Peppin had finished giving evidence, the district attorney selected several documents from his table.

"With the permission of the court," he said, "we desire to present certain affidavits in support of the case of the People against the defendant."

"What does the Territory propose to establish by such affidavits?"

"We propose to establish that this defendant is a person of ill-repute—a known cattle thief, outlaw, and renegade murderer."

"The Court will withhold its ruling," Judge Bristol said, "until made aware of the contents of the purported affidavits. The bailiff will remove the jury pending such ruling. You may proceed, sir."

"These affidavits are based upon the findings of a grand jury sitting in Lincoln County. They allege there are reasonable grounds to indict the defendant for the murders of Frank Baker, William S. Morton, James Carlyle, and Deputy Sheriff Robert Beckwith; and, also, as an accessory before and after the fact of the murder of a person known as 'Buckshot' Roberts, and for other high crimes and misdemeanors."

"Have indictments been returned charging the defendant with those alleged crimes?"

"No, your Honor. The report of the grand jury alleges probable cause, without recommendation."

Judge Bristol was probably aware that, if the introduction of these affidavits were permitted, the verdict of "guilty" that he anticipated might be set aside on appeal. He made a quick decision.

"The ruling of the court is that these affidavits present nothing germane and are not relevant to the case at issue. Had indictments actually been returned, possibly the matter could assume a different character. The purported affidavits having been ruled immaterial, the bailiff will return the jury to the courtroom."

"In that case, Your Honor," the district attorney said, "the prosecution rests its case."

The defense attorneys conferred hurriedly. They had no witness for their client. The whereabouts of those surviving could not be determined, and, if one could have been located, his appearance in court would almost certainly have led to his indictment. The appearance of the Kid as a witness in his own behalf would accomplish nothing. He could only deny that he had killed Brady, and, for this, his plea of "not guilty" would suffice.

"If the learned counsel can introduce no witnesses in defense of the accused," Judge Bristol said, "it is the opinion of the court that the defendant is clearly and legally entitled to make a statement to the jury, if he so elects."

Billy had been following the proceedings carefully. Nothing had happened to alter the hostility he had sensed in the judge and jury at the outset. He felt that nothing he could say would make any difference, but he determined that the real truth of that unfortunate incident should become a matter of public record. He stood and addressed the jury in a quiet voice.

"Lincoln was overrun with outlaws during this time. Our men were hiding out at Dick Brewer's ranch, trying to side-step more trouble. Then we heard Mr. McSween had come back to town and would likely be needing protection. We didn't want him killed, like Mr. Tunstall. Deputy Sheriff Barrier of Mora County was with Mr. McSween and would, we thought, protect him —but he was only one man.

"Dick Brewer reminded us about the ladies being with Mr. McSween, and that worried us more. A lot of the

Spanish women in the village had stampeded long before to safer places. Dick sent twelve of us to Lincoln to ride herd on those in the McSween house. He ordered us to fight shy of trouble, unless it came our way. We rode in and turned our horses into pasture and started toward McSween's house.

"Just as we got to the wall, we saw four men, Brady, Hindman, Peppin, and Mathews, all with rifles and side arms. It looked like someone saw us and reported to the sheriff. We all ducked and took cover behind the wall. When they were just opposite us, someone fired a shot, and Hindman fell. I don't know who fired. There was a lot of shooting, and Brady was killed. Mathews and Peppin ran behind a building.

"When I thought the shooting was over, I jumped the wall to get the rifle Brady dropped. It was mine. Mr. Tunstall gave it to me. Mathews fired at me from the corner of the building. The bullet struck the rifle and glanced, hitting me in the side. I shot and kept shooting at that corner and retreated, the best I could.

"I sent some of the boys to tell Brewer what happened. The rest of us went to McSween's house. When we got in, I found out the officers weren't after us. I don't know who started the shooting, or why, but I do know it wasn't a planned ambush. I didn't shoot at anyone but Billy Mathews.

"Mr. McSween was very angry with us. He was never armed and didn't believe in killing for any reason. And I'm sure the killings did his cause a lot of harm.

"I know all this talk won't help me, but some day you may know I spoke only the truth."

"Very interesting," the district attorney said ironically. "Will you just state again, how many were in your party when Brady was killed?"

"Twelve," the Kid replied.

"You were in command of the group?"

"No, sir. After Mr. Tunstall was killed, we took orders from Dick Brewer. He was Mr. Tunstall's foreman."

"Then it was Brewer who sent you into town to create trouble for the authorities?"

"I explained," Billy said, "he was worried about the folks in the McSween house, especially the women. He said if anything happened to them, there would be war for sure."

"Just one or two more questions, if you please," the district attorney said politely. "You state there were twelve men in this 'peace mission?' "

"Yes, sir."

"Just state, for the record," the district attorney said, quite casually, "the names of the others."

Billy flashed the attorney a quick look. Naming the others would place them in the same jeopardy in which he stood. He was certain he would be found guilty, and he thought that should end the matter.

"Sheriff Brady," Billy said slowly, "met his death a little more than three years ago, and my memory isn't good. I can remember only four—Tom O'Folliard and Charlie Bowdre, both killed by Pat Garrett or his posse; Harvey Morris, he was killed in the attack on the McSween house; and me."

If the district attorney had hoped the Kid would incriminate others, he knew better now. The trial was concluded, and the judge charged the jury. The instructions asked by defense counsel were vague and weak, offering the jury no alternatives other than to acquit or convict the defendant of first-degree murder. No reference was made to a possible verdict of manslaughter or second-degree murder.[6]

Following the charge, the judge addressed the jurors:

---

[6] See Appendix II, Note C, Chap. XXIX.

"Gentlemen, you are the sole judges of the guilt or innocence of the accused. You have heard the evidence produced by the prosecution and the statement made by the defendant. You also have heard read the instructions of the court, submitted by counsel for the Territory and those on behalf of the defendant. These you will take with you into the jury room to guide you in your deliberation. Weigh carefully the evidence, for and against the accused, and return your verdict accordingly. You may now retire and report to the court. The bailiff will now assume charge and permit no outside communication with the jury during its deliberation."

It seemed that no one in the courtroom entertained any doubt that the verdict would be "guilty." There was suspense as the crowd waited impatiently. The jury was returned by the bailiff after a short interval. Judge Bristol resumed his seat.

"Has the jury arrived at a verdict in the case of the People of the Territory of New Mexico against William H. Bonney?" he asked.

The foreman rose. "We have, Your Honor. We, the jury, find the defendant, William H. Bonney, guilty of murder in the first degree."

Judge Bristol picked up a paper from the table before him. He had obviously prepared at least one sentence in advance. Perhaps he had ready another for use if the verdict had been "not guilty"—that will never be known.

"The defendant will rise and face the bench," the judge ordered.

Billy stood up promptly. He exhibited no emotion as the judge began to read:

"After due and careful consideration, the jury of your peers has found you guilty of murder in the first degree. In its considered judgment it has made no recommendation for leniency. Therefore you are hereby remanded to the custody of the sheriff of Lincoln County who, in pursuance of the sentence of this court, will take you, William H. Bonney, alias William Antrim, alias Billy the Kid, to some convenient place in said Lincoln County, and on Friday, the 13th of May, 1881, between the hours of ten o'clock in the forenoon and three o'clock in the afternoon, there hang you by the neck until you are dead, and may God have mercy on your soul. The bailiff will now remove the prisoner."

There was some dissatisfaction with the conduct of the trial and with the verdict, although, for the most part, the verdict was popular with the Las Cruces element. Outside, a New Mexico cattleman and Confederate veteran stepped forward to state his views to a group of the Kid's enemies who were congratulating each other on the outcome of the trial.

"Well, men," he said, "I don't hold with unnecessary bloodshed. I seen too much of that during the war. And I don't admire an ambush, generally speaking. One day my platoon went out to scout along the Cumberland River. We run into a bunch of blue-bellied Yanks hiding in a grove of trees, and they damn-near wiped out the platoon. That was mighty bad, but it was war."

The old-timer paused to spit expertly. He had the full attention of the men as he continued.

"Now take this here Kid and his pals. There weren't no ambush figured on. They were surprised and hid behind that wall, thinking them officers were out to get 'em. Some lad got nervous, or maybe just trigger-happy, and let go and downed the deputy. Then there was some firing, and nine—that's nine—bullets put out the sheriff's lamp.

"Sure, I admit it don't sound good, but it was more a mistake than a ambush. They was twelve of 'em, and this here Kid has to bear the brunt for the whole bunch."

Several newcomers had gathered about the cattleman, and the crowd was murmuring resentfully, but the cattleman continued, unperturbed.

"Now, how about them lawyers that was appointed to defend the boy? They didn't argufy very hard, and they give *hanging* instructions. They knew damn well he wouldn't be acquitted, and they never mentioned no in-between possibilities, like second-degree murder or manslaughter. The boy wasn't given a chance for his life. Looks to me like the whole thing happened because of that feud—"

At this juncture, a tall, bronzed man interrupted.

"Seems to me, Reb, you're doing a lot of talking and making mighty free with your opinions. You claiming the jury didn't call the shots square?"

"Could be the *jury* was not to blame for following them instructions," the old man said. "It seems to me them fancy lawyers didn't *defend* their man too well. As to your remark, I'm thinking and speaking my opinions as I read 'em. If you think I'm talking out of line, just pick it up or leave it lay!" His hand hung ready by his holster.

The crowd, anticipating possible gunplay, moved aside.

The tall man smiled. "Just shorten your loop a little, Reb, for, you see, I *agree* with the views you've been making so free with. If you'll accept an invitation from a blue-bellied Yank, I'll consider it a privilege to buy you a drink!"

Grinning delightedly at each other, the two men shouldered their way through the crowd to the Drover's Hotel where they toasted the Stars and Stripes, the Stars and Bars, the gray and the blue, forgetful of the doomed boy in the jail.

Chapter XXX

SHERIFF Newcomb of Doña Ana County was a fine peace officer, soft-spoken and unassuming. He had the respect of good citizens and outlaws alike. He had served as an army scout in Arizona during the Apache campaigns and had moved to Las Cruces after retiring from the army.

During Billy's confinement and trial, Newcomb had left him to the custody of the officers who had brought him from Santa Fe. The day following the Kid's conviction, Sheriff Newcomb went to Billy in the jail.

"Well, Billy, it looks like you will be started for Lincoln tomorrow. Is there anything I can do for you before you go?"

The Kid flashed the sheriff his habitual smile. "Thanks, Sheriff. There's one thing—I'm out of money, but I could sure use a bag of tobacco and cigarette papers on the ride north."

"Of course, son, I'll be glad to do you this small service."

There was a short, troubled silence, and then the sheriff said, "Billy, is there anything connected with this affair that you would like to tell me?"

The Kid studied the sheriff for some moments and then he said slowly, "Well, there don't seem to be any point in talking any more. Nothing I say will make any difference. I told the whole truth in court. But, if they could have waited until Ira Leonard got back, things would have turned out better."

The sheriff's kindly look encouraged Billy to continue. "I kept thinking Governor Wallace was going to help me. I guess I misunderstood what he meant. Could be he's tied down by that Amnesty Proclamation because I was already under indictment when he made it."

Newcomb nodded. "I know, son. That proclamation was intended to bring peace to Lincoln County and the territory. It helped some, I guess, but it made an out for some outlaws and murderers who should have been hung. Well," the sheriff rose to leave, but paused at the the door. "Billy, do you expect trouble on the ride to Lincoln?"

"No, I don't—but that will depend on the guards."

"There will be three," the sheriff said, "Bob Ollinger, Billy Mathews, and a hard character known hereabouts as Slim Travis. If there is a bad actor in this section, Slim is it. He and Ollinger seem to be good friends."

"Sheriff," Billy said, frowning, "with that outfit riding herd on me, I'll never reach Lincoln alive. Ollinger will kill me first chance he gets. He's a coward and a killer, and I've heard he says he means to add my scalp to them already in his belt. It looks like the deck is stacked against me."

"I know that *hombre,*" the sheriff agreed, "and I can't understand why Garrett would appoint him a deputy. I have an idea we may be able to hobble any notions Ollinger may be cooking up."

Late in the evening, the sheriff came to Billy with a package. "Here you are — makings — tobacco, cigarette papers, and matches. There should be plenty to hold you for a while."

Without waiting for the Kid's thanks, the sheriff continued, "I'm late because I rode out to my ranch. I got to thinking, being an officer of this court, it is my duty to see you're returned to Lincoln safely, so I deputized two of my boys to ride along. I've known these boys since the Apache uprising. They don't talk much, but when it comes to action—well, either one of them makes a striking sidewinder look slow."

"Thank you, Sheriff." Billy smiled. "That was plenty thoughtful. That gets rid of one of the jokers in the deck, because I was sure Ollinger would find a way to kill me. But that leaves another joker—if Ollinger doesn't get me, I'll die like a sheep-killing cur at the end of a rope! And yet"—the Kid hesitated, then continued slowly—"I have a feeling the rope hasn't been braided yet that will go around my neck. There's thirty days, and I'll take a chance in a million, if I see it!"

"I won't see you in the morning," the sheriff said, "but I can promise you'll be safe to Lincoln. Trust my boys to see you through. Good luck and *adios*."

Early the following morning a buckboard pulled up before the jail door. In the front seat was the owner and driver. In the rear seats, Ollinger, Mathews, and Travis sat. Ollinger stepped down and swaggered into the jail while the others waited.

Presently Ollinger emerged with the prisoner. The Kid was handcuffed and shackled with heavy leg irons.

"Get in the seat beside Slim," Ollinger ordered, and he gave the shackled boy a vicious push. The Kid stumbled against the buckboard. Awkwardly and with difficulty, he managed to climb in while the guards watched.

When he was seated, Billy spoke to Ollinger. "You're a louse and a coward, Bob. You're mighty brave, though, with a hog-tied man. Someday you'll get a belly full of lead."

"Shut up," Ollinger growled, "or that lead may find another target before we get to Lincoln!"

Ollinger seated himself beside Mathews, facing Billy and Slim Travis. All three guards rested rifles across their knees.

"All set, Dad," Ollinger said to the driver. "Pour on the whip. Let's go!"

Two horsemen appeared from the gray dawn shadows and took position on either side of the buckboard. Their faces were dark and expressionless. Blankets were strapped to the cantles of their saddles. They were equipped with booted rifles, six-guns, and ammunition belts. Ollinger stared at them in surprise and moved his rifle a little, threateningly.

"Who the hell are you, and what are you doing?" Ollinger demanded.

"One question at a time, *hombre*, and I'll ask the first one. Are you entertaining ideas of firing that rifle?" the nearest rider asked.

Ollinger removed his hands from the weapon.

"That's better—never reach for a gun unless you mean to use it." This piece of advice from the horseman was a gratuitous insult since it was the first rule of handling arms and known to every ten-year-old boy in the West. "Now, I'll answer your question."

The bronzed man drew aside his vest and displayed a deputy's badge. "Me and my partner have been deputized by the sheriff to escort this prisoner to Lincoln and see he's delivered into the custody of Sheriff Garrett."

Ollinger laughed, "Oh, well, that's mighty thoughtful of the sheriff, but we don't need no help. We'll make out fine."

"No doubt—but our orders are to see the prisoner is delivered *alive*," the other replied with unmistakable finality.

Ollinger seemed to understand. He said nothing, and the party got under way.

The light conveyance moved rapidly across the country and the horsemen maintained positions close on either side of the vehicle. Near sunset, the party made camp at the Warner ranch. They ate and prepared to spend the night.

Ollinger had occupied himself all day with persecuting the Kid, and he continued through the evening. Sitting up in his bedroll before the night fire, Ollinger said, "I guess a hanging ain't so bad, if nothing goes wrong. But sometimes the drop don't work proper, or the noose don't slip right, and the neck don't get broke. In them circumstances, Kid, you'll just hang there kicking, with your wind cut off, for a while before you die."

Ollinger turned to Travis. "Slim," he asked with relish, "did you ever see a horseback hanging? It sure is interesting. One day some of us run onto a greaser driving a few cows. He claims he owns 'em, but he don't sound convincing. Throwing a rope over a limb and pulling a man up ain't easy, if he's heavy like this here Mexican, so we put him in the saddle of his bronc and put the noose around his neck. We throw the rope over a big limb, and a couple of fellows hold the other end. Then someone gives the bronc a lick with a quirt. He jumps away sudden, leaving that cow thief hanging mighty pretty." Ollinger paused. "We learned later this greaser did own them cows, so the laugh was on us, for sure," he concluded.

There was a thick silence around the campfire. Billy, using both his manacled hands, tossed a cigarette into the fire, then he said, "I guess you had plenty of time to think out the chances for bad breaks on a hanging, eh, Bob?"

"Meaning what, runt?" Ollinger asked.

"Seems like I recall," Billy said, "Murphy sent you out to arrest a homesteader who located on some land Murphy claimed to own. You brought him in, all right —dead. Your story was he tried to escape, but he was shot in the back, so close a hole was burned in his shirt as big as the palm of your hand. It was so raw you were indicted for murder, but the Murphy crowd got you off. Maybe while you waited for your trial you thought about—"

Ollinger was standing, his gun in his hand. "Shut up, damn you! I'll blow you apart!" he shouted.

From the half light beyond the campfire a cold voice interrupted, "You'll do nothing. You're covered."

Ollinger froze for a second or two; then, slowly, returned his gun to the holster.

"You win this pot, *hombre,*" he said to the deputy, "but when we reach Lincoln, I'll kill you."

"When we reach Lincoln and this job is finished," came the cool reply, "I'll be at your service. In the meantime, my partner and I will be taking turns standing night guard."

In Lincoln, Sheriff Garrett had been giving some thought to the safekeeping of the prisoner. When the trial began, he rode to Fort Stanton and requested of the commandant that Billy should be confined in the guardhouse at the post after he had been convicted and returned to Lincoln.

"I sympathize with your problem," Colonel Purrington replied courteously, "and personally I would be happy to comply with your request. However, following the unfortunate incidents in Lincoln in '78, I have received definite orders from the War Department to avoid committing this post in the civil affairs of this section. I regret that I am unable to comply with your request, but I am sure you appreciate my position."

Garrett returned to Lincoln, convinced that there was but one course open to him. He would confine the Kid on the upper floor of the courthouse.[1] There was a single

---

[1] See Appendix II, Note A, Chap. XXX.

exit from the upper story. It was down a flight of stairs and led to an enclosed yard, and it seemed to Garrett that a room on the upper floor of the courthouse offered reasonable security for the prisoner he confidently expected.

Chapter XXXI

WORD of the Kid's conviction was received at Fort Stanton over the military telegraph that connected several army posts with headquarters at Santa Fe. From there, it was quickly relayed to Lincoln.

In Lincoln, the information was received with diverse emotions by the two elements of the population. The pro-Murphy faction was, naturally, pleased with the outcome. The Spanish-American people and the few surviving Tunstall-McSween sympathizers were saddened by the news. Many women wept, recalling ways in which the boy had befriended them. Prayers were offered for Billy in the little churches, and Spanish imprecations were called down upon the heads of those responsible for the death sentence.

The prisoner knew nothing of this. He was taken directly to the courthouse and up the stairs to the small room Garrett had prepared. The room was furnished with a cot, a small table, and a chair. An oil lamp had been placed in a bracket on the wall, so that the prisoner could be observed throughout the night. At the door were two chairs to be occupied by the guards. For the day guard, Garrett designated Bob Ollinger and J. W. Bell.

J. W. Bell was a deputy of Garrett's, an experienced peace officer. Bell was kind and humane. He soon fell into the habit of whiling away the long hours by playing cards with the Kid. The players used matches and pinto beans in lieu of poker chips. Bell was watchful, and, of course, the small table was always between them. The two laughed hilariously at the Kid's awkward gestures with his closely manacled hands. Bell brought Billy copies of the few newspapers that found their way into the village. Bell liked Billy and performed little acts of kindness for him when he could, but he was a peace officer, sworn to perform a duty, and he did not forget it, nor did he allow the prisoner to forget it!

Ollinger had a different attitude. He made a ceremony of marking off each day on the whitewashed wall with some statement that the prisoner had one less day of life. He had a new-model shotgun, of which he was very proud and which he liked to handle carelessly, or threateningly. One day he said, "Old Reliable, here, is sure-fire—and each barrel is loaded with thirteen buckshot. Plenty unhealthy for anyone entertaining notions, don't you think?"

The Kid only grinned. Billy knew his disregard for the inference angered his would-be tormentor.

"Thirteen is sure unlucky, Bob," he drawled. "Be careful it don't catch up with *you.* Toting around a gun with each barrel loaded with thirteen buckshot makes your chances twice as bad. That's your unlucky number, for sure."

This sally infuriated Ollinger. He glared at the boy, his face flushed with anger. "Well, runt, May 13 sure won't be your lucky number!" and Ollinger left the room.

When he had gone, Bell said, "He sure likes to call you 'runt.' I guess it's because he is so big. I wish you wouldn't ride him that way, though. He might get mad enough to kill you. Men like Bob don't weigh the consequences."

As the weary days of confinement passed, Billy watched for his "chance in a million." His mind was busy with questions. Where was Pat Garrett? Were the night guards always alert? Where did the other guard go when he was left, temporarily, in the care of only one? How far was it to the ground from his upper window?

During the wakeful nights, Billy practiced removing his handcuffs. His wrists were large and muscular, his hands slender, and he had long known he could remove either hand from its cuff at will. He meant to be ready for his chance, and he believed that it would come.

The morning following the Kid's attempt to provoke his curiously superstitious nature, Ollinger came early into the room. He was without the shotgun and was armed only with a revolver thrust into a holster. In his hand he carried a short length of rope.

"Howdy, Bob," Billy greeted him, "where is Old Reliable? Taking no chances with thirteen buckshot? Going to hang yourself instead?"

Ollinger ignored the boy and spoke to Bell. "Can you make a hangman's noose, Bell? There's no trick to it if you know how."

Ollinger glanced at Billy, hoping for some evidence of fear, or at least concern. The boy was smiling a crooked smile.

The burly guard's big hands deftly fashioned a hangman's knot. "You see," he explained, "this noose is made with one end of the rope coiled several times around the long end that is fastened to the gallows. You put this knot just under the ear; then, when the trap is sprung, the neck gets broke like a pipestem. Get the idea, runt?"

Bell moved restlessly, but he said nothing. Nor did Billy reply to the question. Ollinger smiled broadly.

"I heard about a hanging back in '75," Ollinger continued. "A feller was strung up for killing his wife. Sheriff Baca didn't know how to build a noose like this one, so he just made a slipknot. When the trap was sprung, the rope just cuts off the *hombre's* wind. When they think he is dead, they cut him down and shove him in a box.

Well, the laugh was on Sheriff Baca. Someone seen the victim trying to get out of the box, so they have to get a new rope and string him up again. This time they leave him hanging until he was plenty defunct!" Ollinger laughed loudly. "If Sheriff Garrett makes that mistake May 13," he said to Billy, "that will be something I'll admire to see."

Billy had not moved, and the crooked smile was still on his lips, but his eyes had darkened, and the upper part of his boyish face had taken on its dangerous look. However, it was Bell who stood up and spoke quietly to Ollinger.

"Damn you for the cur you are," Bell said. "Any more of this kind of talk and I'll beat you to a pulp with my bare hands."

"Easy does it, John," the Kid interposed. "Let the mangy wolf howl. His palaver don't get in my hair." Billy smiled warmly at Bell. "Everybody knows he's a cowardly louse. It's the poison in him makes him talk like that. Someday, he'll bite himself and catch the rabies, and be shot for the mad dog he is!"

Chapter XXXII

THE morning of April 28 was bright and warm. The sun shone on new green foliage, and breakfast smokes from the village scented the air.

Upstairs in the courthouse, the night guards waited sleepily for relief. From the caretaker's cabin behind the courthouse, hearty odors of coffee and bacon floated out the windows.

Nothing in the atmosphere suggested that the day would bring tragedy, retribution, and escape.

The caretaker, who whistled as he prepared breakfast for himself and the prisoner, was one G. Gauss, universally known as "Old Man" Gauss. He was a small man who always spoke in a low voice. He liked Billy and, in common with many others, believed the boy to be the victim of enemies.

Gauss carried food upstairs and placed it on the small table in Billy's room.

"Rise and shine," he greeted Billy. "Time to put on the feed bag." Gauss leaned near and said in a low voice, "Billy, they must be hell popping over at White Oaks. Feller rode in this morning all lathered up. He told Pat some miners over there are shooting each other up over claims. One's dead. Pat saddled up and took a lead horse. He said"—Gauss dropped his voice to a whisper—"he may be gone for two or three days!"

The caretaker stopped speaking. He assumed a look of deep concern. "Oh, hell, Billy!" Gauss exclaimed. "Pat said if I told you about him leaving Lincoln, he'd scalp me and hang my hair at his gun belt!"

Billy smiled. "Well, thanks, Dad. I think I rope the idea, but I'm not feeling so good this morning and haven't heard a word you said."

The boy gulped part of the hot, black coffee and then set the jar back on the tray.

"Just take this food back and mention to the guards I won't eat this morning. Don't bring me any dinner and—well—thanks."

The caretaker picked up the rejected food and withdrew.

Garrett was well aware of the Kid's resourcefulness, and he knew Billy had many friends loyal and daring enough to attempt his rescue, if they had proper leadership. He had stayed as close to the courthouse as his work permitted, and he had been watchful. He had cautioned the guards repeatedly to be particularly alert. He was reluctant to go to White Oaks, and he planned, and hoped, to return quickly.

Relaxed upon his cot, Billy was thinking. The absence of Pat Garrett, he believed, increased his "chance in a million" manyfold. He formulated and rejected many plans before Bell and Ollinger came at eight o'clock to relieve the night guard.

Ollinger went straight to the wall to mark another black cross on his "calendar." Bell crossed to the cot and spoke to Billy, "Lost your appetite, Billy? Gauss told me you passed up your fodder this morning."

The Kid looked up. He was pale, and his face twisted as if with pain.

"Can I do anything?" Bell asked.

"Thanks, nothing," Billy said. "Maybe, if I sleep some, I'll be better."

He turned his face to the wall. Bell took up his post by the door.

The forenoon passed slowly and uneventfully. At midday, Ollinger arose and stretched. It was his duty to conduct some minor offenders, confined in another part of the courthouse, across the road to the hotel for dinner. He combined this duty with his hour of relief from guarding. Billy knew the routine, and he had waited patiently to make use of this knowledge. Up to now, the presence of Garrett had effectively deterred any plan he had formulated—but today?

When Billy was sure Ollinger had time to be well away from the building, he asked Bell to take him downstairs to the outdoor latrine. This was not an unusual request, and Bell readily agreed. Gauss was busy in his small garden and did not look up as the two men returned to the building.

Billy led by a few steps, and he made his way upstairs as rapidly as his heavy leg irons would permit. At the top of the stairs, instead of turning left toward his prison room, Billy turned right and flattened himself against the wall. Freeing his hands from the handcuffs, he waited.

Just as Bell reached the upper floor, the Kid's hand grasped the deputy's gun and snatched it from the low-slung holster. Surprised, Bell stared at Billy.

"Don't worry, John," Billy said, "I won't hurt you. You've been good to me, but I'm fighting for my life. Just back into that room and I will tie and gag you. Someone will help you as soon as I am gone."

Bell did not move or speak. A second or two passed, then suddenly, wildly, Bell turned and ran down the stairs. The Kid fired, purposely missing. At the same time, he called, "Stop, for God's sake! I don't want to kill you."

What impulse prompted Bell's rash act cannot be known. Perhaps he thought Billy would not fire, or could not hit him. Perhaps he deliberately risked his life to perform his duty. Whatever his reasons, he did the most courageous thing.

The shouted warning was not heeded, and when Bell was at the bottom of the long flight of stairs, one step from escape, Billy fired once more. The second shot struck Bell in the left shoulder, over the heart, but he ran on, out of Billy's sight into the yard, where he fell at the feet of Gauss. J. W. Bell was dead.

Billy thrust the revolver in his waistband and hobbled down the hall to a room known as the armory. He was moving fast and thinking fast. He had no time to worry or to wonder about Bell. He knew the shots had been heard—by Ollinger, by others—perhaps by everyone in the village. Billy pushed open the door and saw "Old Reliable" resting against the wall. He caught up Ollinger's shotgun and hobbled and hopped rapidly to an open window facing the hotel diagonally across the street.

In the dining room of the hotel, a startled Ollinger pushed back his chair from a half-finished meal, exclaiming, "By God, Bell has killed the Kid!" At the door he paused and turned to his two charges. "You *hombres* stay here. If you leave, I'll hunt you down and blow you apart!"

Ollinger ran across the road, and at the corner of the building he was greeted from above by the quiet voice of the Kid saying, "Hello, Bob."

Ollinger glanced up involuntarily, then froze. He was looking into the barrel of his own shotgun, and, behind it, he saw the smiling face of Billy.

"I told you thirteen was your unlucky number, and here's proof," the boy said.

He pressed the trigger, and Ollinger fell. He died instantly with a full charge of buckshot in his chest. Billy fired the second barrel into the fallen form. He looked down at Ollinger a moment, then dropped the weapon out the window beside the body.

Two more lives had been taken. The Lincoln County War was not yet finished.

Behind the building, Gauss rose from where he had been kneeling beside Bell. He heard the blasts of the shotgun, but he could not guess who had fired. He left Bell and circled the building. Billy spoke from the window, "Hold it, Dad. You're in no danger if you do as I tell you. First, where is Bell? Is he hurt bad?"

"He's dead," Gauss replied.

The youth became very grave. "I'm sorry. I only meant to wing him. He would have done the same to me to stop my getaway. I wish it hadn't turned out this way."

There was a short silence.

"Get a file," the Kid said. "Throw it up on the porch in front. Go to the corral and get a saddle horse. Leave it ground-hitched just below. Don't get any ideas, Dad."

Billy returned to the armory. He chose a rifle, a belt of cartridges, and a holster. He found a length of heavy cord and picked it up. With these, he hobbled out onto the balcony. Across the road, a number of men had assembled. They stood motionless, looking up at the porch.

The Kid seated himself on the porch floor, with the rifle across his knees, and applied the file to the chain holding his leg irons. The file was dull. Patiently, with frequent glances at the crowd across the road, Billy worked at the chain. He recognized a few in the crowd who would like a shot at him, but something held them in check. There was no sound except the harsh, rasping noise of the file on steel and a distant bird song.

Finally the link parted, and the boy stood up. With the cord, he fastened the loose end of the chain to his belt. He made a series of peculiar motions which some of the onlookers later described as a kind of war or victory dance. Actually he was moving his feet and legs freely for the first time in weeks, flexing and stretching his cramped muscles. He examined the faces of the watchers; then, with the strap of the rifle over his shoulder, he slid down an upright supporting the balcony to the ground beneath and mounted the horse that stood there.

One Spanish American said softly, "*Viva el Cabrito.*" There was an almost inaudible murmur of agreement among the crowd.

The Kid's face lighted with a smile. Raising his hand in a half salute, he said, "*Gracias, amigos. Hasta la vista. Adios.*"

Touching the strange horse with a light heel, Billy rode at a trot toward the west.[1]

Although communications were notoriously bad in Lincoln County, word of the Kid's escape was quickly broadcast. Among the Spanish-American population, most of the homesteaders, and many of the cattlemen, there were quiet expressions of satisfaction. The whole story was known to these people, and some of them were personally acquainted with citizens who were guiltier than Billy, but who went about freely. Perhaps the boy was on the conscience of Lincoln County residents. Or, perhaps, they only liked him.

In any case, there were others who viewed the Kid's escape with deep concern. John S. Chisum and District Attorney Rynerson, for example, feared personal reprisals. When Chisum learned that Billy was at large, he found an urgent necessity for his immediate presence in Kansas City.

Rynerson's fear was not for himself, but for his herds, and he doubled his force of *vaqueros* and posted night riders, as he awaited action by Sheriff Garrett.

---

[1] See Appendix II, Note A, Chap. XXXII. See also Plate XXVIII in the Appendix.

Chapter XXXIII

OUT of sight of Lincoln, Billy began to follow a plan he had had plenty of time to perfect. He continued along the wagon road for a short distance, then left it to follow the river under cover of the brush.

A few miles west of Lincoln, he cut across country to the homestead of Amando Salas, a friend in whom he had confidence. Night had fallen when he reached the little adobe house. Candlelight shone through the open door into the warm night, and Billy could see the family at their evening meal. Salas heard the unknown horseman, and he quickly extinguished the candle. He stepped outside, rifle on his arm. The Kid rode nearer and received a challenge in broken English.

He drew rein and replied, "*Buenas noches, amigo.* Do you greet a friend with a rifle?"

"Mother of God," Amando exclaimed in wonderment, "Billy! Dismount and enter. My house is yours."

The candle was lighted, and Salas stared at Billy, his surprise undiminished. "How is it you are not in prison, to die in a few days? Tell us of your deliverance. Take food with us."

Billy ate and related the circumstances of his escape.

When he had finished, Salas said gravely, "None will weep for Señor Ollinger, for he was a man of evil heart, but Señor Bell—one would wish he had not been killed, and that you, my friend, had not killed him!"

"He was a brave man," Billy said, "taking his chance in a million, as I was doing. I didn't want to kill him. If he had only stopped—if he had let me tie him up—

if I had had time to take better aim—but the thing is done."

"May God rest his soul," Amando said.

He and his wife crossed themselves in the flickering shadows. Billy was lost in thought.

"Amando," he said, at length, "please help me remove these irons so that I may go. There is need for haste. I would not bring trouble to your house."

Salas brought his few crude tools. He and Billy worked at the irons until the clasps parted, and they fell upon the floor. Billy stood up to leave, and Salas' wife placed in the boy's hand a small parcel of food.

She smiled at him and said in Spanish, "I will thank Our Blessed Lady that you have been saved, and I will pray that she will continue to protect you."

The boy's eyes softened. He smiled at Rosa Salas. "I thank you, little sister, for your kind words and thoughts, and you, Amando, for your help. Now, I must go."

Billy took up his rifle, mounted his horse, and waved farewell to his friends silhouetted in the light from the open door.

From Lincoln, a courier was dispatched to White Oaks to tell Garrett of the escape of the prisoner. Garrett was terribly worried. He felt his reputation as a peace officer had been tarnished. He made hasty preparations to return to Lincoln. Questions spun through his mind. How had the escape been timed so well? Had Billy known he was absent from Lincoln? If so, who had told him? And what of the reward he counted on?

The witnesses Garrett questioned in Lincoln told of the help furnished the fugitive by Gauss. Garrett interviewed the caretaker at length and finished by accusing Gauss of betrayal.

The caretaker was unperturbed. "You want to know

who tipped the Kid you were out of town?" Gauss asked. "Well, you won't no way like the answer, but it was you, Pat."

The sheriff looked incredulous and angry.

Gauss explained. "He only had to look in the horse corral to see that both your horses were gone. If it had only been your regular saddle mount, he might have thought you hadn't gone far, but with both horses gone, it would be easy for a saddlewise *hombre* to figure you took a lead horse and a long ride. He used his head and made his plans. He didn't eat no breakfast—claimed he was sick. I figure he watched and listened all morning. He didn't see nor hear of you. When Ollinger took them *hombres* out to feed, Billy acted sudden. You know the rest."

Garrett was thoughtful. He had been careful, true, but he had underestimated the resourcefulness of the Kid.

He rested a searching gaze upon Gauss. He was still suspicious of the old man, but he could see no evidence of guilt in the caretaker's face.

"It may be as you say, Gauss," he admitted, "but it could be you'll find yourself in a lot of trouble for your part in this affair."

"Meaning what?"

"Just this—helping a prisoner escape, especially one convicted of murder, is a serious matter. You got the Kid tools to free himself and a horse for his getaway."

Gauss laughed.

"You can't throw that legal loop over my horns, Sheriff," he said. "I was working in my garden when I heard some pistol shots. Bell staggers out and falls, and I know the Kid is loose. I stampeded around the building, but there were two shots, and Ollinger had cashed in when I get there. Billy is in the window with a six-gun on me.

What can I do but follow his orders? I ain't making no excuses, Pat."

"It seems to me you might have made a break for it when you were out of sight, or—"

"Bell tried a break, Sheriff," Gauss interrupted.

"Well, all right, Dad," Garrett said. "But what I can't see is why one of those damned cowards looking on didn't cut the Kid down. Out in front he must have made a big target."

"Sheriff, among them *hombres* watching was some of the best fighting men in Lincoln County, but it would have been unhealthy for anyone who got trigger-happy. Most of them," Gauss finished with quiet emphasis, "was glad to see the boy get away!"

This was a truth which had been made known to Garrett. Without a word, he left Gauss and went into his office to make plans to recapture or kill the fugitive.

Garrett's eye fell on the lumber in the courthouse yard —the lumber he had ordered delivered for the gallows. He sent for the village carpenter and ordered coffins for Bell and Ollinger to be made from the material on hand.

After the double funeral, Garrett was frequently absent from the village for a day or two at a time. He sent messages to the scattered villages in the county, urging local constables and marshals to report information about the Kid's movements. This action by Garrett produced no results.

Although no legitimate reports came to him, Garrett heard the many rumors which were flying about: that the Kid had gone to Texas; that he had fled to Arizona; that he had crossed the Rio Grande into Mexico.

The natives were especially unco-operative. No information, or, what was worse, misleading information, was given to Garrett and to his men.

One morning Garrett stopped a young *vaquero* riding north from Alamogordo and asked if he had seen the Kid. "*Si,* I spent the evening with him in the cantina last night. He was very drunk. He talked big about how he killed two men—"

"All right, all right, on your way," Garrett interrupted. "I ought to bend a pistol barrel over your head and leave you here for the buzzards!" Everyone knew the Kid neither drank nor talked big.

The youth grinned at Garrett, touched his hat, and galloped away.

Garrett, hoping for the speedy apprehension of the Kid, had delayed making a return of the death warrant he had in his possession. Finally, on May 24, nearly a month after the Kid had escaped and eleven days after the date of the scheduled execution, Garrett endorsed the warrant: "I hereby certify that the within warrant was not served owing to the fact that the within named prisoner escaped before the time set for serving said warrant. Pat F. Garrett, Sheriff, Lincoln County, New Mexico."

Early in June, Garrett enlisted the services of John W. Poe and Thomas L. McKinney to assist him in the search for Bonney. Poe had been serving as representative of the Cattleman's Protective Association, and McKinney had some experience as a man hunter.

Sometimes together, sometimes separately, these three covered the territory, following all trails, questioning, investigating.

Late one afternoon, Garrett, Poe, and McKinney approached the foothills ranch of Pedro Machado. Pedro was mending a fence near the house, and he greeted the visitors with courtesy. He was terrified, for the Kid was in his house. He denied all knowledge of the fugitive, but he called from the fence, "Mama, our visitors are the sheriff and two friends. Please make coffee, *tortillas,* and bacon so that they may eat and break their journey."

Billy was able to slip out the back door and reach his horse in the cover of irregular ground and scrub trees. Inside the house, the officers were greeted with studied silence by Señora Machado. She placed food before them, moving her clear, dark eyes from one face to another.

When they had finished the meal, she said to Garrett, "Pedro is master of this house, else you would not have eaten, but he does not control my thoughts, or words. You seek the death of Billy as you did that of Tomaso and Carlos (O'Folliard and Bowdre). You say he is evil and must die. Why? Because he has fought his enemies? He has a kind heart. I know it. Because of him, my baby lives."

The woman paused, and her expression softened. "One winter's night, she was very sick, the little one. It seemed she must die. Billy sought shelter here, and when he saw the baby, he rode far—very far—in snow and darkness to bring medicine. They say an innocent child can sense evil—well, she lives, and she loves Billy, and he loves her. Please go now!"

Garrett got to his feet and left the house, stooping to pass through the door. McKinney followed the sheriff outside. Poe remained behind.

Speaking in fluent Spanish, for Señora Machado knew no other language, he said, "I understand. It is the maternal that speaks, and I respect it. I have never seen the Kid, but I have often heard of his loyalty to your people, and of your people to him. Please know that we are but performing our duty as peace officers of the territory." Poe smiled. "Keep your faith, *Señora.* The Kid restored to you the life more precious than your own. Do not think of the misdeeds attributed to him. Whatever happens, think only of your debt to him."

Tears appeared in Señora Machado's eyes. "You have an understanding heart," she said. "When I pray to Our Lady that Billy may escape capture or death, I will pray for your protection, too."

Poe rejoined his companions, and the three men moved on, unaware that the fugutive had escaped apprehension by minutes.

It was now nearing the end of June, and the Kid had been at large since April. Garrett was at a loss to know what new course to pursue. He had followed so many misleading clues down so many roads leading nowhere that he had begun to believe the Kid had left the territory. He thought the matter over for a day or two and reached the conclusion that he must discover, somehow, whether the Kid was really in the vicinity or had fled his jurisdiction. That night in camp, he talked over his plan with his associates.

"Poe, you're not well known in this section since you've mostly operated in the north. Go to Fort Sumner and represent yourself as a government cattle inspector, and, of course, you are one. Visit all the small ranches as if you are looking for blackleg or hoof and mouth disease in the herds. Spend some time around the cantinas. Someone may take on too much bad liquor and be inclined to talk. Listen plenty, but ask no questions."

"McKinney," the sheriff told the other deputy, "you scout down the Pecos and around Roswell. I'll go back to Lincoln and catch up my business. I'll meet you July 12 at Rudolph's ranch. It's about seven miles north of Fort Sumner. We'll separate and ride in the morning."

Rudolph's ranch, widely known as *El Rancho* ("The Ranch"), was a portion of the old Maxwell land grant. Vast herds of cattle ranged the lowland sections of the spread. In the hills, flocks of sheep in the care of Basque herders thrived on the sparser vegetation. The owner of this large enterprise was MacDonald Rudolph.

Rudolph was a blunt, honest man of Scotch-Irish ancestry. Rustling on his range was unknown. His *vaqueros* had orders to shoot to kill any unauthorized possessor of cattle bearing the M-R brand. There was one exception to this order. If the transgressor were taken by surprise and surrendered, he was to be conducted to the most convenient cottonwood and hanged. Shooting, in a case of this kind, Rudolph argued, smelled of murder. Hanging, on the other hand, followed the unwritten law of the range. "A distinction without a difference," to the culprit, certainly. Rudolph's edict had been so well circulated that the gentry of the wide loop never knowingly invaded his range.

It was Rudolph's headquarters that Garrett had designated a rendezvous for himself and the deputies. On July 12, in the evening, Rudolph listened soberly to the sheriff's request for any information, or rumor, which might lead him to the Kid.

"I regret I can't help you, Sheriff," Rudolph replied. "This is a curious affair, and I have questioned the *vaqueros* from time to time. They all say they know nothing about the Kid. Some of them may be lying. I suppose they don't want to inform—or are afraid. From what I know, I would guess informing on a man with so many friends would not be healthy. Most of the natives seem to have a great loyalty for the Kid."

"Then you don't believe he is in this vicinity?" Garrett asked.

"Well," Rudolph said, "at times, I believe he is somewhere around—then, again, I entertain doubts. Is it logical he would cross into Mexico? Or would he remain hereabouts where his friends could inform him of danger?

If he is with his friends, I think you could only take him by accident, for he will know what you are doing."

Rudolph sat for some moments, lost in thought. "I can only suggest one thing. The Maxwell family has been sympathetic to the Kid. They believe in him and trust him. Pete Maxwell is popular with the native population. Perhaps Mr. Poe and Mr. McKinney don't know that Pete's father was the original owner of the Maxwell land grant, and his mother was Spanish. He could probably tell you something about Billy, but I don't know whether he *would!*"

"It's worth a try," Garrett said.

"As for you, Pat," Rudolph said bluntly, "you must know Maxwell doesn't like you. He vigorously opposed your election as sheriff. I've heard he used to employ you as a *vaquero* and fired you for what he says was a good reason. For myself, I know nothing about it, and never believe rumors and unproved accusations."

"Well, thank you, Mr. Rudolph," Garrett drawled. His face was in shadow, but it seemed to his listeners there was irony or amusement, or both, in his voice.

"Pete has freely condemned you for the way in which O'Folliard met is death, and most of the people in the village agree with him. I mention this, Sheriff, so you will know the worth of any information he might give you. I believe, if you approach him as an *official* and not as an *individual*, you may learn something. I'm sorry not to be helpful, and I'm leaving for one of my line camps in the morning. I won't be back for several days. But you're welcome to stay here, and I wish you success."

Garrett was disturbed by Rudolph's frank appraisal of the situation. He resented what Rudolph had implied Maxwell thought of him. Was Rudolph quoting Maxwell? Or was he expressing his own views? Garrett had been frustrated at every turn for weeks, and his mood was irritable and suspicious.

"Pat," John Poe said next morning, "while I've been riding around hunting nonexistent bovine diseases and hanging out in cantinas, I've been trying to reconstruct the mental processes of this Kid. I don't know him, but he seems to be a smart boy."[1]

"Seems to be," Garrett said drily.

"Well," Poe continued, "maybe he figured if he went to other parts he might easily be recognized and betrayed. On the other hand, in this section, his friends might well be counted on to help, protect, and inform him of danger. I really believe he's very near Fort Sumner."

"I've come to the same conclusion," Pat drawled. "But how do we catch him—that's a question!"

"I agree with Rudolph that we're not likely to take him by surprise. It'll just have to be an accident, or a break —and it may take some patience."

"You're probably right," Garrett conceded. "But in spite of what Rudolph said, I mean to make one more try to get some information. We'll question Maxwell. If I think he knows where the Kid is and won't tell, or gives wrong information, I'll see to it he's prosecuted for harboring a criminal!"

"That sounds all right, Pat," Tom McKinney said. "How do we work it?"

"We'll go into Fort Sumner separately after dark tomorrow night and meet at the Pioneer Corral north of town at eleven. From there, we'll go afoot."

---

[1] See Appendix II, Note A, Chap. XXXIII.

Chapter XXXIV

THE mid-July day was hot, and evening brought little relief. From the north, by diverse routes, three horsemen approached Fort Sumner. From the south, a fourth rider followed an overgrown trail that led from the ranch of Francisco Labita to Fort Sumner. Billy was making one of his frequent nocturnal visits to the village. He rode leisurely to the home of Jesus Silva, across the dusty road from Maxwell's home.

Billy dismounted and secreted his horse in Silva's shed. He entered the house quietly. It was dark and silent. He removed his boots and outer shirt and stretched out on a rough bed he had used before. He was weary—weary of hiding, weary of inactivity, weary of thinking of his problems. He sighed deeply and stared into the darkness for a time.

After a long hour, Billy roused his sleeping host.

"Hello, Billy." Silva smiled. "I didn't hear you come. Are you hungry?"

"I am," Billy said with feeling.

"I will make coffee," Silva said, getting out of bed. "You take a butcher knife from the kitchen and go to Pete's meat house. Cut some beef, but you'd better stop and speak to Pete so he won't shoot you for a sneak thief."

Billy laughed as he went into the kitchen.

Over at the Maxwell house, the deputies, Poe and McKinney, waited in the darkness of the porch. Garrett moved quietly to Maxwell's room in a wing facing the road. From the deep shadows at the head of the bed, Garrett roused Pete Maxwell and questioned him.

Maxwell was angered at the unceremonious behavior of Garrett, for whom he had scant regard, anyway, and the rancher retorted hotly, "Sheriff, I am not a man hunter. I believe that is *your* business. Nor am I an informer. You have exceeded your authority by this unwarranted intrusion, and I resent it!"

Outside, the Kid approached the building, butcher knife in hand. He sensed and then, dimly, saw two men seated near the door. He hesitated. Billy was scantily dressed and bootless, the light was poor, he seemed very small and young, and neither of the deputies recognized him.

Rising, Poe said reassuringly, "Don't be frightened, *muchacho*. Put away that ugly knife. No one will harm you."

The Kid was observing that both men wore low-slung revolvers and spurs. He was immediately suspicious and stepped quickly through the open door into Pete Maxwell's room. Approaching the bed, he was silhouetted against the pale light from without. Garrett, in the deep shadow, was not visible to Billy.

"*Quien es? Quien es,* Pete?" the Kid whispered.

The silence in the room was shattered by a revolver shot—and a second. With a small, broken moan, Billy the Kid crumpled onto the floor, a bullet in his breast. He was dead.

Maxwell leaped from the bed and ran out, dragging a sheet with him. Garrett shouted to the deputies, "Don't shoot—that's Maxwell!"

Poe said, "I'm afraid you have shot an innocent man, Sheriff. I think he is one of Maxwell's herders."

"No mistake, John," Garrett replied. "I knew his voice, and I recognized him in the dim light from outside. Somebody bring a light!"

And so Pat Garrett redeemed in full his promise to capture or kill the Kid. He redeemed it in a manner that was to make the tall sheriff a controversial figure for the rest of his days.

Bootless, butcher knife in hand, standing between the relentless foe in the dark room and the armed guard outside, his unanswered question still on his lips, William Bonney died violently, the last victim of the Lincoln County War.

Jesus Silva, watching the coffee brewing in the blackened pot, heard the shots. He knew at once that his friend was dead, and he hurried across the road. Others had already appeared on the porch. Among them was Deluvina, an aging Navajo woman who was a servant to the Maxwell family. She knew Billy and loved him. Shaken by sobs, she faced Garrett and cursed him in English, Spanish, and Navajo, hurling at him every epithet her distraught mind could summon. No one present seemed inclined to quiet her, or to disagree.

"I suggest, sir," Maxwell said to Garrett, raising his voice over the commotion in the small room, "that you and your deputies leave here for the present. I cannot be responsible for what might happen." And Maxwell turned abruptly away.

Garrett and the deputies went to the Pioneer Corral where they had left their horses.

"McKinney," the sheriff ordered, "you saddle up and go to Rudolph's ranch. Find him and get him to come back here with you. Poe, you find Alejandro Seguro and bring him here. He may be able to restrain these greasers if they start any trouble."

Silva, Maxwell, and Deluvina examined the room where the Kid died. One bullet had taken his life, the other was imbedded in the wall. Contrary to reports at the time, Billy was not carrying a gun. Only the butcher knife was found, where it had fallen from the hand of the dying boy.

The body of the Kid was tenderly removed to the home of Silva. There, Deluvina kept a vigil beside the body which was placed on the bed where, only an hour before, Billy had rested.

At dawn, several kindly women of the village entered the room, extinguished the candle, and led Deluvina away to rest.

In the afternoon, Seguro, justice of the peace, ordered an inquest. Rudolph was named foreman of the jury, and the others appointed were Spanish Americans. The verdict was returned in Spanish, and its wording reveals it to have been dictated in the interests of the sheriff. Translated, it reads:

> We the jury unanimously say that Wm. Bonney came to his death from a wound in the breast in the region of the heart, fired from a pistol in the hand of Pat. F. Garrett, and our decision is that the action of the said Garrett was justifiable homicide; and we are united in the opinion that the gratitude of all the community is due said Garrett for his action, and that he deserves to be compensated.
>
> (Signed) M. RUDOLPH, *Foreman*
> ANTONIO SAAVEDRA—x his mark
> P. ORO ANTONIO LUCERO— x his mark
> JOSE SILVA
> SABEL GUTIERREZ—x his mark
> LORENZ JARAMILLO

A stranger legal document is rarely to be found. It is to be noted that three of the five jurors were illiterates who signed with their marks. To have recited in the verdict, "the gratitude of all the community is due said Garrett for his action," was pointless, legally, and certainly contrary in fact to the actual sentiments of the community.

The declaration that "he deserves to be compensated"

has no legal significance, and seems the more extraordinary as Garrett's earlier claim for reward for the capture of the Kid had been rejected on the premise that, in offering the reward, Governor Wallace had exceeded his authority.

As soon as the jury's verdict had been returned, Garrett prepared and forwarded to Governor Wallace his version of what occurred on the night of July 14 in Maxwell's dark room.

Although Garrett's report is at variance with the reports of other witnesses, it is here presented as it appears on the record:

Fort Sumner, N.M.,
July 15, 1881

To His Excellency, the Governor of New Mexico:

I have the honor to inform your Excellency that I have received several communications from persons in and about Fort Sumner, stating that William Bonney, alias the Kid, has been there, or in that vicinity for some time.

In view of these reports I deemed it my duty to go there and ascertain if there was any truth in them or not, all the time doubting their accuracy; but on Monday, July 11, I left home, taking with me John W. Poe and T. L. McKinney, men on whose courage and sagacity I relied implicitly, and arrived just below Fort Sumner on Wednesday, 13th. I remained concealed near the house until night, and then entered the fort about midnight and went to Mr. P. Maxwell's room. I found him in bed and had just commenced talking to him about the object of my visit at such an unusual hour when a man entered the room in stocking feet with a pistol in one hand and a knife in the other. He came over and placed his hand on the bed just beside me, and in a low whisper, "Who is it?" (and repeated the question), he asked of Mr. Maxwell. I at once recognized the man and knew he was the Kid and reached behind me for my pistol, feeling almost certain of receiving a bullet from his at the moment of doing so, as I felt sure he had now recognized me, but fortunately he drew back from the bed at noticing my movement, and, although he had his pistol pointed at my breast, he delayed to fire and asked in Spanish, "*Quien es? Quien es?*" This gave me time to bring mine to bear on him, and the moment I did so I pulled the trigger, and he received his death wound, for the ball struck him in the left breast and pierced his heart. He never spoke but died in a minute. It was my desire to have been able to take him alive, but his coming upon me so suddenly and unexpectedly leads me to believe that he had seen me enter the room, or had been informed by someone of the fact; and that he came there armed with pistol and knife expressly to kill me if he could. Under that impression, I had no alternative but to kill him, or to suffer death at his hands.

I herewith annex a copy of the verdict rendered by the jury called in by the Justice of the Peace (ex-officio coroner), the original of which is in the hands of the prosecuting attorney of the first judicial district.

I am, Governor, very respectfully your Excellency's obedient servant,

PAT F. GARRETT
Sheriff of Lincoln County

While Deluvina kept her silent vigil, Manuel Palomeras, the local carpenter, labored in his shop to build a casket for Billy—the finest he could make of the materials at hand. All day, from humble homesteads, friends of the Kid came into town. Many arrived on horseback, some afoot, others in rude conveyances.

Early in the afternoon, they gathered in the plaza where the casket rested upon wooden trestles draped by a colorful Indian blanket.

The youth was clad in a new white shirt, his light brown, curly hair was neatly groomed. He appeared very young in death.

When the casket was closed, Father Redin, the village priest, read the brief funeral service in Latin; then in Spanish spoke to the silent group.

"My children, I knew Billy well. Though he was not always blameless, there was nothing depraved or sordid in his character. Often he did not follow the teaching of Holy Writ. 'Vengeance is mine, saith the Lord.' Frequently he obeyed other impulses and permitted human vengeance to govern many of his acts, but he was always generous and helpful to those in distress or in need, as many of us so well know.

"When he was drawn into the vortex of an unholy feud that threatened to ravish this peaceful land, and despoil you of your homes and possessions, he deserted the ranks of the oppressors to espouse your cause, believing it to be just, in which he risked his life times without number.

"Following the tragic death of his loyal friend and protector, who came among us from a far-off land, he gave his allegiance to another honorable man who soon met his death, also the victim of assassins.

"Those tragedies altered the entire course of his young life. He became outlawed, persecuted, and hunted, and eventually unjustly condemned to death.

"We cannot condone his many faults, but let us 'Judge not that we be not judged.'" The gentle padre bowed his head. "Receive the soul of Thy servant, O Lord, and grant it eternal peace. Amen."

The cortege moved slowly to the old brush-covered cemetery at the edge of the village. There, the Kid was interred beside his former friends and companions in arms. Only a wooden cross then marked his grave, but subsequently a granite monument was erected upon which was inscribed:

TO THE MEMORY
of
WILLIAM H. BONNEY
Alias
Billy the Kid

THOMAS O'FOLLIARD
and
CHARLES BOWDRE

How appropriately could there also have been carved

on that block of stone the lines of the Immortal Bard of Avon:

> The evil that men do lives after them;
> The good is oft interred with their bones.

So let it be with the Kid.

Epilogue

IT IS indeed difficult to visualize the present little village of Lincoln as once having been the center of a bitter factional feud.

Situated in a peaceful and pastoral valley on the Rio Bonita, the scars of conflict have long since been erased; class hatred no longer survives.

This was a struggle for commercial and political supremacy, a conflict from which neither faction emerged the victor.

There must, of necessity, be two elements present in every controversy. Possibly both may have justification as is so frequently true—who may judge?

One of the contending factions, by reason of its long and undisputed control of the area, came to believe it had a "vested right" to the cattle and merchandising industry of the section.

It regarded the other as an interloper or trespasser, while it sought only to establish itself in the same pursuits, as was clearly its right.

Thus were sown the seeds of strife that were to germinate into the feud, known as the Lincoln County War.

Arson, pillage, and death followed in its wake, out of which there eventually emerged peace.

During the strife the two leaders of one faction met death. The leader of the other died in Santa Fe of natural causes and was succeeded by a younger associate. He was a youth of unquestioned courage and superior attainments—an expert accountant and an executive of exceptional ability.

When peace came to the stricken area, he engaged in commercial pursuits as an honored and respected leader in the social and civic affairs of his community.

He had married the attractive daughter of a prominent pioneer family. To them were born two daughters who grew into gracious and lovely womanhood.

Though residing in a state other than that of their birth, they remained beloved by all who were privileged to have known them.

The old home remains in Lincoln, still known by the family name.

The two cousins survived the conflict. Both fled the scene and were declared outlawed.

One was taken prisoner and was confined in a loathsome jail in Santa Fe but was subsequently released by order of the court.

The other (author of *Frontier Fighter*) eventually returned to his homestead pursuant to the provisions of a governor's amnesty proclamation.

Here again they began anew where their lives had been so tragically interrupted.

Their children, whom it was the author's privilege to have met, still occupy the lands of their fathers along the Ruidoso, greatly esteemed, and prominent in the cultural and civic affairs of the county and the legislative halls of the great state of New Mexico.

Of the peace officers of the period much could be related, but here they can be mentioned only briefly.

One became a rancher, a member of the Texas Rangers, and finally the collector of customs at El Paso.

He met a tragic death near Las Cruces, the victim of assassins' bullets, a crime that has never been solved. He was survived by a son, a prominent executive residing in the great state of Texas.

His chief deputy succeeded him as sheriff of Lincoln

County and later became a prominent banker in the nearby city of Roswell.

Another early peace officer remained in Lincoln, pursuing the vocation of contractor and builder, and here his immediate family still resides.

A granddaughter, a lovely and accomplished young woman, became the private secretary of a former territorial governor who was then state historian, custodian, and curator of the Old Lincoln County Museum.

To this very personable young woman, the author is greatly indebted for many courtesies during the course of his research in the village of Lincoln.

It would appear presumptuous for one to present a story as wholly factual unless he had personal knowledge of the incidents related. He must therefore rely upon such sources of information as may be available and employ the legal phrase, "*the allegations herein are made on information and belief and are predicated on sources believed to be true.*" So may it be here.

Those sources of information are, in brief, from the former territorial governors who witnessed the history in its making, the Library of Congress, the National Archives, the report of the United States Commissioner sent from Washington to investigate conditions relating to the feud, copies of old newspapers of the period, depositions, old letters, and other sources relating to that tragic era.

True, many incidents have been reconstructed, but only to conform with the events related.

The actors in this grim drama have long since passed from the stage, and there can be no curtain call.

Let us honor the memory and have tolerance for those young frontier warriors of now more than three quarters of a century ago, regardless of the cause they espoused.

THE AUTHOR

Postscript

THE LAST YEARS AND TRAGIC DEATH OF PATRICK FLOYD GARRETT

Pat Garrett was not re-elected sheriff of Lincoln County, and was succeeded by his former deputy, John W. Poe.

Out of office, Garrett engaged briefly in the cattle business, his registered brand being P-A-T.

Although doing fairly well in his ranch undertaking, he accepted an invitation from the governor of Texas to organize a company of Rangers for the protection of stockmen along the Texas-New Mexico border. The acceptance of the commission involved the neglect of his cattle outfit, but, being unable to resist the advantages of the opportunity offered, he undertook the work.

In the fall of 1885 he resigned his commission of Captain of Rangers and attempted various undertakings, among which were an irrigating project and the raising of blooded horses, each destined to prove a failure.

Then the wheel of fortune turned. The post of collector of customs at the port of entry at El Paso became vacant. Oddly, his name was sent to the United States Senate by President Theodore Roosevelt for confirmation. Roosevelt had a penchant for the appointment of Western characters to political positions. He knew Garrett had killed the Kid and was proficient with a six-gun. Not at all disturbed by the flood of letters and telegrams protesting the appointment, the President, whose motto was, "Speak softly and carry a big stick," forced the confirmation in 1901. Garrett served four years, then returned to his hobby of stock raising on his small ranch a few miles west of Las Cruces.

Garrett no longer had the prestige of his former offices, nor was he sought after as a celebrity for having killed the Kid, and for him life grew drab.

He became taciturn, morose, and sullen. Upon one occasion, following an argument, he pistol whipped a small rancher with his six-gun, inflicting serious injury, an act that did him no good in the rangeland.

He visited saloons frequently and spent much time playing poker, usually leaving the game a loser. Other players feared him during his moods of sullenness and irritability, and would withdraw from the game.

He was constantly in financial difficulty. Only a few days before he met his death, in desperation he wrote his old friend, George Curry, then territorial governor of New Mexico:

> "Dear Curry:
> I am in a hell of a fix. I have been trying to sell my ranch but no luck. For God's sake, send me $50.00.
>
> Pat"

The small ranch referred to was to prove the contributing, or the actual cause of his death—murder, as it was believed by many.

Garrett had leased it to a former cowboy known as Wayne Brazil, who was engaged in running a large herd of goats on the range. To sell the ranch the herd had to be removed. This, Brazil declined to do, unless a purchaser could be found for his four-footed property.

A few days before his death, Garrett informed Brazil

that he was negotiating with J. P. Miller and Carl Adamson for the sale of the range, if satisfactory arrangements could be made between the parties, and that Miller believed he could effect a sale of the goats.

On February 29, 1908, Garrett, in company with Adamson, drove to the ranch to confer further with Brazil, believing that a solution to the problems blocking the sale had been found.

Returning to Las Cruces, Garrett and Adamson were riding in a buckboard while Brazil, on horseback, rode alongside.

"Midway to town," Brazil later testified, "Garrett suddenly stepped from the conveyance, shotgun in his hands, angrily demanding: 'Brazil, I want you to get those damned goats off my range, or I'll make you take them off.' Knowing his reputation as a gunman, I feared for my life and had no alternative other than to shoot. I recall firing the first shot, and that Adamson called to me not to fire again, but I was too agitated to stop shooting."

Leaving Garrett's body where it had fallen, Brazil and Adamson continued to Las Cruces where Brazil surrendered to the sheriff, claiming the old reliable plea of the West—self-defense.

He was later indicted by the grand jury on the charge of murder. As a legal instrument the indictment was a classic, and may be worthy of note:

> That he, the said Wayne Brazil, on the twenty-ninth day of February, 1908, in Doña Ana County, Territory of New Mexico, with force and arms in and upon one Patrick F. Garrett, there and then, with a certain pistol, loaded with gunpowder and various leaden bullets, did kill and murder the said Patrick F. Garrett.

There being no witness for the prosecution, and with Adamson for the defense, on April 19, 1909, the jury returned a verdict of "not guilty."

Out on the ranch of W. W. Cox, in the Organ Mountains, there was a great barbecue, ostensibly to celebrate Brazil's acquittal. Cowboys and ranchers from the rangeland for miles around attended in great numbers. Soon it developed into ribald rejoicing over the death of Pat Garrett.

Governor George Curry, upon being informed of Garrett's death, immediately left Santa Fe, accompanied by James M. Henry, Attorney General, and Fred Fornoff, Captain of Territorial Police, to make a personal investigation. The governor and Garrett had long been friends, from the early days in Lincoln. Strangely, the check the governor had so generously sent Garrett was discovered in his pocket, yet uncashed.

Governor Curry and his aides sought an interview with Dr. W. C. Field, the autopsy surgeon, who related his findings as he had formally presented them to the grand jury:

"Upon being informed of the tragedy, in company with Sheriff Felipe Lucero, I at once left for the scene of the killing. We found Garrett's body as it had fallen, undisturbed, in a six-inch sand drift beside the road. Garrett's shotgun was about four feet off to one side. There was a glove on his right hand, which naturally covered his trigger finger, but none on the left. There was a pathway in the center of the back of the head, made by a .45-caliber bullet, which had driven Garrett's long hair into the brain and had torn away the right eyebrow, unmistakable evidence, in my opinion, that he had been shot from behind.

"I later extracted another bullet that had penetrated the body from the upper part of the stomach to the upper part of the shoulders. I made careful measurements of distances and closely investigated conditions at the scene of the crime, and declare unequivocably that, in my opinion, the shooting of Pat Garrett was murder in cold blood—murder in the first degree."

Following the acquittal, Wayne Brazil, J. P. (Jim) Miller, and Carl Adamson, who were related by marriage, became more and more suspect. It became known that Miller had no purchaser for either the ranch or the goats. Many questions arose in the minds of the reputable citizens of Las Cruces: What reason had Garrett to seek a quarrel with Brazil, when, as he thought, he was about to effect an adjustment of their controversy? Why had the buckboard been stopped on that lonely reach of road in the hills, where, within the radius of many miles, there was no known habitation? Why had Adamson accompanied Garrett to the Brazil ranch? These and other questions persisted, and it became the consensus of opinion in the section that Miller had master-minded the murder at the behest of Garrett's many enemies, and had slain his victim from ambush on that isolated county road, an opinion that was never susceptible of definite proof.

Jim Miller had the reputation of being a professional killer for hire. He was a mild-mannered man who did not gamble, drink or use tobacco. He was never profane, but he was as deadly as a coiled reptile. About a year after the murder of Garrett, a just retribution brought an end to his nefarious career.

He was accused, with two others, of the murder of a cattleman, and the trio was lodged in jail. Late one night, a group of irate citizens overpowered the jailer and took his prisoners to a near-by barn, and there "hanged them by their necks until they were dead."

Jim Miller met his end with the same indifference and nonchalance with which he had so frequently dealt death to others. As the rope was being placed about his neck, he withdrew from his finger a diamond ring with the request it be sent to his wife, then calmly, manifesting no evidence of fear, he remarked to the silent, waiting vigilance committee, "Gentlemen, I am now at your service."

Thus was Jim Miller, one of the Southwest's bad men, ushered from life into eternity.

Pat Garrett came to his death in his fifty-eighth year. His spare six feet four inches was slightly stooped by age, and his unkempt hair streaked with gray. He had died wearing the proverbial "boots." Possibly it happened as he would have wished. Who may know?

He was buried in the old Las Cruces cemetery, his grave remaining unmarked, then as now, by tombstone or monument.

Patrick Floyd Garrett, the slayer of Billy the Kid, had reached "the end of the trail."

Glossary

Spanish	*English*
ACEQUIA	An irrigating ditch
ADIOS	Good-by
ADOBE	A sun-baked mud brick
AGUARDIENTE	A strong Mexican liquor
AMIGO	Friend
BAILE	Dance or ball
BUENOS NOCHES	Good night
BUENOS TARDES	Good afternoon
CABALLO	Horse
CABRITO	Kid
CANTINA	Saloon or bar
CARCEL	Jail or prison
CHOLO	Contempt term for Mexican national
COMPADRE	Comrade
GRACIAS	Thanks
GRINGO	Term of contempt for Anglos
HASTA LA VISTA	The translation of this expression from Spanish into English is dependent upon its usage. It may be, "Hasten the time when we shall meet again," or, "I'll be seeing you soon"

HOMBRE	Man
JASPÉ	Roasted limestone, then pulverized to make a white plaster
MADRE	Mother
MADRECITA	An endearing term for mother
MÍA (singular feminine)	My or mine
MÍO (singular masculine)	My or mine
MÍ CASA ES SUYA	My house is yours
MUCHACHO	Boy or youth
MUY PRONTO	Very quick or soon
PADRE	Father
POBRE	Poor (as, poor friend)
PRONTO	Quick
QUIEN ES?	Who is it?
REMUDA	Horse herd
RIO BONITA	Beautiful river
RIO GRANDE	Great or grand river
RIO HONDO	Deep river
RIO RUIDOSO	Noisy river
SI (pronounced see)	Yes
VAQUERO	Cowboy or range rider
VINO	Wine
VIVA	Long live! (a greeting)

Roster of Those Who Lost Their Lives* in The Lincoln County War and Its Aftermath

John H. Tunstall
Alexander A. McSween
William A. Bonney
alias BILLY THE KID
Francisco Zamora
Sheriff William Brady
Deputy Sheriff Hindman
Harvey Morris
Vicente Romero
Joe Grant
Charles Crawford
Robert Beckwith
Bud McCloskey
Ignacio Gonzales
Attorney George Chapman
Joseph Bernstein
Dick Brewer
"Buckshot" Roberts
Frank McNab
James Carlyle
Frank Freeman
Tom O'Folliard
Charlie Bowdre
Frank Baker
William Morton
J. W. Bell
Robert Ollinger

* Many others were critically wounded but recovered.

STATEMENTS MADE TO GOVERNOR LEW WALLACE BY THE CITIZENS OF LINCOLN

Relating the Chaotic Conditions Prevailing in Lincoln County

Border Troubles in Lincoln Co. N.M.
Statements of Isaac Ellis
to Governor Wallace

Lincoln County has for many years commercially as well as politically been under the entire control of L. G. Murphy, J. J. Dolan, and J. H. Riley, usually called the "House," while this house was held under the thumb of the "New Mexico Ring." The house had all the U.S. contracts for Fort Stanton and the so called beef contracts for Fort Stanton and the Apache Indian Reserve. To fill these meat contracts the House bought all the necessary cattle from a band of thieves at $4 to $8 a head while cattle is worth in New Mexico $15 to $20. Of course the House and Ring made of these jobs handsome profits, but our Ring the same as other combinations of that character, has quite a big stomach and it is no easy thing to satisfy them. Indian Agent Godfroy pretends that according to his official list he has 1100 Indians to feed while F. W. Angell, special agent of the Departments of State and Interior could only count 375; Godfroy pretended that at that time 5 or 600 Indians had left the reserve with and without permits; instantly Angell ordered out 100 U.S. Cavalry to bring in the 5-600 missing Indians, but unfortunately they could not find but 15 or 20. The U.S. officers commanding this patrol, if I be not mistaken, reported that they did not believe that there were more than 400 Indians on the reserve; however, the House got every week regularly its certificate for the delivery of meat for 1100 Indians. But that was not enough! If instead of 1100 Indians only 400 were in existence, there was of course quite a quantity of sugar, coffee, tobacco, etc. left over. But what could be done with this superabundance? The yearly Indian inspection must not show this and the goods had to be put out of the way. An easy remedy was found, as the House in its store had quite a call for such goods. They were simply loaned by the Agency to the House—wagon load after wagon load was brought to Lincoln, but never did the blinded inhabitants of Lincoln see a single load of those loaned goods going back.

Some two years ago J. H. Tunstall, a young Englishman, came to Lincoln and opened a store. But the House would not submit to opposition and on the 18th of February of this year Tunstall was murdered in cold blood by a so called Sheriff's posse that was composed of the worst murderers and thieves of Southern New Mexico. Warrants were immediately sworn out against these murderers and a number of citizens of Lincoln County left Lincoln for the purpose of arresting the murderers. They had scarcely left Lincoln when our good Governor appeared upon the scene, deposed the justice of the peace who had issued the warrants, declared all his (the justice's) official acts null and void and said that only the warrants of the judge in Mesialla at a distance of 150 miles were good, although two other justices were in the County.

I with other citizens of Lincoln begged of the Governor to call a meeting of the citizens of Lincoln, so that they might have a chance to explain to him the state of affairs. The Gov. refused to call such a meeting, declaring that he needed no further information but such as he had received. Three of our best and most influential citizens went the next day to Fort Stanton to see the Governor, but instead of hearing them he sent them home with a good ruffle. To explain the Governor's behavior in this affair, I only need to say that J. J. Dolan was one of the murderers and Gov. Axtell had a short time before borrowed $1500 of J. J. Dolan and J. H. Riley. Riley said publicly that he and others had the Governor all right, as he owed to them $1500. Which he never needed to pay. Gov. Axtell, however says that he paid back this sum. When Axtell had left Lincoln, the men who tried to arrest Tunstall's murderers were followed up by the Sheriff and the United States troops and were driven to the mountains.

Then a regular war commenced; the citizens of Lincoln seeked to arrest Tunstall's murderers and the Sheriff seeked to arrest the citizens, until at last the Sheriff was killed. Thereupon the County Commissioners appointed for the sheriff's office, J. N. Copeland, one of our most respected citizens. But now Axtell's voice was heard again. T. B. Catron, U.S. Attorney, wrote a long letter to his Excellency, in which among other things, he designated all the inhabitants of Lincoln Co. as thieves, saying farther that he had heavy interests in Lincoln Co. and asked of the Governor U.S. troops for the protection of his property. Catron had all the property of Dolan & Riley transferred to himself for the purpose as it was said, of covering $20,000 that they owed him. The Gov. sent Catron's letter to General Hatch, the Military Commander of New Mexico, with the request and full power to take the necessary steps. General Hatch ordered Col. Dudley, commander at Fort Stanton, to disarm all the inhabitants and gave him the power at his discretion and without further process to arrest citizens and to hold them as prisoners at the Fort. General Pope hearing of this telegraphed that this order must instantly be revoked. A short time after this, 25 men, among them, the present Sheriff Peppin after having on their way to Lincoln killed a farmer and dangerously wounded another, attacked the village of Lincoln, but were driven back, arrested, and taken to Fort Stanton. The following day most all the inhabitants of Lincoln were arrested for having defended their lives and property. Both parties were kept prisoners in Fort Stanton for a few days and then discharged. Sheriff Copeland gave the legal surety but could not give the surety as official collector of taxes legally required to be given within 30 days from his installation, for the reason that the tax list not having been fully made out, the amount of the surety to be given by him, could not be fixed. As soon however as the necessary documents were made out the County Commissioners sent them to the circuit judge with the request of fixing the sum. Three days after this letter was sent, a proclamation of the Governor without date or seal appeared, through which Copeland was deposed and a certain G. W. Peppin who for the last 2 months had been a member of a band of thieves and murderers, was appointed sheriff. Peppin was at the time of his appointment with his band. The law of the territory demands that a sheriff should be a real estate owner, and further the owner of $3000. over and above all property exempt by law from execution. Peppin owns neither real estate nor can he fill the later condition. Peppin gathered 20 of the worst (?) desperadoes of Southern New Mexico, such men as Jesse Evans, John Kinney, G. W. Davis, etc. who all stand committed for murder in our courts, and with them he appeared in Lincoln. The citizens of Lincoln publicly refused to have anything to do with Peppin and his posse.

Peppin and his band had several skirmishes with the citizens, and the fight culminated in the murder of McSween and three others who were with him in his own house. McSween's house was set on fire under the protection of U.S. troops under command of Col. Dudley and McSween and his three friends, after having surrendered to Peppin's deputy, were murdered. The same and the following nights Peppin's band broke into Turnstall's store and plundered it, nothing was left but the iron safe. With rifles in hand they went to Isaac Ellis' store and helped themselves to what they wanted, of course not saying a word about pay. But this was only the beginning. The band roams through the whole Country in all directions, plundering and levying contributions. All county officers had to leave Lincoln, for to stay was sure death, and there are not 10 Americans or Mexican families left in the whole county. Lincoln County is today totally in the hands of thieves, and all law and order loving citizens are forced to seek elsewhere protection and safety of their and their families' lives. If Gov. Axtell had done his duty, and if instead of protecting Tunstall's murderers, he had used the means at his service to bring them before justice, if he had heard the opinions and the councils of our citizens instead of obeying the order of a corrupt clique; if instead of a highway robber and a murderer, he had appointed a good honest man as sheriff, Lincoln Co. would today be free from all troubles; it would be the El Dorado of New Mexico, while today it is the rendezvous of all the scamps (tramps), thieves, and murderers.

Gov. Axtell pretends that there is no such combination in existence as the New Mexico Ring. A pocket book that J. H. Riley has lost sometime ago, contains among other interesting notices the following cypher names of the New Mexico Ring;

T. B. Catron (U.S. Atty)	Grapes
L. G. Murphy The Chief	Box
James J. Dolan Murphy Partner	Ace
John H. Riley Murphy Partner	Joker
Joseph Bernstein Clerk Indian Agency	Soap Weed
Maj. Godfroy (Ind. Agt.)	Hampton
Indians	Trees
W. L. Rynerson (Dist. Atty)	Oyster
1 Nat. Bank Santa Fe	Terror
2 " " " "	Fearful

This is only a part of the Ring that operates in Southern New Mexico. In the Northern part of the Territory there are probably things kept in the same shape.

Signed by — Isaac Ellis

STATEMENT FURNISHED GOVERNOR WALLACE BY JOHN B. WILSON

Territory of New Mexico
County of Lincoln

Before me the undersigned authority personally came and appeared John B. Wilson who after being duly sworn according to law deposeth and saith:

That he is a duly elected justice of the peace in Precinct No. 1 in Lincoln County, New Mexico and that he was ordered by Col. Dudley, commanding Fort Stanton, in New Mexico on or about the 19th of July 1878 to take the affidavits of Col. Purington, Capt. Blair and Dr. Appel, accusing A. A. McSween and others that was in his house on July 16th, 1878 of having committed an assault on the person of one Berry Robinson, a soldier of Fort Stanton, by having shot four or more shots at him with intention to kill as they had been informed and believed. I told Col. Dudley that I was not certain whether it was lawful for me to issue such an order or not and I thought it was the duty of a United States commissioner to issue it as there was a soldier concerned in it and he got very angry at me for refusing to issue it on that ground and told me if I did not take the affidavits and issue the warrant forthwith that he put me in double irons and would report me to the Governor and he called me a coward and said many other bad words to me. I then went to my office and took the affidavits of the above named officers as aforesaid and after they signed and swore to it, I issued the warrant to the Sheriff of Lincoln County for the arrest of A. A. McSween and others that was in the house on the 16th of July 1878 as per affidavits and gave it to George W. Peppin to serve returnable forthwith and said warrants has not been returned into my office up to this date by Peppin or any other person for him. I did not issue said warrant by my own will but by the peremptory order of Col. Dudley he (Dudley) coming in person to my office before I had it ready and told me I was not trying to issue the warrant in a hurry as it was my duty to do. Col. Dudley was the only person that appeared to be so much interested in the issue of the warrants. I was not ordered or solicited by any other person but by Col. Dudley to issue the warrant above mentioned for the arrest of McSween and others to the best of my knowledge. Col. Dudley was more desirous to have McSween and party arrested than all the others parties that was in Lincoln at the time not even the sheriff asked me to issue the warrant I give it to the sheriff without him asking me for it. I further state that Col. Dudley camped with his command about 30 yards northeast of the house of Jose Montana in Lincoln and planted a cannon about 15 yards from and in front and pointing towards said house and told a woman that understood English to tell the people in the house that if there was a shot fired out of the house over his soldiers he would fire the house with the cannon which was pointed at the house at the time Col. Dudley stopped in Lincoln with his command until after McSween's house was burnt and McSween and others killed, then left with his command for Fort Stanton, leaving 3 soldiers at S. Baca's house to protect Baca's family.

JOHN B. WILSON

Attorney Ira E. Leonard
to
Governor Lew Wallace:

Sunday Eve. April 20, 1879

MY DEAR GOVERNOR:

Court is moving on. I have tried no more habeas corpus cases. Am trying to stand them off.

I tell you Governor, the District Attorney here is no friend to law enforcement. He is bent on going after the Kid. He proposes to distroy his evidence and influence and on pushing him to the wall.

He is a Dolan man and is defending him in every manner possible.

Respectfully,
IRA E. LEONARD

NOTE: Reference is here made to District Attorney W. L. Rynerson.

STATEMENT FURNISHED GOVERNOR WALLACE BY SAM CORBET

Territory of New Mexico
County of Lincoln

Before me the undersigned authority personally came and appeared Samuel R. Corbet well known to me to be such, Who being duly sworn according to law deposeth and saith to wit:

That the deponent was clerking in the store belonging to the Estate of John H. Tunstall until it was broken and robbed of its entire contents and since that time has been clerking for Isaac Ellis & sons Merchants of the Town of Lincoln County of Lincoln, Territory of New Mexico. That on or about the 17th of July 1878, Sheriff Peppin's Posse attacked the town of Lincoln and kept up firing from the neighboring hills until the morning of the 19th, when Lieut. Col. M. A. M. Dudley, Capt. George A. Purington, Capt. Blair, Lieut. Goodwon and Dr. Appel, post Surgeon of Fort Stanton with a company of soldiers and two pieces of Artillery arrived here and went into camp about the center of the Town and set one cannon about 20 yards from and pointing towards the house of Isaac Ellis, a short time after Dudley had made his camp. Peppin with about nine men came into the house of Isaac Ellis, armed with guns and six shooters and ordered them to give him coal oil for which they stated they wanted it to use in setting fire to the house of A. A. McSween. They further stated that they had him in the house and they intended to burn him out. They took the coal oil and went back. When opposite the camp of Col. Dudley, he (Dudley) came out and with Peppin talked for some time. Peppin and his posse, then past up the street toward the house of A. A. McSween, in a short time firing commenced around McSween's house and I soon saw smoke arise from his house and firing was kept up until about nine o'clock at night. The following morning the bodies of A. A. McSween and three others were found in the yard riddled with bullets, the house and contents totally destroyed by fire. On the same morning the store belonging to the estate of John H. Tunstall was broken open and robbed of its entire contents, amounting to about Six Thousand Dollars. About nine o'clock in the morning, I went up to the store and found Sheriff Peppin and about eight of his posse in the store. I spoke to sheriff Peppin and asked him if he could not stop his men from taking goods out of the store as I was in charge of the store, and he told me that he was not responsible for nothing and went out. Col. Dudley was in the store and saw men carrying out goods. He walked out with Peppin and they talked awhile in the street. The same day with his command, Col. Dudley went back to Fort Stanton.

SAM CORBET

GEORGE TAYLOR TO GOVERNOR LEW WALLACE

LINCOLN, NEW MEXICO, Apr. 25, '79

Governor Lew Wallace:

MY DEAR GOVERNOR:

I thought I would give you a little sketch of matters here as some things that have happened after you left may be interesting to you.

Last night two of those outlawed scoundrels who are so numerous around here made a dash through the town on horseback and fired into our building.

Judge Leonard had changed the place of his bed and they seemed to be aware of the fact for the bullets were directed where he lay, fortunately the side of the house was struck and no damage done but had they not been going so rapidly when they fired they may have accomplished their purpose which was evidently to kill or injure the Judge so he cannot prosecute them.

Col. Rynerson, the prosecuting attorney for the territory is either afraid of or anxious to screen these villians you have arrested; he is entering into his work with no spirit and leaves all the work for the Judge only interfering to raise obstacles in the way of bringing the rascals to justice.

I have no confidence in him, he has been engaged in numerous scrapes himself, and can't help but have a fellow feeling for men who are in the same trouble he has been in himself.

Wilson, (lawyer living at Lincoln), is in great trouble, the men who employed him are now to get back their horses and arms from him; he is denouncing them as a set of — cutthroats and murderers and swearing he will never defend another one of them. He told me he had heard them make desperate threats against parties who have been prominent in arresting them, and particularly against Judge Leonard against whom they are very hostile. Singularly they have no feeling against Rynerson but all their animosity is directed against the Judge.

You would have laughed had you seen us rushing around for weapons when we were fired into last night. It was a complete surprise as we had not anticipated anything of the kind. I thought when you were here you took too many precautions but I see now I was mistaken. There is no telling when the scoundrels will make a break on us. They are thirsting for revenge and plunder and the minutes the military are withdrawn from here we will have the same bloody contests over again that have taken place here before.

We are now well-armed and ready to give the outlaws a good reception when they come as they surely will if that military scoundrel Col. Dudley is exonerated from his crimes. It is a mystery to me how that man can be permitted to disgrace the army as he does, using it to persecute and murder the honest people of this country and aid and protect the most desperate thieves and outlaws in the United States in their crimes.

The mining interests are looking better every day. I believe we will soon have some good developments made.

I will write you the news as they occur. I hope you will soon return as these outlaws stand in great dread of you and your presence here gives us all a greater sense of security than ever the military as they could not prevent the outrage of last night.

Respectfully,
George Taylor — Lincoln, New Mex.

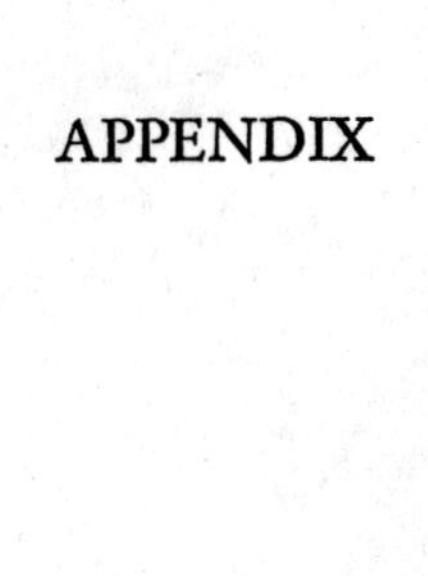

APPENDIX

Appendix I and Commentary

They Knew Billy the Kid

There are many inconsistencies in the story of Pat Garrett, the slayer of the Kid, with respect to the youth's true character and worth. These may be attributed, perhaps, to an attempt at self-justification, coupled with possible qualms of conscience.

Garrett stated:

The Kid's career of crime was not the outgrowth of an evil disposition, nor was it caused by unchecked youthful indiscretions. It was the result of unfortunate circumstances acting upon a bold, ungovernable spirit which no physical restraint could check, no danger appall, and no power less potent than death could conquer.

All who ever knew Billy will testify that his polite, gentlemanly bearing invited confidence and offered promise of protection, the first of which he never betrayed, the latter of which he was never known to withhold. He was never loud or boisterous. There was always a pleasant smile on his face, a soft musical ripple in his voice. There were no bounds to his generosity. Friends, strangers, and even his enemies were welcome to his money, his horse, or anything else which he happened at the time to possess.

The aged, the poor, the sick, the unfortunate, and the helpless never appealed to him in vain for succor. There is the impression among some people that he was exceedingly gross, profane, and beastly in his habits, conversation, and demeanor. Nothing could be further from the truth. In dress, when circumstances would permit, he was always scrupulously neat, taking great pride in his apparel, expressly in his fine boots, worn on small, shapely feet, and a Mexican sombrero. Bold, daring, and reckless, he was open-handed, generous-hearted, frank, and manly.

He was a favorite with all classes and ages; especially was he loved and admired by the old and decrepit and the young and helpless. To such he was a champion, a defender, a benefactor, a right arm.

He was never seen to address a lady, especially an elderly one, except with his hat in his hand; and did her attire or appearance evidence poverty, it was a poem to see the eager, sympathetic, compassionate look in his face as he proffered assistance or afforded information. A little child never lacked a lift across a gutter or the assistance of a strong arm to carry a heavy burden when Billy was in sight.

He loved his mother. He loved and honored her more than anything else on earth. This affection for her was a near obsession, and his devotion to her memory never ceased. He often declared that the tyranny and cruelty of his stepfather drove him from home and a mother's influence, a mother whom he was never again to see.

Thus it was, in 1882, that Patrick Floyd Garrett portrayed Billy the Kid, the youth only twenty-one years of age, who met his death in the darkened room at Fort Sumner, the victim of the sheriff's guns.

Let us now turn the page and observe the strange contradictions that appear in Garrett's portrayal of the life, character, and exploits of the Kid following Garrett's election to the office of sheriff of Lincoln County and his endeavor to obtain the reward for capturing or killing his former friend and companion:

The best and brightest side of Billy's character has been portrayed above. The shield has another side, never exhibited to his best friends or to the weak and helpless. His temper was FEARFUL, and in his angry moods he was dangerous. He had no bark, or if he had, the bite came first. Those who knew him best would watch his eyes for an exhibition of anger. One could scarcely believe that those blazing, baleful eyes and laughing face were controlled by the same spirit. He was the noted desperado of the Southwest, whose deeds of daring and blood made his name a terror in New Mexico, Arizona, and northern Mexico.

When the Kid was flush he spent money freely and kept himself pretty full of whiskey. He and his friends applied themselves industriously to the pursuit of pleasure in and around Fort Sumner where they worshipped religiously at the shrines of Bacchus and Venus.

Here were some misleading and exaggerated statements, for it was common knowledge throughout the territory that the Kid never indulged in intoxicating beverages and was noted for his strict sobriety.

Garrett's account continues:

> Securing some new recruits to his service, the Kid inaugurated a system of plunder that baffled all resistance. A stock owner's only course to secure immunity from loss was to conciliate the Kid and court his friendship. This business they followed industriously throughout the summer and fall.

In voicing the charge of widespread rustling, the sheriff grossly misrepresented the activity of the Kid. The herds of the small cattleman, rancher, and homesteader were never molested by the youth. Frequently he aided them in the recovery of their stolen property from rustlers who had raided their small possessions.

In justice to Garrett, it may be conceded that he made reference to John S. Chisum who suffered serious losses of cattle through the raids of the Kid and his followers. They justified these operations according to the precepts of their own code.

Undeniably, the Rio Feliz Ranch was raided frequently. The Kid's hatred for W. L. Rynerson, then district attorney, knew no bounds. He did not recognize the legal rights of Rynerson who had secured the property through a tax sale at a price very much smaller than the value of the ranch, thus depriving the family of John H. Tunstall, yet in England, of a valuable estate.

Most of the proceeds from the rustling raids were distributed among the dependent relatives of those youths whose lives had been sacrificed during the Lincoln County War.

Other than his raids against John S. Chisum and District Attorney Rynerson, however, the Kid held inviolate the property of the small cattleman, rancher, and homesteader.

Among the many crimes Garrett attributed to the Kid, he stressed three as deliberate murders. The death of Sheriff Brady was a tragic mistake, a misconception of the purpose of the officers as has been related in a former chapter. Although there were twelve men involved in the firing, and it was established at the inquest that Sheriff Brady received nine bullet wounds, Garrett has imputed to the Kid the sole responsibility for the officer's death. He was the only one of the group to be tried, convicted, and sentenced for participation in that unfortunate tragedy. The Kid maintained throughout that he fired at neither officer, but frankly admitted having exchanged shots with J. B. (Billy) Mathews, the leader of the posse that murdered John H. Tunstall, his loyal friend who believed in and trusted him.

In commenting upon the incident, Garrett stated: "This murder was a most dastardly crime on the part of the Kid and lost him many friends who had heretofore excused and screened him."

Similarly, Sheriff Garrett was in error when he attributed the death of James Carlyle to the Kid as a deliberate murder. It was subsequently established that Carlyle was killed by members of his own posse, mistaking him for the Kid in the snowy half-light outside the Greathouse trading post.

In his zeal, Sheriff Garrett again attributed deliberate murder to the Kid—that of Joseph (Soapweed) Bernstein, the Indian agent on the Apache Reservation:

He [Bernstein] was warned of his danger by persons who knew the Kid and his gang, but unheeding, he rode out boldly and commanded them to leave the reservation. The only reply was from the Kid's Winchester, and poor Bernstein answered for his temerity with his life.

For this atrocity the Kid was tried and declared not guilty. He was defended by Ira Leonard. It was subsequently proved that the Indian agent was murdered by a small, deformed, mentally deficient Mexican youth known as Isaacio Sanchez.

Sheriff Garrett, in commenting upon the death of "Buckshot" Roberts during the battle with the Brewer posse at Blazer's Mill, again misstated the circumstances:

> The Kid knew Roberts would not be taken alive by Brewer's posse. As the party approached the building from the east, Roberts came galloping up from the west. The Kid espied him, and he spurred directly towards Roberts as Brewer demanded he surrender. Quick as lightning, Roberts' Winchester was at his shoulder, and a bullet sang past the Kid's ear. The Kid was as quick as his foe, and his aim was more accurate. The bullet from his rifle went crashing through Roberts' body, inflicting a mortal wound.

This version is different from the stories of everyone present at the mill, and it is universally accepted as a fact that Bowdre killed Roberts.

Why, in his commentaries, did Garrett portray the Kid as a thief, renegade, and ruthless murderer, as well as a gentleman? Possibly he was attempting to advance the idea that he killed the youth as a duty incumbent on his office. However derogatory Garrett's remarks may be, there is a different view voiced by many who knew the Kid.

George Curry, former territorial governor, State Historian and Curator of the Old Courthouse and Museum, Lincoln, New Mexico, said, in statements to the author:

> I had no part in the Lincoln County War. During that era I was

only a youth and a civilian employee at Fort Stanton. I knew Governor Wallace, Colonel Dudley, Lawrence G. Murphy, Pat Garrett, and the Kid, as well as others involved in the feud.

Governor Wallace was a spare man, abrupt and austere in manner, but withal he was honest and sincere. He succeeded in bringing a semblance of peace to Lincoln County through obtaining the removal of Colonel Dudley from the command of Fort Stanton and other reforms. Yes, there was much diversity of opinion whether or not he [Wallace] failed to keep faith with the Kid. This was largely based upon partisan bias and prejudice. He was compelled to contend not only with local opposition, but with adverse pressure from the "Santa Fe Ring." After the lapse of so many years, I hesitate to appraise his actions and motives.

Pat Garrett? Yes, I knew him very well indeed, especially following his term of office as collector of the customs at El Paso. He moved to Las Cruces where ill-fortune appeared to pursue him. His every undertaking failed. No longer occupying an important political position, or sought after as a celebrity—the slayer of the Kid—he frequently became mean and irritable. At times he was sullen, surly, and ill-tempered, causing him to be avoided and feared, a contributing factor that eventually led to his murder. I believe, in his later years, the knowledge that he was the instrument of the Kid's death weighed upon his mind, causing him secret regret. . . .

To make a realistic appraisal of the Kid's character, one must have known him. Innumerable distorted accounts of his life and exploits have been written by writers of fiction who knew nothing of him or the old frontier. I knew him as an unassuming youth, courteous and always displaying a friendly grin. It has been said, in critical situations all men experience a degree of fear. I believe this to have been foreign to Billy. He was always calm and unemotional. Elements of danger appeared to exhilarate him. Young though he was, he was a born leader. Had he been reared in a more favorable environment, he would have made a most efficient peace officer; or had John H. Tunstall, his loyal friend and sponsor, not been murdered, I believe he would have guided the Kid to become a useful and respected member of society as it then existed. Many crimes were attributed to him by his enemies, without regard for truth. Though several men became the victims of his gun, it is my considered opinion that in every instance there were justifiable or mitigating circumstances.

Miguel Antonio Otero, former territorial governor, historian, author, member of a pioneer New Mexico family, made these statements to the author:

My first meeting with Billy the Kid was coincidental. By chance, my father, brother, and I were in Las Vegas when Sheriff Garrett brought in his prisoners, captured at Stinking Springs, en route to the jail at Santa Fe for safekeeping. I witnessed the attempt of the mob that had gathered, determined to take them from the officers and administer "summary justice." Besides the Kid, there were three others, Rudabaugh, Wilson, and Pickett. The mob wanted Rudabaugh in particular as he had killed his jailer in Las Vegas, where he was being held for murder, and escaped.

With the aid of the local peace officers, the quartet was eventually placed aboard the train, and bloodshed was averted. At the time, I was but a month younger than the Kid and felt a youthful interest in the lad. My brother and I gained permission from our father to continue to Santa Fe on the same train. There, we were permitted to visit the Kid in jail. We took him cigarette papers, tobacco, and some confections which he greatly appreciated. He was in a pleasant humor, laughing and jesting.

As I reflect upon my first meeting with him, my impressions were most favorable. Nothing would have pleased me more than to have witnessed his escape. I can now say I believe he was "more sinned against than sinning."

In later years, I had many talks with the late Pat Garrett about the Kid. He always spoke of him pleasantly, saying, "I have many times regretted that I had to kill him. The night I met him in Pete Maxwell's bedroom it was simply a case of who got in the first shot. I chanced to be the lucky one. If I had not shot when I did, I would not be here to tell the tale."

Garrett always spoke of the Kid as a great fellow, and has told me many times, "Billy the Kid was one of the nicest little gentlemen I ever saw; kind and considerate, true and loyal to his friends, afraid of nothing on earth that walked on two legs or four. All his deviltry was wished on him by much worse men than he ever dared to be."

Through Garrett's own recital, one may read between the lines and note the apologies and laudations. All in all, Garrett wanted one to believe that duty called him. All of which to my mind is unadulterated rot. If one doubts Garrett's mercenary nature, one has but to take the case of his killing Tom O'Folliard before he killed Charlie Bowdre and captured the Kid.

After the murder of her husband, Alexander A. McSween, Susan McSween married George L. Barber, an attorney at Carrizozo. This marriage terminated in divorce. She resided at White Oaks until her death. Of Billy the Kid, she stated:

Possibly no woman knew Billy better than I. Peril and tragedy create a great bond of understanding. Quiet and unassuming, he displayed the unstudied attributes of a gentleman. When addressing any woman, contrary to the custom of the times, he always removed his hat, displaying his curly light hair. He loved to read. Mr. McSween had a few books, and when Billy would come to our home he would ask permission to use them. History appeared to fascinate him, and he would ask many questions relating to historical events. Music appealed to him, and he would listen intently whenever I turned to the piano, the only one then in Lincoln County.

After the brutal murder of Mr. Tunstall, he transferred his allegiance to my husband, who has been a fast friend and associate of Tunstall. Wherever possible he aided the forces of law and order in the county. During the hearing before the Military Board of Inquiry, trying Colonel Dudley for his dereliction of duty on the tragic night of July 19, Billy rendered Governor Wallace an invaluable service, as he also did when he appeared as a witness against the brutal murderers of the young lawyer, Chapman.

I understood, for this aid, the governor promised him immunity from prosecution on the indictments which were then pending against him, but for some reason he failed to act. I do know the governor requested District Attorney Rynerson to dismiss the charges against Billy that he might avail himself of the provisions of the Amnesty Proclamation, but that official rejected the governor's request. Had it been granted, other lives would not have been needlessly sacrificed, later.

Billy was never the ruthless outlaw, as claimed by his enemies. To the contrary he was always generous, loyal, and helpful to those requiring his aid. His courage was boundless, a courage having the total absence of fear.

How better can those qualities be known than by his leadership during the tragic night when my husband was murdered and my home destroyed?

I had gone twice to Colonel Dudley's camp to implore him to intervene and to save the lives of the brave youths entrapped in the burning building and surrounded by the Dolan-Turner attackers, but I had failed in my missions. Returning the second time, Billy begged me to leave while there was yet time as there were only two rooms yet unreached by the fire. Soon they would have to fight their way out, and I would be in deadly peril. He told me he would endeavor to save the "governor's" life—as he called Mr. McSween—and that I would only prove a great hindrance.

At first I refused to leave my husband. The usual smile faded from Billy's face, and his eyes appeared to plead. I knew he was right, so I moved towards the only remaining exit. Instantly, the boyish grin returned.

He had given no thought to his own peril or that of his companions. As I stepped out into the half-light, a shot was fired, the bullet striking the wall near my side. No doubt the marksman then observed I was a woman, and no further effort was made to hinder my escape.

Viewed in retrospect, I am now convinced that, had I refused to leave, Billy would have regretfully and apologetically in some way have compelled me to leave the burning building. It was not until later that I learned of his efforts to save my husband's life. Billy and Tom O'Folliard were the last to leave the now nearly-destroyed building. O'Folliard led, closely followed by Mr. McSween, with Billy endeavoring to protect him from the rear.

Bob Beckwith, a member of the Dolan-Turner attackers, had secreted himself by the fire-blackened wall of the west wing. As they emerged he fired twice, missing Billy, but a bullet struck my husband, killing him instantly. Believing he may have been only wounded, Billy attempted to raise him to convey him to possible safety, but it was too late; he was beyond all help.

As Beckwith was boldly proclaiming he had killed Mr. McSween and claiming the reward for his murder, Billy arose, heedless of his own peril, and calmly confronted the surprised assassin, remarking, "Yes, you have earned your reward, Bob. Here is the pay-off!" He fired twice, and Beckwith was dead as he fell to the ground. Turning, Billy ran for the gate through a hail of lead, miraculously making his escape, uninjured.

A stranger to fear, courteous, generous, and loyal, was the youth I knew as Billy the Kid.

Don Martin Chavez, a grave Spanish American who mustered thirty-five men to go to the aid of McSween and the besieged men, had this to say concerning the affair, and of Billy the Kid:

Colonel Dudley arrived in Lincoln with a mounted company of troops and a squad of artillery with a Gatling gun and a twelve-pounder. He ordered the fieldpiece placed in front of the Montano house and ordered me to leave with my men. He cursed me; said if a single shot was fired, he would blow the house to pieces.

As there were women and children refugees within, I felt responsible for their lives. I could not defy an officer of the U.S. Army, nor did I dare to fire on his troops. I had no alternative other than to withdraw.

About Billy? He was a perfect gentleman and a youth with a generous heart. Once he gave me a horse, mine having been stolen. He thought nothing of riding the entire night to bring medicine or other aid to some unfortunate family. He never killed a native citizen of New Mexico in his entire career. He did kill in the line of duty as a member of a legal posse, or in defense of his own life. He had courage.

They had to sneak up on him in the dead of night to murder him!

Mrs. José Jaramillo, nee Paulita Maxwell, sister of Pete Maxwell, Fort Sumner, also supplied her comments:

Billy was a good boy. He was always pleasant, laughing, and good-natured. He frequented our home and was always welcome. He was courteous to women, regardless of how lowly their station. He was hounded by men who wanted to kill him, and he was always on the defensive. I have never believed Mr. Garrett's statement that he was armed, the night he entered my brother's room and was killed. No weapon was ever discovered, nor was one produced at the inquest to confirm Mr. Garrett's contention.

Billy was worshipped by Deluvina, the old Navajo Indian woman who had been a domestic in our home since the time of our father, and Billy regarded her with real affection. He rarely came to our home without bringing her some small gift. He would address her as *madre mía* ("my mother"), and her old eyes would light with happiness. I recall he once brought her from Las Vegas a silver crucifix and chain, which she prized above all of her few possessions until her death. At the mention of Billy she would talk volubly about "my little boy," her affectionate name for him. She would relate how Mr. Garrett killed him, anathematizing Garrett as a coward. He was afraid to go back to the room to make sure whom he had shot, she would explain. "I was the first to go in and discover he had killed my little boy."

I hated those men and am glad I have lived long enough to see them all dead and buried.

George Coe, prominent citizen of Lincoln County, author of *Frontier Fighter,* living in Glencoe, New Mexico, made these statements to the author:

I had a hand in the three-days fight in Lincoln. Hendry Brown, Sam Smith, and I were stationed in the Tunstall store to protect it.

We had a difficult time in getting out as the only open side was surrounded, but we made a run for the river without being hit by the many shots fired at us. I cannot say too much in praise of Billy's stand in the McSween home. He risked his all to protect and save Mr. McSween, but the odds were too great. However, he did kill Bob Beckwith, his [McSween's] murderer.

Billy came into Lincoln County in 1877; shortly afterward he went to work for John H. Tunstall who had started a cattle ranch on the Rio Feliz. He said he wanted to make a man of himself. Mr. Tunstall liked Billy and valued him more than anyone else in his employ. He trusted him implicitly with everything he had. The cold-blooded murder of Tunstall completely upset Billy's plans. He became revengeful. If Mr. Tunstall had lived, the Kid would have been known as William H. Bonney, a respectable member of society and a valuable citizen. Billy was a brave, resourceful, and honest boy; he would have been a successful man under any circumstances. I loved the youngster in the old days and can say now, after the passing of many years, that I still love his memory.

When Billy was killed in 1881 by Pat Garrett, I was in Rio Arriba County. Though I heard the news with sorrow, it was by no means a surprise. His enemies were constantly on his trail, making his capture and killing merely a question of time. . . . The motive behind Pat Garrett's relentless pursuit of Billy was that his death meant money and the office of sheriff of Lincoln County. Billy was a thousand times better and braver than any man hunting him, including Pat Garrett.

Frank Coe, rancher, veteran of the Lincoln County War, cousin of George Coe, also a resident of Glencoe, New Mexico, gave the author this account:

I first met Billy the Kid in the year 1877. He was then only a boy of eighteen, and I was not much more than a boy myself. An intimate friendship began at once between us. I found Billy different than most boys of his age. He had been thrown on his own resources from early childhood. From his own statement to me, he hadn't known what it meant to be a boy. From the age of twelve he was associated with men of twenty-five and older. He was eager to learn, and he had an active and fertile mind.

When the fighting broke out, Billy proved himself a valuable man. He was one in five hundred in his fitness for such service. His youth was no handicap since he had developed maturity and the experience of a man twice his age. He knew instinctively what to do in an emergency, and he acted with lightning speed. His natural qualities of leadership made him a great influence with others of our party.

Billy stayed with me at my home for most of one winter, during which time we became staunch friends. I never enjoyed better company. He always found a touch of humor in everything, being naturally full of fun. Though he was serious in emergencies, his humor was often apparent even in such situations. His disposition was remarkably kind; he rarely thought of his own comfort first and was always solicitous of others. He resented an unkind word or slighting remark about a woman or young girl.

George and I shared the same opinion of Pat Garrett. He was an overrated man. He was a cow thief, and everybody knew it. At Fort Sumner, he stole many bull teams and sold them to butchers at Las Vegas. His killings of Charlie Bowdre, Tom O'Folliard, and Billy were little short of deliberate murders. He acted the part of traitor to his best friends, turning against them for money and office.

Pat's conscience must have worried him a lot. He never succeeded in anything, even with the assistance of the President of the United States and several governors of New Mexico.

George L. Barber, pioneer attorney at law, sometime

husband of Susan McSween, Carrizozo, New Mexico, contributed his remarks, also:

Billy the Kid was a mere boy in appearance. He was always gay and high-spirited, but in any emergency he always stood out as a leader, quick, and resolute.

I managed to preserve a neutral position during the Lincoln County War and was not identified with either faction, but I felt the Kid was not half as bad as those who were determined to kill him.

I was in Lincoln the day he made his escape from jail, and I realized then that, despite the fact he had killed his two guards, Bell and Ollinger, he had the community completely on his side.

Aside from a few—those belonging to the old Murphy-Dolan-Riley following—the community was wholly sympathetic towards the Kid. Scarcely anyone believed he had received a fair and just trial, and they were glad to know that by his own ingenuity and nerve he had succeeded in cheating the noose that was soon to end his young life. He fought for his existence and, for a time, won, but not for long, only to fall victim to Pat Garrett's gun.

Appendix II—Notes

Prologue

A. From the Las Cruces *Thirty-Four,* April 30, 1879: "The principal cause of such lawlessness lies deeper than the Lincoln county war, however, and in a measure created that war and has kept it alive. It is nothing more nor less than the prostitution of the law by corrupt men and partisans who have been entrusted with its execution."

Chapter I

A. No formal charges of defrauding the government were ever brought or proved against L. G. Murphy, but government beef contractors had devised a number of ingenious ways of cheating on their contracts, and rumor had it that Murphy was acquainted with these. One plan called for agents of the contractor to steal back the cattle shortly after they had been delivered to the government and payment received. These agents went to considerable pains to leave clues indicating that a marauding band of Indians was responsible for the theft.

Another practice was to show the quartermaster a few prime steers, on the basis of which a contract was executed. The same steers were shown at delivery, but the cattle actually delivered were poor, scrawny, substandard animals.

Indian beef contracts were negotiated on the basis of a head count of reservation Indians. A clever contractor could arrange for an overcount of the Indians and sell more substandard beef on the basis of the mistaken census, neatly doubling the cross.

B. The "long rail" refers to a long, straight brand mark extending from shoulder to flank. The "jingle bob" was a peculiar earmark, made by a deep, vertical cut in the ear which resulted in the ear flopping over. The brand was distinctive and almost defied alteration, but it furnished only a slight obstacle to the rustlers who plagued John Chisum. Buyers, even for obviously stolen cattle, were not difficult to find.

Chapter IV

A. The *carcel*, or jail, was a log-lined cellar, surmounted by a small log building.

B. This matter was fully aired in the *Mesilla Independent*, which published the following letters in January, 1878:

Office of John H. Tunstall
LINCOLN, LINCOLN COUNTY, N.M.
January 18, 1878

"The present sheriff of Lincoln County has paid nothing during his present term of office."—*Governor's Message* for 1878.

EDITOR OF THE *Independent:*

The above extract is a sad and unanswerable comment on the efficiency of Sheriff Brady and cannot be charged upon "croakers." Major Brady, as the records of this county show, collected over Twenty-Five Hundred Dollars, Territorial funds. Of this sum, Alexander A. McSween, Esq., of this place, paid him over Fifteen Hundred Dollars by cheque on the First National Bank of Santa Fe, August 23, 1877, Said cheque was presented for payment by John H. Riley, Esq., of the firm of J. J. Dolan & Company. This last amount was paid by the last-named gentleman to Underwood and Nash for cattle. This passed away over Fifteen Hundred Dollars belonging to the Territory of New Mexico. With the exception of Thirty-Nine Dollars, all the taxes of Lincoln county for 1877, were promptly paid when due. Let not Lincoln county suffer the delinquency of one, two, or three men.

By the exercise of proper vigilance, the taxpayers can readily ascertain what has become of what he has paid for the implied protection of the commonwealth. It is not only his privilege, but his duty. A delinquent taxpayer is bad; a delinquent tax collector is far worse.

J. H. T.

LAS CRUCES, N.M.
Jan. 29, 1878

TO THE EDITOR OF THE *Independent:*

DEAR SIR:—In answer to a communication in reference to taxpayers of Lincoln county, published in your issue of the 26th and signed J. H. T., I wish to state that everything contained therein is false. In reference to Sheriff Brady, I will state that he deposited with our House Territorial Funds amounting to nearly $2,000, subject to his order and payable on demand. Owing to sickness in the family of Sheriff Brady, he was unable to be in Santa Fe in time to settle his account with the Territory. This, I hope, will explain satisfactorily how the Governor in his message had our county delinquent. If Mr. J. H. T. was recognized as a gentleman and could be admitted into respectable circles in our community, he might be better posted in public affairs. For my part, I don't see the object of Mr. J. H. T.'s letter, unless it is to have the public believe that Alexander A. McSween is one of the largest taxpayers in our county, when in fact, he is one of the smallest. Sheriff Brady is willing at any time to show uneasy taxpayers what disposition he has made of the money paid by them; he can also show clean receipts from the Territorial treasurer of his account.

Respectfully,
J. J. DOLAN

These letters show the degree of personal animosity that was developing among neighbors at Lincoln.

C. Murphy was certainly displaying undue interest in the Fritz money. His original intent was that the proceeds of the insurance policy should be placed to the credit of the Murphy firm with Speigelberg. His interest would be understandable, had Fritz owed money to the firm of Murphy & Co. However, this appears not to have been the case.

McSween reported in his deposition made to Frank Warner Angel, Agent of the Department of Justice, in June, 1878, that Murphy owed money to the Fritz estate, and certain conflicting opinions were in existence as to the amount.

Dolan stated to McSween, in the spring of 1875, that the Murphy firm owed the Fritz estate about $48,000. In May, 1877, Murphy asked the probate court that a commission be named to examine the firm's books to determine whether Fritz owed the Murphy firm money, or if, on the contrary, Murphy was indebted to the estate. The report of this committee showed that Murphy owed the Fritz estate $23,376.10. In January, 1878, Murphy filed a claim in probate court against the Fritz estate for $76,000. This claim was disallowed, the court ruling that Murphy owed the Fritz heirs about $3,000.

Chapter V

A. The same deposition referred to in Note C, for Chapter IV.

Chapter VI

A. Results of the post mortem confirmed accounts received by McSween as to how Tunstall met his death.

B. In this letter, written by W. S. Morton, following his capture by the Brewer posse, it appears that he (Morton) had a premonition that he would not be taken to Lincoln alive:

South Springs Ranch, N.M.
March 8, 1878

H. H. Marshall
Richmond, Va.

Dear Sir:

Sometime since I was called upon to assist in serving a writ of attachment on some property wherein resistance had been made against the law.

The parties had started off with some horses which should be attached, and I as Deputy Sheriff, with the posse of twelve men, was sent in pursuit of same. We overtook them, and while attempting to serve the writ, our party was fired on by one John H. Tunstall, the balance of the party having ran off. The fire was returned and Tunstall was killed. This happened on the 18th of February.

The 6th of March I was arrested by the Constable's party, accused of the murder of Tunstall. Nearly all of the sheriff party fired at him (Tunstall) and it is impossible for anyone to say who killed him. When the party which came to arrest me, and one man who was with me, first saw us, about 100 yards distant, we started in another direction when they (eleven in number) fired nearly 100 shots at us.

We ran about five miles, when both of our horses fell, and we made a stand. When they came up, they told us if we would give up, they would not harm us.

After talking awhile, we gave up our arms and were made prisoners. There was one man in the party who wanted to kill me after I had surrendered, and was restrained with the greatest difficulty by others of the party. The Constable himself said he was sorry we gave up, as he had not wished to take us alive. We arrived here last night en route to Lincoln. I have heard that we were not to be taken alive to that place. I am not at all afraid of their killing me, but if they should do so, I wish that the matter should be investigated and the parties dealt with according to law.

If you do not hear from me in four days after receipt of this, I would like you to make inquiries about the affair.

The names of the parties who have me arrested are: R. M. Brewer, J. G. Schurlock, Charles Bowdre, William Bonney, Henry Brown, Frank McNab, one Wayte, Sam Smith, Jim French, and two others named McClosky and Middleton who are friends. There are two parties in arms and violence is expected. The military are at the scene of disorder and trying to keep peace. I will arrive at Lincoln the night of the 10th and will write you immediately if I get through safe.

Have been in the employ of Jas. J. Dolan & Co. of Lincoln for 18 months since the 9th of March, '77, and have been getting 60 dollars per month. Have about $600.00 due me from them and some horses, at their cattle camps.

I hope if it becomes necessary, that you will look into this affair. If anything should happen, I refer you to T. B. Catron, United States Attorney of Santa Fe, N.M., and Col. Rynerson, District Attorney, Mesilla, N. M. They both know all about the affair as the writ of attachment was issued by Judge Warren Bristol of Mesilla, N.M. and everything was legal. If I am taken safely to Lincoln, I will have no trouble, but will let you know.

If it should be as I suspect, please communicate with my brother, Quin Morton, Lewisburg, Va. Hoping that you will attend to this affair if it becomes necessary and excuse me for troubling you if it does not.

I remain yours respectfully,
W. S. MORTON.

Address,
Lincoln,
New Mexico

Chapter VIII

A. This was the same grand jury which examined reports of the deaths of Morton, Baker, and McCloskey and did not find indictments. Although McSween was here exonerated of embezzlement, in the disorder that followed, it is not certain that the Fritz family received payment of the net proceeds of the insurance policy.

Chapter X

A. Somewhat tardily, the federal government was beginning to evidence interest in the desperate situation in remote New Mexico. A flood of protests reached President Rutherford B. Hayes, and one of these suggested the appointment of Lew Wallace, soldier, statesman, and author, to replace Axtell. Hayes appointed Frank Warner Angel as special agent to investigate the trouble in Lincoln County —factional fighting, Fort Stanton, administration of the Mescalero Apache Reservation—and reported political corruption in Santa Fe. Angel completed his investigation in June, 1878. His undated report, which might have enabled the President to prevent further death, fire, and pillage, was not submitted until months later.

B. The reason the Lincoln County War remains controversial should, by now, be apparent. Were the two groups of fighting men *armies?* Or, was one group a legally constituted posse and the other a band of outlaws? If this was the case, which group was which? Who were the criminals? How may the responsibility be fixed upon the principals, none of whom did any shooting?

These questions are as difficult to answer now as they were in 1878, and upon the answers arrived at by each reader depends his evaluation of a situation which had the changing complexion of a game of cops and robbers by children, with the juvenile participants altering their characters with the shifting breeze.

In defense of Billy the Kid, it can be said that, until these warrants were issued, his record was clean, except for a single indictment for the theft of a horse dating back some years. From this time forth, however, the Kid's early death was a foregone conclusion. His reputation as a gunman was a *fait accompli,* and there were always those anxious to attribute to him every murder, robbery, and other unsolved crime in the area.

Chapter XI

A. About this time, L. G. Murphy, who had figured prominently in Lincoln County affairs for years, simply faded away. Although he was one of the prime movers in the conflict, Murphy's health had been declining for some time, and he went to Santa Fe, probably for treatment, leaving his affairs in the control of James J. Dolan and Marion Turner. He died in Santa Fe in October, 1878, apparently without having returned to Lincoln.

McSween, in the deposition, heretofore referred to, to Frank Warner Angel, mentioned J. J. Dolan & Co., "successors to L. G. Murphy & Co." The transfer of the business seems to have taken place prior to August, 1877.

Chapter XII

A. Dudley held the brevet of general. Actually, he was a colonel, drawing the pay of that rank. He is referred to by both titles in this and other accounts.

B. While the officers were discussing matters at "the house," several of the enlisted men went to the aid of Crawford who still lay at the foot of the hill, an hour or so after he was hit. Crawford died of his injury at Fort Stanton that night.

C. The account of the climax of the Lincoln County War is based upon the recollections of Señora Sara Salazar. Señora Salazar's father, Saturnino Baca, and brother-in-law, Hijinio Salazar, participated in the battle, and the Señora herself, as a small girl, witnessed parts of it. The statements of Susan McSween are also referred to, and the stories of the two women are substantially in agreement.

Chapter XIII

A. Litchfield recovered, but was later killed in the Panhandle, an indirect victim of the Lincoln County War. Litchfield took offense at a slurring remark about his disfigurement and went for his gun—too late.

B. The fight at McSween's house elicited some comment from Dudley. Although not entirely consistent with the known facts, it is of interest:

"Men who have the reckless courage to attack a building in bright midday, its walls forming a perfect protection against any modern musketry to its inmates, pierced as this castle of McSween's was with scores of loopholes for rifles on every side and angle, to say nothing of the flat roof protected by a perfect wall of defense, and for hours hugging the walls, exposed to the fire not only from the loopholes but from the buildings held by McSween's men, charging this position across a space perfectly exposed to the fire of McSween's men for a distance of nearly 300 yards, are not of a character to be easily induced to abandon a course they believe is only half completed.

A similar remark can be made of the party holding this structure, who held the same fortification five days, the last nine hours gradually retreating from one room to another, as the heat compelled them to do what no amount of leaden missiles from the rifles of the attacking party could do; and for one hour, finally, all huddled in one room nearly surrounded by flames, some, as it is claimed, preferring to be burnt rather than to surrender to the sheriff's posse. More desperate action than was exhibited on this unfortunate day by both sides is rarely witnessed."

It must be conceded that Dudley paid high tribute to the courage of both factions. However, whether through lack of knowledge or with deliberate intent, certain erroneous statements were made.

The McSween house was not a "castle . . . with scores of loopholes for rifles on every side and angle." It was only a fine residence, pretentious when viewed by the standards of the neighborhood.

The defenders on the flat roof were scarcely "protected by a perfect wall of defense." Rather, they were pitifully exposed to snipers stationed on the hillside, and they soon abandoned this strategically untenable position.

At no time did the Dolan-Turner men "[charge] this position across a space perfectly exposed to the fire of McSween's men" from *any* distance. The character of the terrain made such a charge impossible. Actually, the defenders were completely surrounded by sharpshooters concealed by thick adobe walls, and by snipers on the hillsides.

The men trapped in the burning building and opposed by thrice their number were cut off from escape and faced the alternatives of chancing surrender, or running a gantlet of fire for a slim hope of survival.

Dudley was certainly accurate when he stated that "More desperate action than was exhibited on this unfortunate day by both sides is rarely witnessed."

The day would seem all the more "unfortunate" when it is recalled that a word from Dudley would have stopped the needless sacrifice of human life.

C. At the brief services conducted by Dr. Ealy, Susan McSween placed her husband's Bible in his coffin, but retained Kinney's note. The note remained in her possession until her home (in White Oaks) was destroyed by fire when she was very old.

D. It may be noted that Hijinio Salazar was a youth of only fourteen years the night of July 19, 1878. It was not unusual for a boy of that age to be a full-fledged fighting man. Billy the Kid had been on his own for two years at age fourteen and was, himself, eighteen years old on the date of the fiery fight.

Chapter XIV

A. During this time, an army officer was widely quoted as having said, "We should again declare war upon the Republic of Mexico and force that country to take back that land of hell-raising outlaws, savages, and rattlesnakes."

B.

PEACE
AMNESTY PROCLAMATION
CITIZENS OF LINCOLN COUNTY
INVITED TO RETURN AND
RESUME THEIR PEACEFUL PURSUITS

For the information of the people of the United States and of the citizens of the Territory of New Mexico in especial, the undersigned announces that the disorders lately prevalent in Lincoln County, said Territory, have been happily brought to an end. Persons having business and property interests therein and who are themselves peaceably disposed, may go to and from that County without hindrance or molestation. Individuals resident there, but who have been driven away, or who from choice sought safety elsewhere, are invited to return, under assurances that ample measures have been taken and are now and will be continued in force, to make them secure in person and property. And that the people of Lincoln County may be helped more speedily to the management of their civil affairs, as contemplated by law, and to induce them to lay aside forever the divisions and feuds, which, by national notoriety, have been so prejudicial to their locality and the whole Territory, the undersigned, by virtue of authority in him vested, further proclaims a general pardon for misdemeanors and offenses committed in the said County of Lincoln against the laws of said Territory in connection with the aforesaid disorders between the first day of February, 1878, and the date of this proclamation.

And it is expressly understood the foregoing pardon is upon the conditions and limitations following:

It shall not apply except to officers of the United States Army stationed in the said County during the said disorders, and to persons who, at the time of the commission of the offense or misdemeanor of which they may be accused, were with good intent, resident citizens of the said Territory, and who shall have hereafter kept the peace, and conducted themselves in all respects as becomes good citizens.

Neither shall it be pleaded by any person in bar of conviction under indictment now found and returned for any such crimes or misdemeanors, nor operate the release of any party undergoing pains and penalties consequent upon sentence heretofore had for any crime or misdemeanor.

In witness whereof I have hereunto set my hand and caused the seal of the Territory of New Mexico to be affixed.

Done at the city of Santa Fe
this 13th day of November A.D., 1878
LEWIS WALLACE

SEAL
By the Governor
W. G. RITCH
Secretary

C. About this time, Wallace's political enemies (they were numerous and included a hostile press) sarcastically proclaimed, "His Excellency has removed the Territorial Capitol from Santa Fe to Fort Stanton, frequently taking it with him to the isolated little village of Lincoln for his personal convenience."

Chapter XV

A. From the contemporary newspaper, *Thirty-Four,* Las Cruces:

FORT STANTON, N.M.
Feb. 23, 1879

EDITOR OF *Thirty-Four:*

Wednesday some of the leaders of the two parties had a meeting and agreed to bury the hatchet. They promenaded the streets of Lincoln arm in arm and had a regular good time. That evening early, Chapman arrived from Las Vegas and put his horses in Mrs. McSween's corral. Then went to a neighbor's to get some bread to make a poultice for his face. He was suffering from a severe attack of neuralgia. He was returning about 10 o'clock and met Dolan, Jesse Evans, and Bill Campbell, with Billy Bonney (the "Kid") and Tom O'Folliard of the McSween party. Dolan and his party had insisted on their accompanying them and they had consented to do so rather than show any unfriendliness.

When they met, one of the Dolan party asked, "Who are you and where are you going?" Chapman answered and told them he was attending to his business. He was told to talk differently or they would make him. "You cannot scare me, boys. I know you and it's no use. You have tried that before." "Then," said Campbell, "I'll settle you," and fired his pistol, the ball going in at the breast and coming out at the back. As he fell, Dolan shot him with his Winchester. Then they set fire to his body. It is thought they soaked his clothes with whisky to make them burn.

When they first met, "Kid" tried to get away and ran around an angle in the lane wall, but Evans held the other fast and made him look on during the whole affair. Next day a coroner's jury was held, but the Dolan party was in town armed and the people so bulldozed no evidence could be brought out.

These are the facts as near as I can get at them, but no one dares to speak of them except in whispers. If it was known I am writing to you my life would not be worth insuring two hours and I don't think you will be safe to publish this letter. I want to get away as soon as possible and don't want any more Lincoln County in mine.

Yours, MAX

P. S. Chapman was unarmed. He never carried arms.

"Max," whoever he was, did not have the story straight in all its details, and the facts he states were not fully established, either by the coroner's jury or at the subsequent trials of the principals, but this is an account of the way the incident looked to one who evidently observed part of it.

B. As far as can be determined, Evans was not heard of again in New Mexico.

Chapter XVI

A. This suggestion is difficult to reconcile with the terms of the Amnesty Proclamation and with subsequent developments, but there seems little doubt that it was made.

Chapter XVIII

A. Tins of food.

B. Lew Wallace was moved to express his wonderment at this unusual friendship. In a letter dated March 31, 1879, addressed to the Hon. Carl Schurz, then Secretary of the Interior (1877-1881), he noted that a prisoner held in Lincoln was an object of tender regard and that he had heard a group serenading the prisoner on one occasion. The note was light in tone and was not a particularly generous reference to the boy who had recently demonstrated to the governor his courage and honor.

Chapter XXI

A. A native whitewash, painstakingly prepared from burned limestone.

B. A slangy reference to Chisum's brand, long rail and jingle bob. See Note B, Chap. I.

Chapter XXIII

A. It would appear that General Hatch and the Secretary of War did not fully approve the findings of the Military Court of Inquiry. While no disciplinary action was taken against Colonel Dudley, his sphere of usefulness as commander of Fort Stanton had terminated, and he was transferred to another frontier post. He was succeeded by Colonel Purrington.

Chapter XXV

A. Many Basque had left the Pyrenees to become shepherds in the New World. They were universally recognized as expert sheepmen.

B. The term "pistol whip" is widely misunderstood to mean the striking of the victim with the *butt* of the gun. Actually, the weapon was drawn from the holster with the fingers holding the butt. To reverse ends would require two movements and entail the loss of seconds. Further, it left the muzzle of the gun pointing toward the individual drawing the weapon, and the contact might discharge the gun, inflicting injury upon its wielder. "Pistol whipping," then, is the striking with the *barrel* of the weapon. It inflicts an effective —though seldom fatal—blow.

C. Under the heading, "Examination of Frank Coe on Writ of Habeas Corpus," among other things *The Independent* stated:

"Coe was charged with being one of the party who killed Roberts at Blazer's mill, on the Mescalero Apache Indian reservation, about one year ago. . . . [The] Grand Jury, after a careful examination of the case, failed to find an indictment against Frank Coe. . . .

"Some two months ago Mr. Coe went into Santa Fe on business, when he was arrested by Marshal Sherman and confined in the Santa Fe jail. . . . Coe was arrested without a warrant . . . and kept in jail some six weeks. . . .

"It appears from the evidence that Coe had nothing whatever to do with the killing of Roberts. . . . Roberts himself stated just before he died that he was certain Frank Coe took no part in the fight. . . . . . . his happening to be present when Roberts was killed was sufficient excuse for the 'Dolan' party to place his name on the list of those marked for the bullet. . . ."

D. A fiery native brew.

Chapter XXVI

A. A report was quickly circulated throughout the territory to the effect that Billy the Kid had wantonly murdered Carlyle when he attempted to escape from a building where he was held prisoner by the Kid and his "band of outlaws."

Chapter XXVIII

A. James H. East, one of Garrett's possemen, later wrote a friend describing the incident:

"Lon Chambers was on guard, and our horses were hidden in Pete Maxwell's stables. Sheriff Garrett, Bob Williams, Tom Emory, and Barney Mason were playing poker on a blanket spread on the floor. Tom O'Folliard was shot through the body near the heart and lost control of his horse which turned and came up near us. Tom cried, 'Don't shoot any more for I'm dying.' We helped him off his horse and took him in and laid him down on my blanket as Pat and the boys returned to their poker game. I got Tom some water, and he died about thirty minutes after being shot."

B. Garrett said: "I gave a signal by bringing my gun to my shoulder." This provided him with several seconds before others could do likewise, so it seems fairly obvious that he must have killed Bowdre. His full account, as quoted, reads:

"Before it was fully daylight, a man appeared at the entrance with a horse's nosebag in his hand, and I took him to be the Kid. His size and dress, especially his hat, corresponded exactly with the description I had been given of the Kid. So I gave a signal by bringing my gun to my shoulder; my men did likewise, and seven bullets sped on their errand of death. Our victim was Charlie Bowdre."

C. The remains of the soldiers interred at Fort Sumner were removed to Santa Fe by the federal government and buried in a national cemetery. The old cemetery reverted to public use and is now desolate and weed-grown. At one corner are the graves of the Kid, O'Folliard, and Bowdre, marked by a granite monument and enclosed with heavy wire netting.

A short distance away can be found the graves of Lucian B. Maxwell, the original owner of the great Maxwell land grant, and his son Pete Maxwell, in whose room the Kid met his death. Both are marked by modest monuments.

Here, also, hidden in a brush-covered plot, is the grave of Juanita, Pat Garrett's first bride, who found in death a refuge from remorse of conscience.

D. Respecting the taking of the mules, see the Kid's letter to Governor Wallace, Fort Sumner, December 12, 1880.

Chapter XXIX

A. The reference here is to Governor Wallace's letter of March 15, 1879, to Billy. See Plate XIV in the Appendix.

B. From a contemporary issue of *The Fort Worth Star:*

The prosecution obtained a change of venue, claiming a fair trial in Lincoln County would be impossible. The case was transferred to the Dona Ana County docket and tried at La Mesilla, Judge Warren Bristol presiding.

In the little, squalid courthouse the trial was begun. The courtroom was packed with a motley crowd of spectators; blanketed Indians, swarthy Mexicans, and cowpunchers, rough and unshaven, from the wind-swept mesas of New Mexico.

At the back of the room sat the Judge behind an old-fashioned, flat-topped desk, which was on a platform raised slightly from the floor. In front of the desk was a small space reserved for the lawyers. Only rough wooden benches were provided for the spectators. Sitting at one side of the Judge's desk was Billy the Kid. Rather pleasant looking was Billy. Wavy, light hair, expressive eyes, seeming just a little defiant now, but looking as though they were made for laughter. There was the mark of keen intellect on his forehead and the clean-cut sweep of his jaw. All around him sat men with guns on their hips. It looked almost ridiculous; all those armed men sitting about a helpless-looking youth, with only the suspicion of down beginning to appear upon his chin.

As a further precaution Billy was kept handcuffed and in leg irons all during his trial. There was drama when the jury filed back into the courtroom to report its verdict.

Silent and contemptuous he stood before the Judge and heard his sentence pronounced—"TO BE HANGED BY THE NECK UNTIL YOU ARE DEAD."

C.

Territory of New Mexico,

vs.

William Bonney, Alias Kid, Alias William Antrim,

In the District Court of Doña Ana
County, March 1881 term.

Instructions asked for by Defendant's Counsel.

The court is asked to instruct the Jury as follows:
to-wit:

1st Instruction asked:

Under the evidence the Jury must either find the defendant guilty of murder in the 1st degree or acquit him.

2nd Instruction asked:

The Jury will not be justified in finding the defendant guilty of murder in the 1st degree unless they are satisfied from the evidence, to the exclusion of all reasonable doubt, that the defendant actually fired the shot that caused the death of the deceased Brady, and that such shot was fired by the defendant with a premeditated design to effect the death of the deceased, or that the defendant was present and actually assisted in firing the fatal shot or shots that caused the death of the deceased, and that he was present and in a position to render such assistance and actually rendered such assistance from a premeditated design to effect the death of the deceased.

3rd Instruction asked:

If the Jury are satisfied from the evidence to the exclusion of all reasonable doubt that the defendant was present at the time of the firing of the shot or shots that caused the death of the deceased Brady, yet, before they will be justified in finding the defendant guilty, they must be further satisfied from the evidence and the evidence alone, to the exclusion of all reasonable doubt, that the defendant either fired the shot or shots that killed the deceased, or some one of them, or that he assisted in firing the same, either by his advice, encouragement, or procurement or command, from a premeditated design to effect the death of Brady. If the Jury entertain any reasonable doubt upon any of these points they must find a verdict of acquittal.

A. J. FOUNTAIN
J. B. BAIL
Attorney for Defendant

Chapter XXX

A. The large Murphy store and residence had been acquired by the county and remodeled, and was now serving as the county courthouse.

Chapter XXXII

A. As evidence of the inadequacy of communications during this period, it may be observed the Kid made his escape on April 28. On April 30, two days later, Governor Wallace signed the death warrant at Santa Fe, ordering the execution of the Kid on May 13. Apparently the governor had not yet learned that the Kid had escaped.

Judge Bristol had sentenced the Kid to be hanged following his conviction at Mesilla, and, on the April date, Wallace ordered his execution—in a kind of dual sentence. Governor George Curry stated that he knew of no legal precedent calling for this action on the part of Wallace, and was unable to account for it.

The death warrant read:

DEATH WARRANT

To the sheriff of Lincoln county, New Mexico—
Greetings:

At the March term, A.D. 1881, of the District Court for the Third Judicial District of New Mexico, held at La Mesilla in the county of Doña Ana, William Bonney, *alias* Kid, *alias* William Antrim, was duly convicted of the crime of Murder in the First Degree; and on the fifteenth day of said term, the same being the thirteenth day of April, A.D., 1881, the judgment and sentence of said court were pronounced against the said William Bonney, *alias* Kid, *alias* William Antrim, upon said conviction according to law; whereby the said William Bonney, *alias* Kid, *alias* William Antrim, was adjudged and sentenced to be hanged by the neck until dead by the Sheriff of the said county of Lincoln, within said county.

Therefore, you, the Sheriff of the said county of Lincoln, are hereby commanded that, on Friday, the thirteenth day of May, A.D. 1881, pursuant to the said judgment and sentence of the said court, you take the said William Bonney, *alias* Kid, *alias* William Antrim, from the county jail of the county of Lincoln where he is now confined, to some safe and convenient place within the said county, and there, between the hours of ten o'clock, A.M. and three o'clock, P.M. of said day, you hang the said William Bonney, *alias* Kid, *alias* William Antrim by the neck until he is dead. And make due return of your acts hereunder.

Done at Santa Fe in the Territory
of New Mexico, this 30th day
of April, A.D. 1881.
Witness my hand and the great seal
SEAL of the Territory.
LEW WALLACE
Governor, New Mexico

By the Governor
W. G. RITCH
Secretary
N. M.

Chapter XXXIII

A. Poe, youngest of the trio of man hunters, was, by education and natural endowment, a leader of men. He early manifested the superior qualities which were eventually to lead to his election as the most respected and efficient sheriff turbulent Lincoln County had known. In later life, Poe took his place as a prominent and substantial citizen of the territory.

Lincoln, March 15. 1879.

W. H. Bonney.

Come to the house of old Squire Wilson (not the lawyer) at nine (9) o'clock next Monday night alone. I don't mean his office, but his residence. Follow along the foot of the mountain south of the town, come in on that side, and knock at the east door. I have authority to exempt you from prosecution if you will testify to what you say you know.

The object of the meeting at Squire Wilson's is to arrange the matter in a way to make your life safe. To do that the utmost secresy is to be used. <u>So come alone.</u> Don't tell anybody—not a living soul—where you are coming or the object. If you could trust Jesse Evans, you can trust me.

Lew. Wallace.

Courtesy Indiana Historical Society Library

LEW WALLACE'S LETTER OF MINUTE INSTRUCTIONS ARRANGING A MEETING BETWEEN HIMSELF AND BILLY

(See text, pp. 140-41.)

San Patricio

3-20-18

Thursday 20th
1879

Friend Wilson.

Please tell
You know who that I do not
know what to do, now as those
Prisoners have escaped. to Send word
by bearer, a note through You
it may be that he has made different
arragements if not and he still wants
it the same to Send: William Hudgins:
as Deputy. to the Junction tomorrow
at three Oclock with some men you know
to be all right. Send a note telling
me what to do

W H Bonney

P. S. do not Send Soldiers

Courtesy Indiana Historical Society Library

BILLY'S NOTE TO SQUIRE WILSON ASKING INSTRUCTIONS

(See text, p. 146.)

PLATE XV

Fort Stanton, March 20. 1879

W. H. Bonney.

The escape makes no difference in arrangements. ~~I will comply with my part, if you will with yours.~~

To remove all suspicion of ~~arrangement~~ understanding, I think it better to put the arresting party in charge of Sheriff Kimbrell, who will be instructed to see that no violence is used.

This will go to you tonight. ~~If you still insist upon Sturgis, let me know.~~ If I dont get ~~receive~~ other word from you, the party (all citizens) will be at the junction by 3 o'clock tomorrow.

Lew. Wallace.

Courtesy Indiana Historical Society Library

WALLACE'S REPLY TO BILLY (MARCH 20, 1879)

(See text, p. 147.)

San Patricio
Lincoln County
Thursday 20th 18

General. Lew, Wallace;

Sir. I will keep the appointment I made. but be Sure and have men come that You can depend on I am not afraid to die like a man fighting but I would not like to be killed like a dog unarmed, tell Kimbal to let his men be placed around the house. and for him to come in alone; and he can arrest us. all I am afraid of is that in the Fort we might be poisoned, or killed through a Window at night. but You can arrange that all right. tell the Comanding Officer to Watch) Lt Goodwin(he would not hesitate to do anything there Will be danger on the Road of Somebody Waylaying us to kill us on the road to the Fort.

Courtesy Indiana Historical Society Library

THE KID'S LONG LETTER IN WHICH HE AGREED TO THE GOVERNOR'S PLAN

(See text, pp. 150-52.)

PLATE XVII

On the Pecos. all that I can remember
are the So Called Dolan Outfit but they
are all up here now: and on Rio Grande
this man Cris Moten I belive his name is
he drove a herd of 1800 head three Years ago
last December in Company with Frank Wheeler
Frank Baker deceased Jesse Evans George Davis
alias Tom Jones, Tom Hill. his name in Texas being
Tom Chelson also deceased. they drove the Cattle to
the Indian Reservation and sold them to John Riley
and J J Dolan. and the cattle were turned in for Beef for the
Indians the Beckwith family Made their boasts that they
came to Seven Rivers a little over four Years ago
with one Milch Cow borrowed from John Chisum
they had when I was there Year ago one thousand Six
hundred head of cattle. the male members of the family are Henry
Beckwith and John Beckwith Robert Beckwith was killed
the time McSweens house was burned.
Charles Robert Olinger and Wallace Olinger
are of the same gang. their Cattle ranch is
situated at Rock Corral twelve Miles below Seven Rivers
on the Pecos. Paxton and Pierce are still below
them forty miles from Seven Rivers there are four

Courtesy Indiana Historical Society Library

THE KID'S LONG LETTER (continued)

PLATE XVIII

of them Paxton: Pierce: Jim Raymer, and Buck Powel.
they had when I seen them lost about one thousand
head of cattle: at Rocky Arroya there is another Ranch
belonging to Smith who Operated on the Penaco
last year with the Jesse Evans gang those and
the places I mentioned are all I know of
this man Cris Moten at the time they stole them
Cattle was in the employ of J. J. Dolan an Co
I afterwards Seen Some of the cattle at the
Rinconada Bonita on the reservation those were
the men we were in search of when we went to
the agency. the Beckwith family were attending
to thier own Business when this War Started but
G. W. Peppin told them that this was
John Chisums War and so they took a hand
thinking they would lose their Cattle in case
that he chisum won the fight. this is all the
information I can give you on this point
Yours Respectfully Billie

Courtesy Indiana Historical Society Library

THE KID'S LONG LETTER (continued)

PLATE XIX

You Will never Catch those
fellows on the road Watch
Fritzes, Captain Bacas ranch
and the Brewerys they Will either
go to Seven Rivers or to Jicarillo
Montains they Will stay around close
untill the Scouting parties come in
give a Spy a pair of Glasses and let
him get on the Mountain back of Fritzes and
Watch and if they are there ther will be provisions
carried to them. it is not my place
to advise you. but I am anxious
to have them caught, and perhaps
know how men hide from Soldiers, better
than you. please excuse me for having so much to say
and I still remain Yours Truly

W. H. Bonney

P.S.
I have changed my mind Send Kimbal to
Gutieres just below San Patricio one mile. because
Sanger and Ballard are or were great friends of Camuels
Ballard told me ~~today~~ yesterday to leave for you were doing
everything to catch me. it was a blind to get me to leave

tell Kimbal not to come before 3 o'clock for I may not be here before

Courtesy Indiana Historical Society

THE KID'S LONG LETTER (continued)

PLATE XX

Fort Sumner

Dec 12th 1880

Gov: Lew Wallace

Dear Sir

I noticed in the Las Vegas Gazette a peice which stated that, "Billy" "the" Kid, the name by which I am known in the Country was the Captian of a Band of Outlaws who hold Forth at the Portales. There is no such Organization in Existence. So the Gentleman must have drawn very heavily on his Imagination. My business at the White Oaks the time I was waylaid and my horse killed was to See Judge Leonard who has my case in hand. he had written to me to Come up, that he thought he could get Everything Straightend up I did not find him at the Oaks & Should have gone to Lincoln if I had met with no accident. After mine and Billie Wilsons horses.

Courtesy Indiana Historical Society Library

BILLY'S LETTER TO GOVERNOR WALLACE RELATING INCIDENTS AT THE GREATHOUSE RANCH

(See text, pp. 236-37.)

PLATE XXI

were Killed we both made our way to a
Station, forty miles from the Oaks kept by
Mr Greathouse. When I got up next morning
The house was Surrounded by an outfit led
by one Carlyle, Who came into the house and
demanded a Surrender. I asked for their
Papers and they had none. So I Concluded
it amounted to nothing more than a mob
and told Carlyle that he would have to
Stay in the house and lead the way out
that night. Soon after a note was brought
in Stating that if Carlyle did not Come out
inside of five minutes they would Kill the
Station keeper (Greathouse) who had left the
house and was with them. in a Short time a
Shot was fired on the outside and Carlyle thinking
Greathouse was Killed jumped through the
window. breaking the Sash as he went
and was killed by his own Party they thinking
it was me trying to make my Escape.
the Party then withdrew.

they returned the next day and burned an old
Man named Spencer's house and Greathouses. also

Courtesy Indiana Historical Society Library

BILLY'S LETTER TO GOVERNOR WALLACE (continued)

I made my way to this Place afoot and
During my absence Deptuty Sheriff Garrett
Acting under Chisums orders went to the Portales
and found Nothing. on his way back he went
by Mr Yerbys ranch and took a pair of mules
of mine which I had left with Mr Bowdre
who is in Charge of mr Yerbys Cattle.
he (Garrett) Claimed that they were stolen
and Even if they were not he had a right
to Confiscate any Outlaws property.
I have been at Sumner Since I left
Lincoln making my living Gambling
the mules were bought by me the truth of which
I can prove by the best Citizens around Sumner
J. S. Chisum is the man who got me into
Trouble and was benifited Thousands by it
and is now doing all he can against me
There is no Doubt but what there is a great deal
of Stealing going on in the Territory. and a great
deal of the Property is taken across the Plains as
it is a good outlet but So far as my being

Courtesy Indiana Historical Society Library

BILLY'S LETTER TO GOVERNOR WALLACE (continued)

at the head of a Band there is nothing of it in Several Instances I have recovered Stolen Property when there was no Chance to get an Officer to do it.

one instance for Hugo Zuber Postoffice Puerto De Luna. another for Pablo Analla Same Place.

if Some impartial Party were to investigate this matter they would find it far Different from the impression put out by Chisum and his Tools.

Yours Respect

William Bonney

Courtesy Indiana Historical Society Library

BILLY'S LETTER TO GOVERNOR WALLACE (continued)

Santa Fe
Jan." 1st
1881

Gov." Lew Wallace
Dear Sir
I would like to see You
for a few moments if You can
Spare time
Yours Respect."
W. H. Bonney

Santa Fe New Mexico
March 2nd/81

Gov." Lew Wallace
Dear Sir
for the last
time I ask, Will You Keep
Your promise. I start below
tomorrow Send answer by bearer
Yours Respt
W H Bonney

Courtesy Indiana Historical Society Library

BILLY'S BRIEF REQUEST FOR AN INTERVIEW AND HIS CURT, DEMANDING NOTE OF MARCH 2, 1881. BOTH WENT UNANSWERED

(See text, pp. 259-60.)

PLATE XXV

Santa Fe. In Jail
March 4th 1881

Gov. Lew Wallace

Dear Sir

I wrote You a little note
the day before Yesterday, but have
received no answer. I Expect You have forgotten, what You promised me, this Month two
Years ago, but I have not, and I think You
had ought to have come and seen me as I
requested you to. I have done Everything that
I promised You I would, and You have done
nothing that You promised me.
I think when You think the matter over, You
will Come down and See me, and I can then
Explain Everything to You.
Judge Leonard, Passed through here on
his way East, in January and promised to
Come and See me on his way back, but he did
not fulfill his Promise, it looks to me like I am
getting left in the Cold. I am not treated right-

Courtesy Indiana Historical Society Library

BILLY THE KID'S APPEAL OF MARCH 4, 1881

(See text, pp. 260-61.)

PLATE XXVI

by Sherman. he lets Every Stranger
that comes to See me through Curiousity
in to See me, but will not let a single one of
my friends in, not Even an Attorney
I guess they mean to Send me up without giving me
any show. but they will have a nice time doing it
I am not intirely without friends
I Shall Expect to See you Sometime today
Patiently Waiting
I am Very Truly Yours Respect=
Wm H. Bonney

Courtesy Indiana Historical Society Library

BILLY THE KID'S APPEAL OF MARCH 4, 1881 (continued)

PLATE XXVII

To the Sheriff of Lincoln County, New Mexico, Greeting:

At the March term, A.D. 1881, of the District Court for the Third Judicial District of New Mexico, held at La Mesilla in the county of Doña Ana, William Bonny, alias Kid, alias William Antrim, was duly convicted of the crime of Murder in the First Degree; and on the fifteenth day of said term, the same being the thirteenth day of April, A.D. 1881, the judgment and sentence of said court were pronounced against the said William Bonny, alias Kid, alias William Antrim, upon said conviction according to law; whereby the said William Bonny, alias Kid, alias William Antrim, was adjudged and sentenced to be hanged by the neck until dead, by the Sheriff of the said county of Lincoln, within said county.

Therefore, you, the Sheriff of the said county of Lincoln, are hereby commanded that on Friday, the thirteenth day of May, A.D. 1881, pursuant to the said judgment and sentence of the said court, you take the said William Bonny, alias Kid, alias William Antrim from the county jail of the county of Lincoln where he is now confined, to some safe and convenient place within the said county, and there, between the hours of ten o'clock, A.M., and three o'clock, P.M., of said day, you hang the said William Bonny, alias Kid, alias William Antrim by the neck until he is dead. And make due return of your acts hereunder.

Done at Santa Fe in the Territory of New Mexico, this 30th day of April, A.D. 1881. Witness my hand and the great seal of the Territory.

Lew Wallace,
Governor New Mexico

By the Governor
W. G. Ritch
Secretary N.M.

PHOTOSTATIC COPY OF DEATH WARRANT OF THE KID IN THE HANDWRITING OF GOVERNOR WALLACE

(See Appendix II, pp. 363-64.)

PLATE XXVIII

Territory
vs
Wm Bonney alias
Kid
Death Warrant
Lincoln, Lincoln County
New Mexico May 24th 1881
I hereby certify that the
within Warrant was not
Served owing to the
fact that the within
named prisoner
escaped before the
time Set for Serving
said Warrant.

Pat F. Garrett
Sheriff
Lincoln County
New Mexico

FILED
JUN
3
1881
W. G. RITCH
Sec. N. M

PHOTOSTATIC COPY OF PAT GARRETT'S RETURN ON THE WARRANT
FOR THE EXECUTION OF THE KID

(See text, p. 294.)

PLATE XXIX